New Concise Maths 4

George Humphrey

Gill & Macmillan

For Michael Dunne,
mathematician supreme

Gill & Macmillan
Hume Avenue
Park West
Dublin 12
with associated companies throughout the world
www.gillmacmillan.ie

© George Humphrey 2003

ISBN-13: 978 07171 3343 7

Print origination by Mathematical Composition Setters Ltd, Salisbury, Wiltshire

*The paper used in this book is made from the wood pulp of managed forests. For
every tree felled, at least one tree is planted, thereby renewing natural resources.*

CONTENTS

Revision Exercises

**Each revision exercise concentrates on a particular question on the
examination paper and is divided into three parts:
Part A's, RA, Part B's, RB and Part C's, RC.**

PREFACE

New Concise Mathematics 4 is the first of two volumes covering Leaving Certificate Mathematics, Higher Level.

Full analysis of the pattern and level of difficulty of the examination questions was taken into account. The book reflects the author's experience that students learn better from worked examples than from abstract discussion of principles. The emphasis is on clear and concise presentation of the material. Long explanations are avoided, on the principle that these are best left to the teacher. A comprehensive range of worked examples, with helpful comments highlighted in colour, is included. The author has very carefully graded the exercises through testing them in class. Concepts are built up in a logical manner. Each chapter is broken down into short, manageable sections. A numbered, step-by-step approach, highlighted in colour, is used to help with problem solving. Key terms are defined simply, and highlighted. This has been found to save valuable class time, otherwise spent copying notes from the board. The proofs required are in their own separate chapter.

The last part of the book is a 'revision book' within the book. This provides a comprehensive range of graded questions. Each revision exercise contains an extensive selection of 'part a', 'part b' and 'part c' type questions similar in standard to the Leaving Certificate questions. Tackling these exercises is an excellent form of revision.

I would especially like to thank my colleague Geoffrey Reeves, St Andrew's College, Booterstown, who helped when mathematical clarification was required. I would also like to thank Patricia Wrynn, Coláiste Chiaráin, Leixlip; Margaret Klotz, Alexandra College, Milltown; and Elizabeth Caird, St Dominic's Secondary School, Ballyfermot, for making many constructive suggestions, which are included in the final text. Thanks must also go to Geraldine Finucane, Stuart Scott and Niall Alexander, students in Trinity College, Dublin, who took on the task of checking my answers and making many valuable contributions.

Finally, I wish to express my thanks to the staff of Gill & Macmillan and to Patrick Roberts in particular, for their advice, guidance and untiring assistance.

George Humphrey
St Andrew's College
Dublin

CHAPTER 1

ALGEBRA

Simplifying Algebraic Expressions and Fractions

Special Factors

1. $a^2 - b^2 = (a - b)(a + b)$	Difference of two squares
2. $a^3 - b^3 = (a - b)(a^2 + ab + b^2)$	Difference of two cubes
3. $a^3 + b^3 = (a + b)(a^2 - ab + b^2)$	Sum of two cubes

Special Expansions

1. $(a + b)^2 = a^2 + 2ab + b^2$	2. $(a - b)^2 = a^2 - 2ab + b^2$
3. $(a + b)^3 = a^3 + 3a^2b + 3ab^2 + b^3$	4. $(a - b)^3 = a^3 - 3a^2b + 3ab^2 - b^3$

These factors and expansions occur frequently and should be memorised.

Example ▼

Factorise **(i)** $6a^2b - 9ab^2$ **(ii)** $25x^2 - 16y^2$ **(iii)** $8x^3 - 27y^3$ **(iv)** $1 + 1000p^3$

Solution:

(i)
$$6a^2b - 9ab^2$$
$$= 3ab(2a - 3b)$$
(HCF is $3ab$)

(ii)
$$25x^2 - 16y^2$$
$$= (5x)^2 - (4y)^2$$
$$= (5x - 4y)(5x + 4y)$$

(iii)
$$8x^3 - 27y^3$$
$$= (2x)^3 - (3y)^3$$
$$= (2x - 3y)[(2x)^2 + (2x)(3y) + (3y)^2]$$
$$= (2x - 3y)(4x^2 + 6xy + 9y^2)$$

(iv)
$$1 + 1000p^3$$
$$= (1)^3 + (10p)^3$$
$$= (1 + 10p)[(1)^2 + (1)(10p) + (10p)^2]$$
$$= (1 + 10p)(1 + 10p + 100p^2)$$

Multiplication and Division of Algebraic Fractions

Operations with algebraic fractions follow the same rules as in arithmetic. Before attempting to simplify when multiplying or dividing algebraic fractions, factorise where possible and divide top and bottom by common factors. The contents of a bracket should be considered as a single term.

Example ▼

Simplify $\dfrac{4x^2 - 10x}{9x^2 + 6x} \div \dfrac{2x - 5}{3x + 2}$.

Solution:

$$\frac{4x^2 - 10x}{9x^2 + 6x} \div \frac{2x - 5}{3x + 2}$$

$$= \frac{4x^2 - 10x}{9x^2 + 6x} \times \frac{3x + 2}{2x - 5} \qquad \text{[turn the fraction we divide by upside down and multiply]}$$

$$= \frac{2x(2x - 5)(3x + 2)}{3x(3x + 2)(2x - 5)} \qquad \text{[factorise the top and bottom]}$$

$$= \frac{2}{3} \qquad \text{[divide top and bottom by the common factors, } x, (3x + 2) \text{ and } (2x - 5)]$$

Addition and Subtraction of Algebraic Fractions

To add or subtract algebraic fractions do the following:

1. Factorise denominators (if necessary).
2. Find the L.C.M. of the denominators.
3. Express each fraction in terms of this L.C.M. and simplify.

Example ▼

Express as one fraction in its lowest terms:

$$\frac{3}{x + 5} - \frac{2}{x + 3} + \frac{5x + 19}{x^2 + 8x + 15}$$

Solution:

$$\frac{3}{x + 5} - \frac{2}{x + 3} + \frac{5x + 19}{x^2 + 8x + 15}$$

$$= \frac{3}{(x + 5)} - \frac{2}{(x + 3)} + \frac{5x + 19}{(x + 5)(x + 3)} \qquad \text{[factorise the denominators; their L.C.M. is } (x + 5)(x + 3)]$$

$$= \frac{3(x + 3) - 2(x + 5) + (5x + 19)}{(x + 5)(x + 3)} \qquad \text{[each fraction expressed in terms of this L.C.M.]}$$

$$= \frac{3x + 9 - 2x - 10 + 5x + 19}{(x + 5)(x + 3)} \qquad \text{[remove brackets on top]}$$

$$= \frac{6x + 18}{(x + 5)(x + 3)} \qquad \text{[factorise the top]}$$

$$= \frac{6(x + 3)}{(x + 5)(x + 3)} \qquad \text{[factorise the top]}$$

$$= \frac{6}{x + 5} \qquad \text{[divide top and bottom by } (x + 3)]$$

Simplify   (i) $\dfrac{x - \dfrac{9}{x}}{1 - \dfrac{3}{x}}$, $x \neq 3$ (ii) $\dfrac{3x-5}{x-2} + \dfrac{1}{2-x}$, $x \neq 2$

Solution:

(i) $\dfrac{x - \dfrac{9}{x}}{1 - \dfrac{3}{x}}$

$= \dfrac{x^2 - 9}{x - 3}$

(multiply each part by x)

$= \dfrac{(x-3)(x+3)}{(x-3)}$

(factorise the top)

$= x + 3$

(divide the top and bottom by $(x-3)$)

(ii) $\dfrac{3x-5}{x-2} + \dfrac{1}{2-x}$

$= \dfrac{3x-5}{x-2} - \dfrac{1}{x-2}$

(as the denominators differ only in sign)

$= \dfrac{3x-5-1}{x-2}$

$= \dfrac{3x-6}{x-2}$

$= \dfrac{3(x-2)}{(x-2)}$

(factorise the top)

$= 3$

(divide top and bottom by $(x-2)$)

Simplify each of the following:

1. $4x(3x^2 + 5x + 6) - 2(10x^2 + 12x)$

2. $(x+2)^2 + (x-2)^2 - 8$

3. $(a+b)^2 - (a-b)^2 - 4ab$

4. $(2a+b)^2 - 4a(a+b)$

Factorise each of the following:

5. $x^2 + 3x$ **6.** $3xy - 6y^2$ **7.** $a^2b + ab^2$ **8.** $9x^2 - 16y^2$ **9.** $121p^2 - q^2$

10. $1 - 25a^2$ **11.** $x^2 - 2x - 8$ **12.** $3x^2 + 13x - 10$ **13.** $6x^2 - 11x + 3$ **14.** $27a^3 + 8b^3$

15. $1 - 64x^3$ **16.** $125 - 8p^3$ **17.** $1 + 125x^3$ **18.** $216 - x^3$ **19.** $1000x^3 + y^3$

Simplify each of the following:

20. $\dfrac{a^2 - 16}{a - 4}$ **21.** $\dfrac{x^2 + 5x}{x^2 + 7x + 10}$ **22.** $\dfrac{a^3 + b^3}{a^2 - ab + b^2}$ **23.** $\dfrac{x^2 + x - 2}{x^2 - x} \times \dfrac{x^2 - 3x}{x^2 - x - 6}$

24. $\dfrac{a^2 - 4}{a - 2} \times \dfrac{a^2 - a - 20}{a^2 - 3a - 10}$ **25.** $\dfrac{x^2 + 8x + 15}{x^2 - 9} \div \dfrac{xy + 5y}{x^2 - 3x}$ **26.** $\dfrac{3a^2}{5b^2} \div \sqrt{\dfrac{9a^2}{100b^2}}$

Express each of the following as one fraction in its lowest terms:

27. $\dfrac{5x-6}{x^2+x-6} - \dfrac{3}{x+3}$

28. $\dfrac{2x}{x^2-1} - \dfrac{1}{x-1}$

29. $\dfrac{4}{4-a^2} - \dfrac{1}{2-a}$

30. $\dfrac{5}{2x-3} - \dfrac{3}{2x^2-3x} - \dfrac{1}{x}$

31. $\dfrac{a}{ab+b^2} - \dfrac{b}{a^2+ab}$

32. $\dfrac{2}{x} - \dfrac{4}{x^2+2x} - \dfrac{1}{x+2}$

Show that each of the following reduces to a constant and find that constant:

33. $\dfrac{x-2}{x-3} + \dfrac{1}{3-x}$

34. $\dfrac{2x-3}{x-2} + \dfrac{1}{2-x}$

35. $\dfrac{5x-3}{3x-2} - \dfrac{x-1}{2-3x}$

36. $\dfrac{1}{1-x} + \dfrac{x}{x-1}$

37. $\dfrac{4x-7}{x-2} + \dfrac{1}{2-x}$

38. $\dfrac{x-2}{x^2+2x} + \dfrac{3}{x^2+3x} - \dfrac{x+4}{x^2+5x+6}$

Simplify each of the following:

39. $\dfrac{x+y}{\dfrac{1}{x}+\dfrac{1}{y}}$

40. $\dfrac{\dfrac{a}{b}-\dfrac{b}{a}}{\dfrac{1}{b}-\dfrac{1}{a}}$

41. $\dfrac{1-\dfrac{3}{x}}{x-\dfrac{9}{x}}$

42. $\dfrac{x-\dfrac{2}{x+1}}{\dfrac{2x}{x+1}-1}$

43. $\dfrac{\dfrac{x+1}{x-1}-\dfrac{x-1}{x+1}}{\dfrac{1}{x+1}+\dfrac{1}{x-1}}$

44. $\left(x+\dfrac{1}{x}\right)^2 - \left(x-\dfrac{1}{x}\right)^2$

45. $\left(\dfrac{1+a^2}{1-a^2}\right)^2 - \left(\dfrac{2a}{1-a^2}\right)^2$

46. Let $f(x) = \dfrac{x^3-1}{x^2-1}$, $\quad x \neq \pm 1$, $\quad$ and $\quad g(x) = \dfrac{x^2+x+1}{x^2-x-2}$, $\quad x \neq -1, 2$,

if $f(x) \div g(x) = ax + b$, find the value of a and b.

47. If $f(x) = \dfrac{1}{x}$, show that $f(p) - f(q) = f\left(\dfrac{pq}{q-p}\right)$.

48. Simplify $(x+a)^3 + (x-a)^3$ and then factorise your simplified expression.

Changing the Subject of a Formula

When we rearrange a formula so that one of the variables is given in terms of the others we are said to be '**changing the subject of the formula**'. The rules in changing the subject of a formula are the same as when solving an equation, that is we can:

1. **Add** or **subtract** the same quantity to both sides.
   (In practice this involves moving a term from one side to another and changing its sign.)
2. **Multiply** or **divide** both sides by the same quantity.
3. **Square** both sides, **cube** both sides, etc.
4. Take the **square root** of both sides, take the **cube root** of both sides, etc.

Note: Whatever letter comes after the word 'express' is to be on its own.

(i) If $\dfrac{1}{b} + \dfrac{1}{a} = \dfrac{1}{c}$, express c in terms of a and b.

(ii) $\sqrt[3]{\dfrac{3p-2}{2p+1}} = q$, express p in terms of q.

Solution:

(i)

$$\dfrac{1}{b} + \dfrac{1}{a} = \dfrac{1}{c}$$

$ac + bc = ab$ [multiply each term by abc to remove fractions]

$c(a + b) = ab$ [take out common factor c on the left-hand side]

$$c = \dfrac{ab}{a+b}$$ [divide both sides by $(a + b)$]

(ii)

$$\sqrt[3]{\dfrac{3p-2}{2p+1}} = q$$

$$\left(\dfrac{3p-2}{2p+1}\right)^{1/3} = q$$ [replace $\sqrt[3]{}$ with $(\ )^{1/3}$]

$$\left[\left(\dfrac{3p-2}{2p+1}\right)^{1/3}\right]^3 = (q)^3$$ [cube both sides]

$$\dfrac{3p-2}{2p+1} = q^3$$ [$(x^{1/3})^3 = x^{1/3 \times 3} = x^1 = x$]

$3p - 2 = (2p + 1)q^3$ [multiply both sides by $(2p + 1)$]

$3p - 2 = 2pq^3 + q^3$ [remove brackets]

$3p - 2pq^3 = q^3 + 2$ [terms with p on the left-hand side]

$p(3 - 2q^3) = q^3 + 2$ [take out common factor p on the left-hand side]

$$p = \dfrac{q^3 + 2}{3 - 2q^3}$$ [divide both sides by $(3 - 2q^3)$]

Exercise 1.2 ▼

1. If $\dfrac{2a - b}{3} = c$, express a in terms of b and c.

2. If $p - \dfrac{t}{q} = r$, express q in terms of p, t and r.

3. If $\dfrac{a}{b} = \dfrac{b}{c} + d$, express c in terms of a, b and d.

4. If $r = \dfrac{q^2 - pr}{q + p}$, express p in terms of q and r.

5. If $x = \dfrac{2t-1}{t-1}$, express t in terms of x.

6. If $\sqrt{5x-2} = y$, express x in terms of y.

7. If $\sqrt{\dfrac{y+1}{y-1}} = x$, express y in terms of x.

8. If $\dfrac{1}{u} + \dfrac{1}{v} = \dfrac{1}{f}$, express f in terms of u and v.

9. If $t = k\sqrt{\dfrac{l}{g}}$, express l in terms of t, k and g.

10. If $\dfrac{p}{2} = \sqrt{\dfrac{1}{x^2-1}}$, express x^2 in terms of p.

11. If $px - b = a - qx$, express x in terms of a, b, p and q.
  If $\sqrt{2p} = 4a$ and $q = -8b^2$, show that $8x = \dfrac{1}{a-b}$.

12. If $\sqrt[3]{x+1} = y$, express x in terms of y.

13. If $\sqrt[3]{\dfrac{ax^2}{1-r}} = y$, express x in terms of y, a and r.

14. If $p = \sqrt{\dfrac{q^2-2r^2}{2q^2+r^2}}$, express r in terms of p and q.

15. If $p = q + \sqrt{q^2-1}$, express q in terms of p.

Undetermined Coefficients

When two expressions in x (or any other variable) are equal to one another for all values of x, we can equate the coefficients of the same powers of x in the two expressions. This is known as the '**principle of undetermined coefficients**'.

Method:

> 1. Remove all fractions and brackets.
> 2. Form equations by equating coefficients of like terms.
> 3. Solve the equations to find the coefficients.

(i) If $a(x + b)^2 + c = 2x^2 + 12x + 23$, for all x, find the value of a, of b and of c.

(ii) If $(ax + k)(x^2 - px + 1) = ax^3 + bx + c$, for all x, show that $c^2 = a(a - b)$.

Solution:

(i) Expand the left-hand side and equate coefficients.

$$a(x + b)^2 + c = 2x^2 + 12x + 23$$
$$a(x^2 + 2bx + b^2) + c = 2x^2 + 12x + 23$$
$$ax^2 + 2abx + ab^2 + c = 2x^2 + 12x + 23$$
$$(a)x^2 + (2ab)x + (ab^2 + c) = 2x^2 + 12x + 23$$

Equating coefficients of like terms:

$a = 2$ ①	$2ab = 12$ ②	$ab^2 + c = 23$ ③
	↓	$2(3)^2 + c = 23$
put $a = 2$ into ②	$2(2)b = 12$	$18 + c = 23$
	$4b = 12$	$c = 5$
	$b = 3$	
	put $a = 2$ and $b = 3$ into ③	

∴ $a = 2$, $b = 3$ and $c = 5$

(ii) Expand the left-hand side and equate coefficients.

$$(ax + k)(x^2 - px + 1) = ax^3 + bx + c$$
$$ax^3 - apx^2 + ax + kx^2 - kpx + k = ax^3 + ox^2 + bx + c \quad \text{(put in } ox^2\text{)}$$
$$ax^3 + (-ap + k)x^2 + (a - kp)x + k = ax^3 + ox^2 + bx + c$$

Equating coefficients of like terms:
(Basic idea is to remove the constants **not** in the answer required)

$-ap + k = 0$ ①	$a - kp = b$ ②	$k = c$ ③

From ③, $k = c$. Replace k with c in ① and ②, as k is not in the answer required.

$-ap + k = 0$ ①	$a - kp = b$ ②
↓	↓
$-ap + c = 0$ ④	$a - cp = b$ ⑤

What we do next is get p on its own from ④ and put this in ⑤.
This removes p which is not in the answer.

$-ap + c = 0$ ④	$a - cp = b$ ⑤
$-ap = -c$	↓
$ap = c$	$a - c\left(\dfrac{c}{a}\right) = b$
$p = \dfrac{c}{a}$	$a - \dfrac{c^2}{a} = b$
	$a^2 - c^2 = ab$
	$-c^2 = ab - a^2$
	$c^2 = a^2 - ab$
	$c^2 = a(a - b)$

1. If $3ax + 5aby = 12x + 40y$ for all values of x and y, find the value of a and b.

2. $a(2x + 3) + b(x - 4) = 4x + 17$ for all values of x. Write two equations in a and b.
   Hence, or otherwise, find the value of a and the value of b.

3. $3(x^2 + 2x) + 7 = p(x^2 + 2) + qx(x - 3) + r$ for all values of x.
   Find the value of p, the value of q and the value of r.

4. $2x(x + 3) = a(x^2 + 1) + b(x^2 - x) + c$ for all values of x.
   Find the value of a, the value of b and the value of c.

5. $(x + 2)(x^2 + px + q) = x^3 + 5x^2 + 2x - 8$ for all values of x. Find the value of p and the value of q.

6. $(x + a)(2x^2 + bx + 1) = 2x^3 + x^2 - 14x + 3$ for all values of x. Find the value of a and the value of b.

7. $p(x + 1)(x + 2) + q(x + 1) + r = 3x^2 + 5x + 7$ for all values of x.
   Find the value of p, the value of q and the value of r.

8. If $2x^2 + 12x + 13 = p(x + q)^2 + r$ for all x, find the value of p, of q and of r.

9. If $n^2 - 4 = a(n - 1)(n - 2) + b(n - 1) + c$, for all values of n, find the value of a, the value of b and the value of c.

10. $(2x + k)(px + q) = x(2px + 2q - p) + r$, for all x. Show that: **(i)** $k = -1$ **(ii)** $q + r = 0$.

11. $(4x + r)(x^2 + s) = 4x^3 + px^2 + qx + 2$, for all x. Show that $pq = 8$.

12. $(ax + k)(x^2 - px + 1) = ax^3 + bx + c$, for all x. Show that:
    (i) $k = c$ **(ii)** $c = ap$ **(iii)** $b = a(1 - p^2)$.

13. Show that $(a + b)^3 = a^3 + 3a^2b + 3ab^2 + b^3$.
    If $x^3 + px^2 + qx + r = (x + h)^3$ for all x, show that: **(i)** $p^2 = 3q$ **(ii)** $q^3 = 27r^2$.

Surds

Properties of Surds:

$$\textbf{1. } \sqrt{ab} = \sqrt{a}\sqrt{b} \qquad\qquad \textbf{2. } \sqrt{\frac{a}{b}} = \frac{\sqrt{a}}{\sqrt{b}} \qquad\qquad \textbf{3. } \sqrt{a}\sqrt{a} = a$$

Simplification of Surds

The key idea is to find the largest possible perfect square number greater than 1 that will divide evenly into the number under the square root and use property 1.

The perfect squares greater than 1 are 4, 9, 16, 25, 36, 49, 64, 81, 100, ..., etc.

Write each of the following in the form of $a\sqrt{b}$, where b is prime:

(i) $\sqrt{32}$ (ii) $\sqrt{45}$ (iii) $\sqrt{75}$

Express in the form $\dfrac{a}{b}$, $a, b \in \mathbf{N}$:   (iv) $\sqrt{\dfrac{9}{4}}$ (v) $\sqrt{2\frac{7}{9}}$

(vi) Express $\dfrac{10}{\sqrt{2}}$ in the form $k\sqrt{2}$.

Solution:

(i) $\sqrt{32} = \sqrt{16 \times 2} = \sqrt{16}\sqrt{2} = 4\sqrt{2}$

(ii) $\sqrt{45} = \sqrt{9 \times 5} = \sqrt{9}\sqrt{5} = 3\sqrt{5}$

(iii) $\sqrt{75} = \sqrt{25 \times 3} = \sqrt{25}\sqrt{3} = 5\sqrt{3}$

(iv) $\sqrt{\dfrac{9}{4}} = \dfrac{\sqrt{9}}{\sqrt{4}} = \dfrac{3}{2}$

(v) $\sqrt{2\frac{7}{9}} = \sqrt{\dfrac{25}{9}} = \dfrac{\sqrt{25}}{\sqrt{9}} = \dfrac{5}{3}$

(vi) $\dfrac{10}{\sqrt{2}} = \dfrac{10}{\sqrt{2}} \times \dfrac{\sqrt{2}}{\sqrt{2}}$ (multiply top and bottom by $\sqrt{2}$)

      $= \dfrac{10\sqrt{2}}{2} = 5\sqrt{2}$

Note: The process of removing a surd from the denominator of an expression is called **'rationalising the denominator'**.

Addition and Subtraction

Only like surds can be added or subtracted. Express each surd in its simplest form and add or subtract like surds.

Example ▼

(i)   Express $\sqrt{18} + \sqrt{50} - \sqrt{8}$ in the form $a\sqrt{b}$, where b is prime.
(ii) $\sqrt{20} - \sqrt{5} + \sqrt{45} = k\sqrt{5}$; find the value of k.

Solution:

(i) $\sqrt{18} + \sqrt{50} - \sqrt{8}$
     $= 3\sqrt{2} + 5\sqrt{2} - 2\sqrt{2}$
     $= 8\sqrt{2} - 2\sqrt{2}$
     $= 6\sqrt{2}$

(ii) $\sqrt{20} - \sqrt{5} + \sqrt{45}$
     $= 2\sqrt{5} - \sqrt{5} + 3\sqrt{5}$
     $= 5\sqrt{5} - \sqrt{5}$
     $= 4\sqrt{5} = k\sqrt{5}$
     $\therefore \; k = 4$

Conjugate Surds

$a + \sqrt{b}$ is a compound surd. Its conjugate is $a - \sqrt{b}$ or $-a + \sqrt{b}$.
$\sqrt{a} - \sqrt{b}$ is a compound surd. Its conjugate is $\sqrt{a} + \sqrt{b}$ or $-\sqrt{a} - \sqrt{b}$.
They have the same components, with one of the signs changed.
The product of a surd and its conjugate is always a rational number.
Think of the difference of two squares: $(a - b)(a + b) = a^2 - b^2$, which is rational.

Example ▼

Show that $\dfrac{-1 + \sqrt{3}}{1 + \sqrt{3}} = 2 - \sqrt{3}$

Solution:

$$\frac{-1 + \sqrt{3}}{1 + \sqrt{3}} = \frac{-1 + \sqrt{3}}{1 + \sqrt{3}} \times \frac{1 - \sqrt{3}}{1 - \sqrt{3}} \qquad \text{(multiply top and bottom by } 1 - \sqrt{3}\text{, the conjugate surd of } 1 + \sqrt{3})$$

$$= \frac{-1 + \sqrt{3} + \sqrt{3} - 3}{1 - \sqrt{3} + \sqrt{3} - 3} \qquad \text{(multiply top by the top and bottom by the bottom)}$$

$$= \frac{-4 + 2\sqrt{3}}{-2} \qquad \text{(simplify top and bottom)}$$

$$= 2 - \sqrt{3} \qquad \text{(divide each part on top by } -2)$$

Note: We could have also multiplied the top and bottom by $-1 + \sqrt{3}$, also the conjugate surd of $1 + \sqrt{3}$

Exercise 1.4 ▼

Express each of the following in the form $a\sqrt{b}$, where b is prime:

1. $\sqrt{12}$ **2.** $\sqrt{18}$ **3.** $\sqrt{20}$ **4.** $\sqrt{72}$ **5.** $\sqrt{48}$ **6.** $\sqrt{45}$

7. $\sqrt{125}$ **8.** $\sqrt{63}$ **9.** $\sqrt{500}$ **10.** $\frac{1}{2}\sqrt{80}$ **11.** $\frac{1}{3}\sqrt{108}$ **12.** $\frac{3}{5}\sqrt{75}$

Express each of the following in the form $\dfrac{p}{q}$, $p, q \in \mathbf{N}$:

13. $\sqrt{\dfrac{4}{9}}$ **14.** $\sqrt{\dfrac{36}{49}}$ **15.** $\sqrt{\dfrac{100}{81}}$ **16.** $\sqrt{2\tfrac{1}{4}}$ **17.** $\sqrt{1\tfrac{9}{16}}$ **18.** $\sqrt{4\tfrac{21}{25}}$

Express each of the following in the form $a\sqrt{b}$, where b is prime:

19. $\dfrac{12}{\sqrt{3}}$ **20.** $\dfrac{6}{\sqrt{2}}$ **21.** $\dfrac{15}{\sqrt{5}}$ **22.** $\dfrac{28}{\sqrt{7}}$ **23.** $\dfrac{12}{\sqrt{18}}$ **24.** $\dfrac{60}{\sqrt{80}}$

Express each of the following in the form $\dfrac{a\sqrt{b}}{c}$, where b is prime:

25. $\dfrac{5}{\sqrt{2}}$ **26.** $\dfrac{4}{\sqrt{3}}$ **27.** $\dfrac{6}{\sqrt{8}}$ **28.** $\dfrac{15}{2\sqrt{5}}$ **29.** $\dfrac{8}{\sqrt{18}}$ **30.** $\dfrac{25}{\sqrt{45}}$

31. $\sqrt{50} - \sqrt{200} + \sqrt{98} = k\sqrt{2}$. Find the value of k^2.

32. Express $(2 - \sqrt{3})^2$ in the form $a + b\sqrt{c}$, where $a, b, c \in \mathbf{Z}$.

33. Express $(7 + \sqrt{5})^2 - (7 - \sqrt{5})^2$ in the form $k\sqrt{5}$, $\quad k \in \mathbf{N}$.

34. Express $\dfrac{1}{3\sqrt{5}} - \dfrac{1}{2\sqrt{20}}$ in the form $k\sqrt{5}$, $\quad k \in \mathbf{Q}$.

35. Show that:

(i) $\dfrac{1}{\sqrt{2}+1} = \sqrt{2} - 1$

(ii) $\dfrac{1}{2-\sqrt{3}} = 2 + \sqrt{3}$

(iii) $\dfrac{\sqrt{2}+1}{\sqrt{2}-1} = 3 + 2\sqrt{2}$

(iv) $\dfrac{\sqrt{5}-1}{\sqrt{5}-2} = 3 + \sqrt{5}$

(v) $\dfrac{\sqrt{3}+\sqrt{2}}{\sqrt{3}-\sqrt{2}} = 5 + 2\sqrt{6}$

(vi) $\dfrac{\sqrt{5}-1}{3-\sqrt{5}} = \dfrac{1+\sqrt{5}}{2}$

(vii) $\dfrac{1}{\sqrt{3}-1} + \dfrac{1}{\sqrt{3}+1} = \sqrt{3}$

(viii) $\dfrac{1}{\sqrt{2}-1} - \dfrac{1}{\sqrt{2}+1} = 2$

36. Express $\dfrac{1}{a} - \dfrac{1}{b}$ as a single fraction.

Hence, or otherwise, express $\dfrac{1}{a} - \dfrac{1}{b}$ in the form $-k\sqrt{k}$, when $a = 1 - \sqrt{2}$ and $b = 1 + \sqrt{2}$.

37. Factorise $x^2 - y^2$.

Hence, or otherwise, evaluate $\sqrt{x^2 - y^2}$, when $x = \left(\sqrt{a} + \dfrac{1}{\sqrt{a}}\right)$ and $y = \left(\sqrt{a} - \dfrac{1}{\sqrt{a}}\right)$, $a > 0$.

Simultaneous Linear Equations

Simultaneous linear equations in two variables are solved with the following steps:

1. Write both equations in the form $ax + by = k$ and label the equations ① and ②.
2. Multiply one or both of the equations by a number in order to make the coefficients of x or y the same, but of opposite sign.
3. Add to remove the variable with equal coefficients but of opposite sign.
4. Solve the resultant equation to find the value of the remaining unknown (x or y).
5. Substitute this value in equation ① or ② to find the value of the other unknown.

Solution Containing Fractions

If the solution contains fractions the substitution can be difficult.
In such cases the following method is useful:

| 1. Eliminate y and find x. | 2. Eliminate x and find y. |

Solve for x and y the simultaneous equations

$$\frac{x+1}{2} - \frac{y+3}{3} = 4, \qquad x + \frac{y-3}{2} = \frac{1}{2}$$

Solution:

Write each equation in the form $ax + by = k$ and label the equations ① and ②.

$\dfrac{x+1}{2} - \dfrac{y+3}{3} = 4$	$x + \dfrac{y-3}{2} = \dfrac{1}{2}$
$\dfrac{6(x+1)}{2} - \dfrac{6(y+3)}{3} = 6(4)$	$2(x) + \dfrac{2(y-3)}{2} = 2(\tfrac{1}{2})$
(multiply each part by 6)	(multiply each part by 2)
$3(x+1) - 2(y+3) = 24$	$2x + (y-3) = 1$
$3x + 3 - 2y - 6 = 24$	$2x + y - 3 = 1$
$3x - 2y = 27$ ①	$2x + y = 4$ ②

Now solve between equations ① and ②:

$3x - 2y = 27$ ①	$2x + y = 4$ ②
$\underline{4x + 2y = 8}$ ② $\times 2$	$2(5) + y = 4$
$7x = 35$ (add)	$10 + y = 4$
$x = 5$	$y = -6$
(put $x = 5$ into ① or ②)	

Thus, $x = 5$ and $y = -6$.

Simultaneous linear equations in three variables are solved with the following steps:

1. Write all three equations in the form $ax + by + cz = k$ and label the equations ①, ② and ③.
2. Select one pair of equations and eliminate one of the variables; call this equation ④.
3. Select another pair of equations and eliminate the **same** variable; call this equation ⑤.
4. Solve the equations ④ and ⑤.
5. Put the answers from step 4 into ① or ② or ③ to find the value of the third variable.

Example ▼

Solve for x, y and z:

$$x + 2y + z = 3$$
$$5x - 3y + 2z = 19$$
$$3x + 2y - 3z = -5$$

Solution:

All three equations are in the form $ax + by + cz = k$.
Label the equations ①, ② and ③.
Eliminate z from two different pairs of equations.

$$x + 2y + z = 3 \quad ①$$
$$5x - 3y + 2z = 19 \quad ②$$
$$3x + 2y - 3z = -5 \quad ③$$

$$
\begin{aligned}
-2x - 4y - 2z &= -6 \quad ① \times -2 \\
5x - 3y + 2z &= 19 \quad ② \\
\hline
3x - 7y &= 13 \quad ④ \text{ (add)}
\end{aligned}
$$

$$
\begin{aligned}
3x + 6y + 3z &= 9 \quad ① \times 3 \\
3x + 2y - 3z &= -5 \quad ③ \\
\hline
6x + 8y &= 4 \quad ⑤
\end{aligned}
$$

Now solve between equations ④ and ⑤ to find the values of x and y.

$$
\begin{aligned}
-6x + 14y &= -26 \quad ④ \times -2 \\
6x + 8y &= 4 \quad ⑤ \\
\hline
22y &= -22 \\
y &= -1
\end{aligned}
$$
(put $y = -1$ into ④ or ⑤)

$$
\begin{aligned}
3x - 7y &= 13 \quad ④ \\
3x - 7(-1) &= 13 \\
3x + 7 &= 13 \\
3x &= 6 \\
x &= 2
\end{aligned}
$$

Now put $x = 2$ and $y = -1$ into ① or ② or ③ to find the value of z.

$$
\begin{aligned}
x + 2y + z &= 3 \quad ① \\
(2) + 2(-1) + z &= 3 \qquad \text{(put in } x = 2 \text{ and } y = -1) \\
2 - 2 + z &= 3 \\
z &= 3
\end{aligned}
$$

Thus, $x = 2$, $y = -1$ and $z = 3$.

Note: Any of the variables x, y or z could have been eliminated at the beginning.

If one equation contains only two unknowns, then the other two equations should be used to obtain a second equation in the same two unknowns, e.g. solve:

$$3x + 2y - z = 3 \quad ① \qquad 5x - 3y + 2z = 3 \quad ② \qquad 5x + 3z = 14 \quad ③$$

Here, from equations ① and ②, y should be eliminated to obtain an equation in x and z, which should then be taken with equation ③.

Exercise 1.5 ▼

Solve for x and y:

1. $3x + 2y = 9$
$\quad x - y = -2$

2. $4x + 3y = -23$
$\quad x + 2y = -12$

3. $5x + 4y = 22$
$\quad 3x + 5y = 21$

4. $x = 5 - y$
$\quad \dfrac{4x}{3} + 8 = \dfrac{y}{2}$

5. $3x - 2y = 19$
$\quad \dfrac{x}{3} + \dfrac{y}{2} = 5$

6. $2x + y = 3(y - x) + 7$
$\quad \dfrac{x}{3} = 2 - \dfrac{y}{4}$

7. $\dfrac{2x-5}{3} + \dfrac{y}{5} = 6$

$\dfrac{3x}{10} + 2 = \dfrac{3y-5}{2}$

8. $\dfrac{3x}{5} - \dfrac{y}{4} = 8$

$\dfrac{2x}{3} = 13 - \dfrac{3y}{4}$

9. $2x + 3y = -2$

$3x + 7y = -6$

Solve for x, y and z:

10. $3x + 5y - z = -3$
$2x + y - 3z = -9$
$x + 3y + 2z = 7$

11. $2x + 3y - z = -7$
$5x - 2y - 4z = 3$
$3x + y + 2z = -7$

12. $3x - y + 3z = 1$
$x + 2y - 2z = -1$
$4x - y + 5z = 4$

13. $x + y - z = 0$
$x - y + z = 4$
$x - y - z = -8$

14. $x + 2y - z = -1$
$2x + y + 3z = 14$
$3x - y - z = -14$

15. $2x + y - z = -3$
$x + 3y + 2z = 1$
$3x - 2y + z = 10$

16. $2x + y - z = -3$
$x + 3y + 2z = 1$
$3x - y = 9$

17. $x + y + z = 1$
$2x - 3y - 2z = -9$
$2x - 3z = -16$

18. $x + y = -1$
$y + 3z = -11$
$3x + 5z = -12$

19. **(i)** Solve the simultaneous equations:
$3x + y + z = 16$
$2x - y + 3z = 24$
$x - y - z = 0$

(ii) Hence, or otherwise, solve:
$3a^2 + (b-2) + (2c-1) = 16$
$2a^2 - (b-2) + 3(2c-1) = 24$
$a^2 - (b-2) - (2c-1) = 0$

20. If the curve $y = ax^2 + bx + c$ contains the points $(0, 5)$, $(1, 4)$ and $(-1, 10)$ find the value of a, the value of b and the value of c.

21. $f(x) = px^2 + qx + r$. If $f(-2) = 7$, $f(1) = -2$ and $f(2) = 3$, find the value of p, the value of q and the value of r.

QUADRATIC AND CUBIC EQUATIONS

Quadratic Equations

Any equation of the form $ax^2 + bx + c = 0$, $a \neq 0$, is called a quadratic equation.
To solve a quadratic equation we either:

> **1.** Factorise and let each factor = 0; or
>
> **2.** Use the formula $x = \dfrac{-b \pm \sqrt{b^2 - 4ac}}{2a}$.

Example ▼

(i) Solve $6x^2 - 11x - 10 = 0$.
(ii) Solve $x^2 + 4x - 1 = 0$, giving your solutions in surd form.

Solution:

(i)
$$6x^2 - 11x - 10 = 0$$
$$(3x + 2)(2x - 5) = 0 \qquad \text{(factorise the left-hand side)}$$
$$3x + 2 = 0 \quad \text{or} \quad 2x - 5 = 0 \qquad \text{(let each factor = 0)}$$
$$3x = -2 \quad \text{or} \quad 2x = 5$$
$$x = -\tfrac{2}{3} \quad \text{or} \quad x = \tfrac{5}{2} \qquad \text{(solve each simple equation)}$$

(ii) $x^2 + 4x - 1 = 0$ (answers in surd form ∴ use formula)

$$x = \frac{-b \pm \sqrt{b^2 - 4ac}}{2a}$$

$$\boxed{x^2 + 4x - 1 = 0 \\ a = 1, b = 4, c = -1}$$

$$x = \frac{-4 \pm \sqrt{(4)^2 - 4(1)(-1)}}{2(1)}$$
$$x = \frac{-4 \pm \sqrt{16 + 4}}{2}$$
$$x = \frac{-4 \pm \sqrt{20}}{2}$$

$$\boxed{\sqrt{20} \\ = \sqrt{4 \times 5} \\ = \sqrt{4}\sqrt{5} \\ = 2\sqrt{5}}$$

$$x = \frac{-4 \pm 2\sqrt{5}}{2}$$
$$x = -2 \pm \sqrt{5}$$
$$\therefore x = -2 + \sqrt{5} \quad \text{or} \quad x = -2 - \sqrt{5}.$$

In some questions we can use the roots of one quadratic equation to help us to solve another quadratic equation by using a substitution.

Example ▼

Solve the equation $x - 11 + \dfrac{24}{x} = 0$.

Hence, solve $\quad (y^2 - 2y) - 11 + \dfrac{24}{(y^2 - 2y)} = 0.$

Solution:

$$x - 11 + \frac{24}{x} = 0$$

$x^2 - 11x + 24 = 0$ (multiply each part by x)

$(x - 3)(x - 8) = 0$ (factorise the left-hand side)

$x - 3 = 0 \quad$ or $\quad x - 8 = 0$ (let each factor $= 0$)

$\qquad x = 3 \quad$ or $\qquad x = 8$ (solve each simple equation)

$\text{let } (y^2 - 2y) = x \qquad \text{(this is the substitution)}$

$$y^2 - 2y = 3 \qquad\qquad \text{or} \qquad\qquad y^2 - 2y = 8$$

$$y^2 - 2y - 3 = 0 \qquad\qquad\qquad\qquad y^2 - 2y - 8 = 0$$

$$(y + 1)(y - 3) = 0 \qquad\qquad\qquad\quad (y + 2)(y - 4) = 0$$

$y + 1 = 0 \quad$ or $\quad y - 3 = 0 \qquad\qquad y + 2 = 0 \quad$ or $\quad y - 4 = 0$

$\quad y = -1 \quad$ or $\qquad y = 3 \qquad\qquad\quad y = -2 \quad$ or $\qquad y = 4$

$$\therefore \quad y = -2, -1, 3, 4$$

Exercise 2.1 ▼

Solve each of the following equations:

1. $2x^2 + 5x - 12 = 0$

2. $x^2 - 3x = 0$

3. $x^2 - 4 = 0$

4. $3x^2 + 14x + 8 = 0$

5. $5x^2 + 14x - 3 = 0$

6. $x^2 - 6x + 9 = 0$

7. $2x^2 = 3x$

8. $6x^2 - x = 2$

9. $9x^2 - 12x + 4 = 0$

10. $8x^2 = 9 - 6x$

11. $15x^2 + x - 6 = 0$

12. $4x^2 - 25 = 0$

Solve each of the following equations, giving your solutions in surd form:

13. $x^2 + 6x + 4 = 0$

14. $x^2 - 4x + 1 = 0$

15. $x^2 - 8x + 13 = 0$

16. $x^2 - 2x - 2 = 0$

17. $x^2 - 4x - 14 = 0$

18. $x^2 + 10x - 23 = 0$

Write each of the following equations in the form $ax^2 + bx + c = 0$, and hence, solve each equation:

19. $1 - \dfrac{5}{x} + \dfrac{6}{x^2} = 0$

20. $3 + \dfrac{2}{x - 2} = \dfrac{1}{x}$

21. $\dfrac{1}{2} = \dfrac{1}{x - 1} - \dfrac{1}{x}$

22. $\dfrac{1}{2} - \dfrac{1}{x} = \dfrac{1}{x + 3}$

23. $\dfrac{5}{2} = \dfrac{1}{x - 1} + \dfrac{3}{x + 2}$

24. $\dfrac{2}{9} = \dfrac{1}{x - 5} - \dfrac{1}{x + 1}$

25. Solve $\dfrac{1}{4} - \dfrac{1}{x+2} = \dfrac{1}{x-2}$, giving your answers in the form $a \pm b\sqrt{c}$.

26. Solve $x^2 - x - 20 = 0$. Hence, solve $\left(2k + \dfrac{2}{k}\right)^2 - \left(2k + \dfrac{2}{k}\right) - 20 = 0.$

27. Solve $3x^2 + 16x - 12 = 0$. Hence, solve $3\left(y - \dfrac{7}{y}\right)^2 + 16\left(y - \dfrac{7}{y}\right) - 12 = 0.$

28. Solve $x^2 - 2x - 24 = 0$. Hence, solve $\left(x + \dfrac{4}{x}\right)^2 - 2\left(x + \dfrac{4}{x}\right) - 24 = 0.$

29. Solve $x^2 - 6x + 8 = 0$. Hence, solve $\left(x + \dfrac{1}{x}\right)^2 - 6\left(x + \dfrac{1}{x}\right) + 8 = 0.$

30. Solve: **(i)** $x^4 - 13x^2 + 36 = 0$ **(ii)** $x^4 - 17x^2 + 16 = 0$.

Modulus and Irrational Equations

Modulus Equations

The modulus of x, written $|x|$, is defined as its positive or absolute value.
For example, $|5| = 5$ and $|-2| = 2$.
A modulus equation is one where the variable is contained within a modulus.
For example, $|x - 1| = 4$, is a modulus equation.
Note: If $|x| = 3$, then $x = 3$ or $x = -3$.

Modulus equations are solved with the following steps:

> **1.** Arrange to have the modulus part by itself on one side of the equation.
> **2.** Square both sides (this removes the modulus bars).
> **3.** Solve the resultant equation.

Note: If there are two modulus parts, arrange to have one modulus part on each side.

Example ▼

Solve $2|x - 2| - |x + 3| = 0$

Solution:

$2|x - 2| - |x + 3| = 0$

$\quad\quad 2|x - 2| = |x + 3|$ (one modulus on each side)

$\quad (2|x - 2|)^2 = (|x + 3|)^2$ (square both sides)

$4(x^2 - 4x + 4) = x^2 + 6x + 9$ $((ab)^2 = a^2b^2)$

$4x^2 - 16x + 16 = x^2 + 6x + 9$ (remove brackets)

$\quad 3x^2 - 22x + 7 = 0$

$\quad (3x - 1)(x - 7) = 0$

$3x - 1 = 0$ or $x - 7 = 0$

$\quad 3x = 1$ or $x = 7$

$\quad x = \tfrac{1}{3}$ or $x = 7$

Irrational Equations

An irrational equation is one where the variable is contained under a square root.

For example, $\sqrt{x+2} = x - 4$ is an irrational equation.

Irrational equations are solved with the following steps:

> **1.** Arrange to have the surd (root) part on its own on one side.
> **2.** Square both sides.
> **3.** Solve the resultant equation.
> **4.** Test every solution in the **original** equation.

Note: Sometimes after squaring both sides there will still be a surd part left in the equation. In this case, arrange to have this surd part on its own on one side and then square both sides again.

Example

Solve $x = \sqrt{19 - 2x} + 2$

Solution:

$$x = \sqrt{19 - 2x} + 2$$
$$(x - 2) = (\sqrt{19 - 2x}) \qquad \text{(rearrange with surd part on its own)}$$
$$(x - 2)^2 = (\sqrt{19 - 2x})^2 \qquad \text{(square both sides)}$$
$$x^2 - 4x + 4 = 19 - 2x \qquad \text{(remove brackets)}$$
$$x^2 - 2x - 15 = 0 \qquad \text{(write in the form } ax^2 + bx + c = 0)$$
$$(x + 3)(x - 5) = 0 \qquad \text{(factorise left-hand side)}$$
$$x + 3 = 0 \quad \text{or} \quad x - 5 = 0 \qquad \text{(let each factor = 0)}$$
$$x = -3 \quad \text{or} \quad x = 5 \qquad \text{(solve each simple equation)}$$

Check $x = -3$: $\quad -3 = \sqrt{19 - 2(-3)} + 2 = \sqrt{25} + 2 = 5 + 2 = 7 \quad$ **False**

Check $x = 5$: $\quad 5 = \sqrt{19 - 2(5)} + 2 = \sqrt{9} + 2 = 3 + 2 = 5 \quad$ **True**

$\therefore \quad x = 5$ is the only solution.

Note: Squaring both sides introduced a new root, called an extraneous root, $x = -3$. This does not satisfy the original equation and hence is rejected.

Note: The square root of a number is defined as the 'positive square root'.
For example, $\sqrt{16} = 4$, not ± 4.

Exercise 2.2 ▼

Solve each of the following equations:

1. $|x - 1| = 4$

2. $|x - 2| = 3$

3. $|x + 3| = 5$

4. $|2x - 1| = 3$

5. $|3x - 1| - 4 = 0$

6. $2|x - 1| = 3$

7. $|x + 1| = |x - 2|$

8. $|2x + 1| = |x - 1|$

9. $|2x - 1| - x = 0$

10. $|4 - 3x| - |2x - 1| = 0$

11. $|3x - 1| - |1 - 2x| = 0$

12. $2|x - 1| = |x + 1|$

13. $2|x + 1| - |x + 3| = 0$

14. $3|x + 1| = |2x - 1|$

15. $|2 - x| = \frac{1}{2}|x|$

16. $\left|\dfrac{x - 2}{3}\right| = 1$

17. $\left|\dfrac{3x + 1}{x - 1}\right| = 2$

18. $\left|\dfrac{2x + 1}{x + 2}\right| = \dfrac{1}{2}$

19. $x = \sqrt{5x - 4}$

20. $x = \sqrt{x + 6}$

21. $x + 6 = 5\sqrt{x}$

22. $x - 2 = \sqrt{2x - 1}$

23. $2x - 1 = \sqrt{8x + 1}$

24. $2x - 7 = \sqrt{x^2 - 3x - 1}$

25. $x = \sqrt{3x - 5} + 1$

26. $x - \sqrt{x + 3} = 3$

27. $x + 1 = 3\sqrt{x - 1}$

Questions 28–33 require squaring twice:

28. $\sqrt{x + 1} = \sqrt{x + 9}$

29. $1 + \sqrt{x} = \sqrt{3(x - 1)}$

30. $2\sqrt{x} = \sqrt{4x - 11} + 1$

31. $\sqrt{3x + 1} = \sqrt{5x + 1}$

32. $\sqrt{x + 2} = \sqrt{2x + 7}$

33. $\sqrt{3x - 2} = 2 + \sqrt{x - 2}$

34. Solve **(i)** $\dfrac{|1 - 3x|}{\sqrt{x^2 + 1}} = \sqrt{8}$ **(ii)** $\dfrac{5|x - 1|}{\sqrt{x^2 + 1}} = \sqrt{10}$

Simultaneous Equations, One Linear and One Quadratic

The **method of substitution** is used to solve between a linear equation and a quadratic equation.

The method involves three steps:

1. From the linear equation express one variable in terms of the other.
2. Substitute this into the quadratic equation and solve.
3. Substitute separately the value(s) obtained in step 2 into the linear equation in step 1 to find the corresponding value(s) of the other variable.

Example ▼

Solve the simultaneous equations $2x - 3y - 1 = 0$ and $x^2 + xy - 4y^2 = 2$.

Solution:

1. $2x - 3y - 1 = 0$ \qquad (get x, or y, on its own from the linear equation)

   $2x = 3y + 1$

   $x = \left(\dfrac{3y + 1}{2}\right)$ \qquad (x on its own)

2. \qquad\qquad $x^2 + xy - 4y^2 = 2$

   $\left(\dfrac{3y + 1}{2}\right)^2 + \left(\dfrac{3y + 1}{2}\right)y - 4y^2 = 2$ \qquad $\left(\text{put in } \left(\dfrac{3y + 1}{2}\right) \text{ for } x\right)$

   $\dfrac{(9y^2 + 6y + 1)}{4} + \dfrac{(3y^2 + y)}{2} - 4y^2 = 2$

$$(9y^2 + 6y + 1) + 2(3y^2 + y) - 16y^2 = 8 \qquad \text{(multiply each part by 4)}$$
$$9y^2 + 6y + 1 + 6y^2 + 2y - 16y^2 = 8$$
$$-y^2 + 8y - 7 = 0$$
$$y^2 - 8y + 7 = 0$$
$$(y - 1)(y - 7) = 0$$
$$y - 1 = 0 \qquad \text{or} \qquad y - 7 = 0$$
$$y = 1 \qquad \text{or} \qquad y = 7$$

3. Substitute separately $y = 1$ and $y = 7$ into the linear equation.

$y = 1$: $\qquad\qquad x = \dfrac{3y + 1}{2} = \dfrac{3(1) + 1}{2} = \dfrac{4}{2} = 2$

$y = 7$: $\qquad\qquad x = \dfrac{3y + 1}{2} = \dfrac{3(7) + 1}{2} = \dfrac{22}{2} = 11$

Thus, the solutions are $x = 2$, $y = 1$ or $x = 11$, $y = 7$.

Exercise 2.3 ▼

Solve the following pairs of simultaneous equations:

1. $x + 2y = 5$
    $x^2 + y^2 = 10$

2. $x - y = 1$
    $xy = 42$

3. $3x - y - 5 = 0$
    $xy - x = 0$

4. $x + y - 6 = 0$
    $x^2 + 2y^2 - 24 = 0$

5. $x - y - 3 = 0$
    $x^2 - 3y^2 = 13$

6. $x + y = 8$
    $x^2 + xy + y^2 = 52$

7. $2x + y = 3$
    $x^2 + xy + y^2 = 3$

8. $3x + y - 5 = 0$
    $2x^2 + 2xy + y^2 = 10$

9. $x + y = 3$
    $2x^2 + 3xy + 2y^2 = 16$

10. $\dfrac{3x}{y} = 1 + \dfrac{7}{y}$
    $x^2 - xy + y^2 = 7$

11. $1 = \dfrac{2}{x} - \dfrac{2y}{x}$
    $x^2 + 2xy - 8 = 0$

12. $\dfrac{x}{y} + 1 = \dfrac{10}{y}$
    $x^2 - y^2 = 40$

13. $2x - 3y - 1 = 0$
    $x^2 - 2xy - 3y^2 + 3 = 0$

14. $5x - 2y + 2 = 0$
    $x^2 + 4y^2 + x + 2y - 58 = 0$

15. $2x + 3y + 4 = 0$
    $(x + 3y)(2x - y) = 4$

Sum and Product of the Roots of a Quadratic Equation

The quadratic equation $ax^2 + bx + c = 0$ can be written $x^2 + \dfrac{b}{a}x + \dfrac{c}{a} = 0$.

The roots of this equation are usually denoted by α and β.
Now we can write down a quadratic equation with roots α and β.

$$x = \alpha \qquad \text{and} \qquad x = \beta$$
$$x - \alpha = 0 \qquad \text{and} \qquad x - \beta = 0$$
$$(x - \alpha)(x - \beta) = 0$$
$$x^2 - \alpha x - \beta x + \alpha\beta = 0$$
$$x^2 - (\alpha + \beta)x + \alpha\beta = 0$$

Thus, $\qquad\qquad\qquad x^2 - (\alpha + \beta)x + \alpha\beta = x^2 + \dfrac{b}{a}x + \dfrac{c}{a}$

Equating the coefficients of x and the constant terms:

$$\alpha + \beta = -\frac{b}{a} \quad \text{and} \quad \alpha\beta = \frac{c}{a}$$

The quadratic equation can be written:

$$x^2 - (\alpha + \beta)x + \alpha\beta = 0$$
$$\text{or}$$
$$x^2 - (\text{sum of the roots})\,x + (\text{product of the roots}) = 0$$

This can be used to obtain a new quadratic equation whose roots are known or are given as functions of α and β.

Example ▼

If α and β are the roots of the equation $2x^2 - 6x + 1 = 0$, find the value of:

(i) $\alpha + \beta$ **(ii)** $\alpha\beta$ **(iii)** $\alpha^2 + \beta^2$ **(iv)** $\alpha^3\beta + \alpha\beta^3$

(v) $|\alpha - \beta|$ **(vi)** $\dfrac{1}{\alpha^2} + \dfrac{1}{\beta^2}$ **(vii)** $\alpha^3 + \beta^3$

Find a quadratic equation with roots $\dfrac{\alpha}{\beta}$ and $\dfrac{\beta}{\alpha}$ and write your answer in the form $px^2 + qx + r = 0$ where $p, q, r \in \mathbf{Z}$.

Solution:

$$2x^2 - 6x + 1 = 0$$
$$x^2 - 3x + \tfrac{1}{2} = 0 \qquad \text{(make coefficient of } x^2 \text{ equal to 1)}$$

(i) $\alpha + \beta = 3$ **(ii)** $\alpha\beta = \tfrac{1}{2}$

What we do next is write each of the other expressions in terms of $(\alpha + \beta)$ and $\alpha\beta$ or use previous parts of the question.

(iii)
$$\alpha + \beta = 3$$
$$(\alpha + \beta)^2 = (3)^2$$
$$\alpha^2 + 2\alpha\beta + \beta^2 = 9$$
$$\alpha^2 + \beta^2 = 9 - 2\alpha\beta$$
$$\alpha^2 + \beta^2 = 9 - 2(\tfrac{1}{2})$$
$$\alpha^2 + \beta^2 = 9 - 1 = 8$$

(iv)
$$\alpha^3\beta + \alpha\beta^3$$
$$= \alpha\beta(\alpha^2 + \beta^2) \qquad \text{(factorise)}$$
$$= \tfrac{1}{2}(8)$$
$$= 4$$

(v)
$$(\alpha - \beta)^2 = \alpha^2 - 2\alpha\beta + \beta^2$$
$$(\alpha - \beta)^2 = (\alpha^2 + \beta^2) - 2\alpha\beta$$
$$(\alpha - \beta)^2 = 8 - 2(\tfrac{1}{2})$$
$$(\alpha - \beta)^2 = 8 - 1$$
$$(\alpha - \beta)^2 = 7$$
$$(\alpha - \beta) = \pm\sqrt{7}$$
$$\therefore \quad |\alpha - \beta| = \sqrt{7}$$

(vi)
$$\dfrac{1}{\alpha^2} + \dfrac{1}{\beta^2}$$
$$= \dfrac{\alpha^2 + \beta^2}{\alpha^2\beta^2}$$
$$= \dfrac{\alpha^2 + \beta^2}{(\alpha\beta)^2}$$
$$= \dfrac{8}{(\tfrac{1}{2})^2} = \dfrac{8}{\tfrac{1}{4}} = 32$$

(vii) $\alpha^3 + \beta^3$

$\quad = (\alpha + \beta)(\alpha^2 - \alpha\beta + \beta^2) \qquad$ (factorise, sum of two cubes)

$\quad = (\alpha + \beta)[(\alpha^2 + \beta^2) - \alpha\beta] \qquad$ (group into previous expressions)

$\quad = (3)[(8) - \tfrac{1}{2}]$

$\quad = (3)(7\tfrac{1}{2}) = 22\tfrac{1}{2}$

$x^2 - $ (sum of the roots)$x + $ (product of the roots)$ = 0$

$x^2 - \left(\dfrac{\alpha}{\beta} + \dfrac{\beta}{\alpha}\right)x + \left(\dfrac{\alpha}{\beta}\right)\left(\dfrac{\beta}{\alpha}\right) = 0$

$x^2 - \left(\dfrac{\alpha^2 + \beta^2}{\alpha\beta}\right)x + 1 = 0$

$x^2 - \left(\dfrac{8}{\tfrac{1}{2}}\right)x + 1 = 0$

$x^2 - 16x + 1 = 0$

$$\dfrac{\alpha}{\beta} + \dfrac{\beta}{\alpha} = \dfrac{\alpha^2 + \beta^2}{\alpha\beta}$$

$$\alpha^2 + \beta^2 = 8$$
$$\alpha\beta = \tfrac{1}{2}$$

Example ▼

One root of the equation $ax^2 + bx + c = 0$ is five times the other.
Show that $5b^2 = 36ac, \qquad a \neq 0.$

Solution:

Let the roots be α and 5α.

$\quad ax^2 + bx + c = 0$

$\quad x^2 + \dfrac{b}{a}x + \dfrac{c}{a} = 0 \qquad$ (make coefficient of x^2 equal to 1)

$\quad \therefore \quad \alpha + 5\alpha = -\dfrac{b}{a} \qquad$ and $\qquad (\alpha)(5\alpha) = \dfrac{c}{a}$

$\quad\quad\quad 6\alpha = -\dfrac{b}{a} \quad ① \qquad$ and $\qquad 5\alpha^2 = \dfrac{c}{a} \quad ②$

α is in both equations and not in the solution required.
Therefore, get α on its own from ① and put this into ②.

$$6\alpha = -\dfrac{b}{a} \quad ① \qquad\qquad\qquad 5\alpha^2 = \dfrac{c}{a}$$

$$\alpha = \left(-\dfrac{b}{6a}\right) \qquad\qquad\qquad 5\left(-\dfrac{b}{6a}\right)^2 = \dfrac{c}{a}$$

$$\text{put this into ②} \qquad\qquad\qquad 5\left(\dfrac{b^2}{36a^2}\right) = \dfrac{c}{a}$$

$$\dfrac{5b^2}{36a^2} = \dfrac{c}{a}$$

$$5ab^2 = 36a^2c$$

$$5b^2 = 36ac$$

1. If α and β are the roots of the equation $x^2 + 2x + 5 = 0$, find the value of:

   (i) $\alpha + \beta$ (ii) $\alpha\beta$ (iii) $\alpha^2\beta + \alpha\beta^2$ (iv) $\alpha^2 + \beta^2$

   (v) $\alpha^3\beta + \alpha\beta^3$ (vi) $(\alpha - \beta)^2$ (vii) $\alpha^3 + \beta^3$ (viii) $(\alpha^2 - \beta)(\beta^2 - \alpha)$

   (ix) $\dfrac{1}{\alpha} + \dfrac{1}{\beta}$ (x) $\dfrac{\alpha}{\beta} + \dfrac{\beta}{\alpha}$ (xi) $\dfrac{2\beta}{1 + \dfrac{\beta}{\alpha}}$ (xii) $\dfrac{1}{\alpha\beta} - \dfrac{1}{\beta} - \dfrac{1}{\alpha}$

2. If α and β are the roots of the equation $x^2 - 4x - 3 = 0$, find the value of:

   (i) $3\alpha + 3\beta$ (ii) $\alpha^2\beta^2$ (iii) $\alpha^2 + \beta^2$ (iv) $\alpha^3 + \beta^3$

   (v) $\dfrac{4}{\alpha} + \dfrac{4}{\beta}$ (vi) $\dfrac{\alpha}{\beta} + \dfrac{\beta}{\alpha}$ (vii) $\alpha(1 + \beta) + \beta(1 + \alpha)$ (viii) $\left(\alpha + \dfrac{1}{\beta}\right)\left(\beta + \dfrac{1}{\alpha}\right)$

   Form a quadratic equation, with integer coefficients, whose roots are:

   (ix) $2\alpha, 2\beta$ (x) α^2, β^2 (xi) $\alpha + 3, \beta + 3$ (xii) $3\alpha + 1, 3\beta + 1$

   (xiii) $\alpha - 1, \beta - 1$ (xiv) $\dfrac{1}{\alpha}, \dfrac{1}{\beta}$ (xv) $\dfrac{\alpha}{\beta}, \dfrac{\beta}{\alpha}$ (xvi) $\alpha(1 - \beta), \beta(1 - \alpha)$

3. The roots of the equation $2x^2 + 6x + 3 = 0$ are α and β. Find the value of:

   (i) $\alpha + \beta$ (ii) $\alpha\beta$ (iii) $3\alpha + 3\beta$ (iv) $\alpha^2 + \beta^2$

   The roots of the equation $2x^2 + px + q = 0$ are $2\alpha + \beta$ and $2\beta + \alpha$.
   Find the value of p and the value of q.

4. The roots of the quadratic equation $2x^2 - 6x + 5 = 0$ are $(\alpha - 2)$ and $(\beta - 2)$.

   (i) Find the value of   (a) $\alpha + \beta$ (b) $\alpha\beta$

   (ii) Form a quadratic equation, with integer coefficients, with roots α and β.

5. If α and β are the roots of the equation $x^2 - px + q = 0$, show that:

   (i) $\alpha^2 + \beta^2 = p^2 - 2q$ (ii) $(\alpha - \beta)^2 = p^2 - 4q$.

6. Given that one root of the equation $2x^2 - 12x + k = 0$ is twice the other root, find the value of k.

7. One root of the equation $x^2 - px + q = 0$ is twice the other.
   Show that $2p^2 = 9q$.

8. The equation $x^2 - 2px + q = 0$ has roots α and $\alpha + 2$.
   Verify that $p^2 = q + 1$.

9. The equation $x^2 - 12x + k = 0$ has roots α and α^2.
   Find the two possible values of k.

10. The equation $x^2 - ax + 16 = 0$ has roots α and α^3.
    Find the two possible values of a.

11. One root of the equation $ax^2 + bx + c = 0$ is three times the other.
    Show that $3b^2 = 16ac$.

12. One root of the equation $px^2 + qx + r = 0$ is four times the other.
    Show that $4q^2 - 25pr = 0$.

13. For what values of k is one of the roots of $x^2 - 4(k + 1)x + (k^2 - k + 7) = 0$ equal to three times the other?

14. (i) The quadratic equation $x^2 + (2k + 2)x + (2k + 5) = 0$ has roots α and β.
Express, in terms of k, **(a)** $\alpha + \beta$ **(b)** $\alpha\beta$ **(c)** $2\alpha^2\beta + 2\alpha\beta^2$.
(ii) The equation $x^2 - px + q = 0$ has roots $2\alpha + \alpha\beta$ and $2\beta + \beta\alpha$.
   (a) Show that $p = 6$.
   (b) Express q in terms of k.
   (c) Find the values of k for which $q = 0$.

Factor Theorem

A polynomial in x is a collection of powers of x added together.
For example, $2x^2 - 3x + 5$, $5x^3 + 6x^2 - x + 4$ are polynomials.

Note: **1.** There cannot be negative or fractional powers in a polynomial.
       2. A polynomial is often denoted as $f(x)$.

Factor Theorem

If an algebraic expression is divided by one of its factors, then the remainder is zero. The expression $(x - k)$ is a factor of a polynomial $f(x)$, if the remainder when we divide $f(x)$ by $(x - k)$ is zero.

Generalising this:

> **1.** If $f(k) = 0$, then $(x - k)$ is a factor of $f(x)$.
> **2.** If $(x - k)$ is a factor of $f(x)$, then $f(k) = 0$.

The factor theorem can be extended:

> **1.** If $f\left(\dfrac{b}{a}\right) = 0$, then $(ax - b)$ is a factor of $f(x)$.
>
> **2.** If $(ax - b)$ is a factor of $f(x)$, then $f\left(\dfrac{b}{a}\right) = 0$.

The factor theorem can be used to factorise polynomials or to find unknown coefficients in a polynomial.

Here are some examples:

Factor	Put factor = 0 and solve	Factor Theorem
$x + 4$	$x = -4$	$f(-4) = 0$
$x - 3$	$x = 3$	$f(3) = 0$
$2x + 1$	$x = -\frac{1}{2}$	$f(-\frac{1}{2}) = 0$

Note: If $(x + a)$ and $(x + b)$ are both factors of a polynomial $f(x)$, then so is their product, $(x + a)(x + b) = x^2 + (a + b)x + ab$, also a factor, and vice versa.

Example ▼

If $(2x - 1)$ is a factor of the polynomial $f(x) = 2x^3 - 5x^2 - kx + 3$, find the value of k.
Hence, find the other two factors.

Solution:

$f(x) = 2x^3 - 5x^2 - kx + 3$

If $(2x - 1)$ is a factor, then $f(\frac{1}{2}) = 0$.

$$f(\tfrac{1}{2}) = 0$$
$$2(\tfrac{1}{2})^3 - 5(\tfrac{1}{2})^2 - k(\tfrac{1}{2}) + 3 = 0 \qquad \text{(replace } x \text{ with } \tfrac{1}{2})$$
$$2(\tfrac{1}{8}) - 5(\tfrac{1}{4}) - k(\tfrac{1}{2}) + 3 = 0$$
$$\tfrac{1}{4} - \tfrac{5}{4} - \tfrac{1}{2}k + 3 = 0$$
$$1 - 5 - 2k + 12 = 0 \qquad \text{(multiply each part by 4)}$$
$$-2k + 8 = 0$$
$$-2k = -8$$
$$k = 4$$

Now divide $2x^3 - 5x^2 - 4x + 3$ by $(2x - 1)$

$$\begin{array}{r} x^2 - 2x - 3 \\ 2x-1 \overline{\big)\ 2x^3 - 5x^2 - 4x + 3} \\ \underline{2x^3 - x^2} \\ -4x^2 - 4x \\ \underline{-4x^2 + 2x} \\ -6x + 3 \\ \underline{-6x + 3} \\ 0 \end{array}$$

Now factorise $x^2 - 2x - 3$
$$x^2 - 2x - 3$$
$$= (x + 1)(x - 3)$$
Thus, the other two factors are:
$$(x + 1) \text{ and } (x - 3)$$

Example ▼

Let $f(x) = 2x^3 + mx^2 + nx + 2$ where m and n are constants.
Given that $x - 1$ and $x + 2$ are factors of $f(x)$, find the value of m and the value of n.

Solution:

$$f(x) = 2x^3 + mx^2 + nx + 2.$$

If $(x - 1)$ is a factor, then $f(1) = 0$.
$$f(1) = 0$$
$$2(1)^3 + m(1)^2 + n(1) + 2 = 0$$
$$2 + m + n + 2 = 0$$
$$m + n = -4 \quad ①$$

If $(x + 2)$ is a factor, then $f(-2) = 0$.
$$f(-2) = 0$$
$$2(-2)^3 + m(-2)^2 + n(-2) + 2 = 0$$
$$-16 + 4m - 2n + 2 = 0$$
$$4m - 2n = 14$$
$$2m - n = 7 \quad ②$$

We now solve the simultaneous equations ① and ②:

$$\begin{array}{l} m + n = -4 \quad ① \\ 2m - n = 7 \quad ② \\ \hline 3m = 3 \text{ (add)} \\ m = 1 \end{array}$$

$$\begin{array}{l} m + n = -4 \quad ① \\ 1 + n = -4 \\ n = -5 \end{array}$$

Thus, $m = 1$ and $n = -5$

$x^2 - px + q$ is a factor of $x^3 + 3px^2 + 3qx + r$.

(i) Show that $q = -2p^2$.

(ii) Show that $r = -8p^3$.

Solution:

Method 1: Equating the coefficients

Let $(x + k)$ be the third factor.

Thus,
$$(x + k)(x^2 - px + q) = x^3 + 3px^2 + 3qx + r$$
$$x^3 - px^2 + qx + kx^2 - kpx + qk = x^3 + 3px^2 + 3qx + r$$
$$x^3 + (-p + k)x^2 + (q - kp)x + qk = x^3 + 3px^2 + 3qx + r$$

Equating coefficients of like terms:

$\quad -p + k = 3p$ ① $\qquad q - kp = 3q$ ② $\qquad qk = r$ ③

(Basic idea is to remove the constant k, which is not in the solution required)

$\quad -p + k = 3p$ ① $\qquad$ (get k on its own from ①)

$\qquad k = 4p$ $\qquad$ (k on its own)

Put $k = 4p$ into ② and ③.

(i) $\qquad q - kp = 3q$ ②

$$q - (4p)p = 3q$$
$$q - 4p^2 = 3q$$
$$-4p^2 = 2q$$
$$-2p^2 = q$$

(ii) $\qquad qk = r$ ③

$$q(4p) = r$$
$$4pq = r$$
$$4p(-2p^2) = r$$
$$-8p^3 = r$$

$$\left(\begin{array}{c} q = -2p^2 \\ \text{from (i)} \end{array} \right)$$

Method 2: Using long division

$$
\begin{array}{r}
x + 4p \\
x^2 - px + q \overline{\big)\, x^3 + 3px^2 + 3qx + r} \\
\underline{x^3 - px^2 \quad + qx} \\
4px^2 + 2qx + r \\
\underline{4px^2 - 4p^2x + 4pq} \\
(2q + 4p^2)x + (r - 4pq)
\end{array}
$$

Since $(x^2 - px + q)$ is a factor, the remainder must equal 0.

Thus $\qquad 2q + 4p^2 = 0$ ① $\qquad\qquad$ or $\qquad\qquad r - 4pq = 0$ ②

$$2q = -4p^2 \qquad\qquad\qquad\qquad r - 4p(-2p^2) = 0$$
$$q = -2p^2 \qquad\qquad\qquad\qquad r + 8p^3 = 0$$
$$\text{Put this into ②:} \qquad\qquad\qquad r = -8p^3$$

1. Verify that $(x - 1)$ is a factor of $x^3 + 2x^2 - x - 2$ and find the other two factors.

2. Verify that $(x + 3)$ is a factor of $x^3 + 9x^2 + 23x + 15$ and find the other two factors.

3. Verify that $(2x - 1)$ is a factor of $6x^3 + 7x^2 - 9x + 2$ and find the other two factors.

4. Verify that $(2x - 3)$ is a factor of $2x^3 - 15x^2 + 34x - 24$ and find the other two factors.

5. Verify that $(x - 1)$ is a factor of $x^3 - (2k + 1)x^2 + (k^2 + 2k)x - k^2$.

6. If $(x + 2)$ is a factor of the polynomial $f(x) = 6x^3 + kx^2 + 11x - 6$, find the value of k. Hence, find the other two factors.

7. If $(2x + 1)$ is a factor of the polynomial $f(x) = 2x^3 + 7x^2 + kx + 2$, find the value of k. Hence, find the other two factors.

8. Let $f(x) = px^3 + 3x^2 - 9x + q$ where p and q are constants.
   Given that $(x + 1)$ and $(x - 2)$ are factors of $f(x)$, find the value of p and the value of q.

9. Let $p(x) = 2x^3 - ax^2 - bx + 42$ where a and b are constants.
   Given that $(x - 2)$ and $(x + 3)$ are factors of $p(x)$, find the value of a and the value of b.

10. Let $f(x) = 2x^3 + ax^2 + bx - 6$ where a and b are constants.
    Given that $f(-2) = 0$ and $f(\frac{1}{2}) = 0$, find the value of a and the value of b.

11. Let $f(x) = x^3 - (h + 2)x + 2k$ and $p(x) = 2x^3 + hx^2 - 4x - k$.
    Given that $(x + 3)$ is a common factor of $f(x)$ and $p(x)$, find the value of h and the value of k.

12. Factorise $x^2 + x - 6$.
    Let $f(x) = px^3 + x^2 - 20x + q$ where p and q are constants.
    Given that $x^2 + x - 6$ is a factor of $f(x)$, find the value of p and the value of q.

13. Given that $px^3 + 8x^2 + qx + 6$ is exactly divisible by $x^2 - 2x - 3$, find the value of p and the value of q.

14. If $(x - 2)^2$ is a factor of $x^3 + px + q$, find the value of p and the value of q.

15. $(x - a)^2$ is a factor of $x^3 + 3px + q$.
    Show that: (i) $p = -a^2$ (ii) $q = 2a^3$.

16. $x^2 + bx + c$ is a factor of $x^3 - p$. Show that:
    (i) $c = b^2$ (ii) $bc = p$ (iii) $b^3 = p$ (iv) $c^3 = p^2$.

17. $x^2 - px + 1$ is a factor of $ax^3 + bx + c$ where $a \neq 0$. Show that:
    (i) $p = \dfrac{c}{a}$ (ii) $c^2 = a(a - b)$.

Solving Cubic Equations

Any equation of the form $ax^3 + bx^2 + cx + d = 0$, $a \neq 0$, is called a **cubic** equation. We use the factor theorem to find one root, and hence one factor.

A cubic equation is solved with the following steps:

> **1.** Find the first root k by trial and error, i.e. try $f(1), f(-1), f(2), f(-2)$, etc. (Only try numbers that divide evenly into the constant in the equation.)
> **2.** If $x = k$ is a root, then $(x - k)$ is a factor.
> **3.** Divide $f(x)$ by $(x - k)$ which always gives a quadratic expression.
> **4.** Let this quadratic $= 0$ and solve by factors or formula.

Note: Each cubic equation we are asked to solve must have at least one integer root.

Example ▼

Solve the equation $2x^3 + x^2 - 13x + 6 = 0$.

Solution:

Let $f(x) = 2x^3 + x^2 - 13x + 6$.

1. The first root will be a factor of 6.
∴ We need try only those values which are factors of 6, i.e. ±1, ±2, ±3, ±6.

$$f(1) = 2(1)^3 + (1)^2 - 13(1) + 6 = 2 + 1 - 13 + 6 = -4 \neq 0$$
$$f(-1) = 2(-1)^3 + (-1)^2 - 13(-1) + 6 = -2 + 1 + 13 + 6 = 18 \neq 0$$
$$f(2) = 2(2)^3 + (2)^2 - 13(2) + 6 = 16 + 4 - 26 + 6 = 0$$

∴ $x = 2$ is a root

2. ∴ $x - 2$ is a factor

3. Divide $(2x^3 + x^2 - 13x + 6)$ by $(x - 2)$

$$
\begin{array}{r}
2x^2 + 5x - 3 \\
x - 2 \enclose{longdiv}{2x^3 + x^2 - 13x + 6} \\
\underline{2x^3 - 4x^2} \\
5x^2 - 13x \\
\underline{5x^2 - 10x} \\
-3x + 6 \\
\underline{-3x + 6} \\
0
\end{array}
$$

4. Let $2x^2 + 5x - 3 = 0$

$$(2x - 1)(x + 3) = 0$$

$2x - 1 = 0$ or $x + 3 = 0$

$x = \tfrac{1}{2}$ or $x = -3$

Thus, the three roots of the equation

$$2x^3 + x^2 - 13x + 6 = 0$$

are -3, $\tfrac{1}{2}$ and 2.

Rough graph of $f(x) = 2x^3 + x^2 - 13x + 6$:

Note: If we draw the graph of $f(x) = 2x^3 + x^2 - 13x + 6$ we can see that the roots of the equation $f(x) = 0$ occur where the graph of $f(x)$ cuts the x-axis.

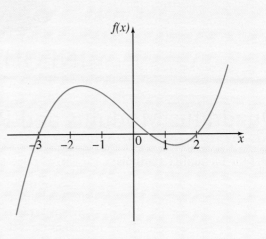

Exercise 2.6 ▼

1. Find the three linear factors of $x^3 - x^2 - 14x + 24$.
   Hence, solve the equation $x^3 - x^2 - 14x + 24 = 0$.

2. Factorise $2x^3 - x^2 - 2x + 1$. Hence solve the equation $2x^3 + 1 = x^2 + 2x$.

3. Show that $x = \frac{1}{2}$ is a root of the equation $2x^3 - 5x^2 - 4x + 3 = 0$ and find the other two roots.

4. Show that $x = 2$ is a root of the equation $x^3 + 4x^2 - 11x - 2 = 0$ and find the other two roots, giving your answer in the form $a \pm b\sqrt{b}$.

5. If $x = -\frac{1}{2}$ is one root of the equation $2x^3 - 9x^2 + kx + 6 = 0$, find the value of k.
   Find the other two roots of the equation.

6. Let $p(x) = ax^3 - 5x^2 - bx + 18$.
   If -2 and 3 are roots of the equation $p(x) = 0$, find the value of a and the value of b.
   If $p(k) = 0$, $k \neq -2, 3$, find the value of k.

7. If k is a root of the equation $3x^3 + (k + 3)x^2 + (7 - k - 4k^2)x - 4 = 0$, find the values of k.

8. Find the values of the constants p, q and r for which $(x - 4)(x - 2)(x + p) = x^3 - 7x^2 + qx + r$ for all values of $x \in \mathbf{R}$. Using these values of q and r solve the equation $x^3 - 7x^2 + qx + r = 0$.

9. Verify that $-4p$ is a root of the equation $x^3 + 3px^2 - 6p^2x - 8p^3 = 0$. Hence, or otherwise, find the three roots of $x^3 + 3px^2 - 6p^2x - 8p^3 = 0$ in terms of p.

INEQUALITIES

Quadratic, Modulus and Rational Inequalities

The four inequality symbols:

> $>$ means 'greater than'
> $\geqslant$ means 'greater than or equal to'
> $<$ means 'less than'
> $\leqslant$ means 'less than or equal to'

Algebraic expressions that are linked by one of the four inequality symbols are called '**inequalities**'. Solving inequalities is exactly the same as solving equations, with the following exception:

> If we multiply or divide both sides of an inequality by the **same negative** number we must reverse the direction, or order, of the inequality.

Modulus and Rational inequalities can be turned into quadratic inequalities. Therefore, it is very important to be able to solve quadratic inequalities.

Quadratic inequalities are solved with the following steps:

1. Replace $\geqslant$, $\leqslant$, $>$ or $<$ with $=$ (make it an equation).
2. Solve the equation to find the roots.
3. Test a number between the roots in the **original** inequality (usually 0).
4. Two possibilities arise:
   (a) If the inequality holds, then the solution lies between the roots.
   (b) If the inequality does not hold, then the solution does not lie between the roots.

Note: We can also test a number **outside** the roots.
       The roots of the equation are also called the '**critical values**' of the inequality.

Example ▼

Solve each of the following inequalities for $x \in \mathbf{R}$:

(i) $x + 6 \geqslant 2x^2$

(ii) $|2x - 3| < |x + 3|$

(iii) $\dfrac{x + 2}{x - 1} < 3, \qquad x \neq 1$

Solutions:

(i) $\quad\quad\quad x + 6 \geqslant 2x^2$

1. $\quad\quad\quad\quad x + 6 = 2x^2$ $\quad\quad\quad\quad$ (replace $\geqslant$ with $=$)

2. $\quad\quad -2x^2 + x + 6 = 0$

$\quad\quad\quad 2x^2 - x - 6 = 0$ $\quad\quad\quad\quad$ (multiply both sides by -1)

$\quad\quad (2x + 3)(x - 2) = 0$

$\quad\quad\quad 2x + 3 = 0 \quad$ or $\quad x - 2 = 0$

$\quad\quad\quad\quad 2x = -3 \quad$ or $\quad\quad x = 2$

$\quad\quad\quad\quad\; x = -\frac{3}{2} \quad$ or $\quad\quad x = 2$

3. Test 0, between the roots, in the **original** inequality.

$\quad\quad\quad 0 + 6 \geqslant 2(0)^2$

$\quad\quad\quad\quad 6 \geqslant 0 \quad$ True

4. $\quad \therefore$ the solution lies between $-\frac{3}{2}$ and 2.

$\quad\quad \therefore$ Solution is $-\frac{3}{2} \leqslant x \leqslant 2$.

(ii) $\quad\quad\quad |2x - 3| < |x + 3|$

Square both sides. This reduces the problem to that of solving a quadratic inequality.

(**Note:** We can square both sides as we are sure both sides are non-negative)

$\quad\quad\quad\quad |2x - 3| < |x + 3|$

$\quad\quad\quad (2x - 3)^2 < (x + 3)^2$ $\quad\quad\quad$ (square both sides)

$\quad 4x^2 - 12x + 9 = x^2 + 6x + 9$ $\quad\quad$ (remove brackets and replace $<$ with $=$)

$\quad\quad\quad 3x^2 - 18x = 0$

$\quad\quad\quad\quad x^2 - 6x = 0$

$\quad\quad\quad\quad x(x - 6) = 0$

$\quad\quad\quad x = 0 \quad$ or $\quad x - 6 = 0$

$\quad\quad\quad x = 0 \quad$ or $\quad\quad x = 6$

Test 2, between the roots, in the **original** inequality.

$\quad |2(2) - 3| < |2 + 3|$

$\quad\quad\quad 1 < 5 \quad$ True $\quad \therefore$ the solution is between 0 and 6.

$\quad \therefore$ Solution is $0 < x < 6$.

(iii) $\quad\quad\quad \dfrac{x + 2}{x - 1} < 3$

As $(x - 1)$ could be positive or negative, we multiply both sides by $(x - 1)^2$ which is positive. This reduces the problem to that of solving a quadratic inequality.

$\quad\quad\quad \dfrac{x + 2}{x - 1} < 3$

$\quad\quad \dfrac{(x - 1)^2(x + 2)}{(x - 1)} < 3(x - 1)^2$ $\quad\quad\quad$ (multiply both sides by $(x - 1)^2$)

$$(x - 1)(x + 2) = 3(x - 2x + 1) \qquad \text{(simplify and replace < with =)}$$
$$x^2 + x - 2 = 3x^2 - 6x + 3$$
$$-2x^2 + 7x - 5 = 0$$
$$2x^2 - 7x + 5 = 0$$
$$(2x - 5)(x - 1) = 0$$
$$2x - 5 = 0 \qquad \text{or} \qquad x - 1 = 0$$
$$2x = 5 \qquad \text{or} \qquad x = 1$$
$$x = \tfrac{5}{2} \qquad \text{or} \qquad x = 1$$

Test 0, **not** between the roots, in the **original** inequality.

$$\frac{0 + 2}{0 - 1} < 3$$

$$-2 < 3 \qquad \text{True} \qquad \therefore \text{ Solution is } \textbf{not} \text{ between 1 and } \tfrac{5}{2}.$$
$$\therefore \text{ Solution is } x < 1 \text{ or } x > \tfrac{5}{2}.$$

Exercise 3.1 ▼

Solve each of the following inequalities for $x \in \mathbf{R}$:

1. $x^2 - x - 2 \leqslant 0$

2. $x^2 - 2x - 8 > 0$

3. $2x^2 - 11x + 5 < 0$

4. $3x^2 + 2x \leqslant 5$

5. $2x^2 + x \leqslant 3$

6. $x^2 - 2x \geqslant 0$

7. $3x^2 < 2x$

8. $x^2 - 4 \leqslant 0$

9. $x^2 - 25 \geqslant 0$

10. $4x^2 - 9 \leqslant 0$

11. $9x^2 - 1 > 0$

12. $(2x - 3)^2 \geqslant 4$

13. $|x + 2| \leqslant 1$

14. $|x - 2| \geqslant 3$

15. $|2x - 3| \leqslant 7$

16. $|2 - x| \leqslant 2$

17. $2|x - 3| \geqslant 1$

18. $|2x - 1| \leqslant |x + 2|$

19. $|x + 3| \leqslant |2x - 3|$

20. $|3x + 4| \geqslant |x + 2|$

21. $2|x + 1| < |x + 3|$

22. $\dfrac{x + 1}{x - 1} < 3$

23. $\dfrac{x + 1}{x - 2} > 2$

24. $\dfrac{2x - 7}{x + 3} < 1$

25. $\dfrac{5 - x}{x - 2} < 1$

26. $\dfrac{2}{x - 1} > 3$

27. $\dfrac{2x - 1}{x - 4} < 1$

28. $\dfrac{2x + 1}{x + 5} < 0$

29. $\dfrac{4x - 1}{x - 3} < 2$

30. $\dfrac{2x + 1}{x + 2} < \dfrac{1}{2}$

31. $\dfrac{2x - 3}{x - 5} > \dfrac{3}{2}$

32. $\dfrac{1}{x} < \dfrac{1}{2}$

33. $\dfrac{5x - 2}{x^2 + 4} > 1$

34. $\left| \dfrac{x - 2}{3} \right| < 1$

35. $\left| \dfrac{1}{x + 2} \right| > \dfrac{1}{2}$

36. $\left| \dfrac{x + 2}{x - 1} \right| \leqslant 3$

Nature of the Roots of a Quadratic Equation

Consider the quadratic equation $ax^2 + bx + c = 0$, $a \neq 0$.

The roots of the equation are given by:

$$x = \frac{-b \pm \sqrt{b^2 - 4ac}}{2a}$$

The value of the expression $(b^2 - 4ac)$ will determine the nature of the roots of the equation and is called the **discriminant** of the equation. The three diagrams below of the curve $y = ax^2 + bx + c$ $(a > 0)$ show the three possible cases.

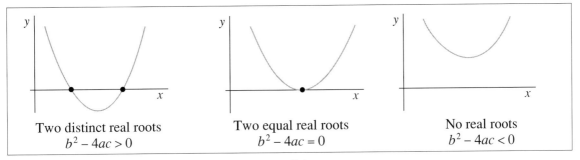

| Two distinct real roots | Two equal real roots | No real roots |
| $b^2 - 4ac > 0$ | $b^2 - 4ac = 0$ | $b^2 - 4ac < 0$ |

Note: For real roots we combine the first two conditions:

$$\text{If } b^2 - 4ac \geqslant 0 \text{ the roots are real}$$

Two equal real roots are also called '**repeated roots**'.

Example ▼

Find the value of k for which the equation $(5k + 1)x^2 - 8kx + 3k = 0$ has real roots.

Solution:

$$(5k + 1)x^2 - 8kx + 3k = 0$$
$$a = (5k + 1) \qquad b = -8k \qquad c = 3k$$
$$b^2 - 4ac \geqslant 0 \qquad \text{(condition for real roots)}$$
$$(-8k)^2 - 4(5k + 1)(3k) \geqslant 0$$
$$(64k^2) - 4(15k^2 + 3k) \geqslant 0$$
$$64k^2 - 60k^2 - 12k \geqslant 0$$
$$4k^2 - 12k \geqslant 0$$
$$k^2 - 3k \geqslant 0 \qquad \text{(quadratic inequality)}$$
$$\text{Let } k^2 - 3k = 0 \qquad \text{(replace} \geqslant \text{with =)}$$
$$k(k - 3) = 0$$
$$k = 0 \qquad \text{or} \qquad k - 3 = 0$$
$$k = 0 \qquad \text{or} \qquad k = 3$$

Test 1, between the roots in $k^2 - 3k \geqslant 0$.

$$(1)^2 - 3(1) \geqslant 0$$
$$-2 \geqslant 0 \qquad \text{False} \qquad \therefore \text{Solution is \textbf{not} between 0 and 3.}$$

$\therefore$ Solution is $k \leqslant 0$ or $k \geqslant 3$.

In the next example we make use of the fact that (any real number)$^2 \geqslant 0$.

Example ▼

Show that the roots of the equation $(k - 2)x^2 + (2 - 3k)x + 2k = 0$ are always real, $k \in \mathbf{R}$.

Solution:

$$(k - 2)x^2 + (2 - 3k)x + 2k = 0$$
$$a = (k - 2), \qquad b = (2 - 3k) \qquad c = 2k$$

$$\begin{aligned} b^2 - 4ac &= (2 - 3k)^2 - 4(k - 2)(2k) \\ &= (4 - 12k + 9k^2) - 4(2k^2 - 4k) \\ &= 4 - 12k + 9k^2 - 8k^2 + 16k \\ &= k^2 + 4k + 4 \\ &= (k + 2)^2 \end{aligned}$$

$(k + 2)^2$ cannot be negative, as it is a square, for any value of $k \in \mathbf{R}$.
$\therefore\ b^2 - 4ac \geqslant 0$ and so the roots are always real.

Exercise 3.2 ▼

In each case calculate $b^2 - 4ac$ and describe the nature of the roots as either:

1. Real roots **2.** Equal roots **3.** No real roots

	Equation	$b^2 - 4ac$	Nature of the roots
1.	$x^2 - 2x - 8 = 0$		
2.	$x^2 - 10x + 25 = 0$		
3.	$2x^2 + 3x + 6 = 0$		
4.	$(p - 3)x^2 + (2p - 1)x + (p + 2) = 0$		
5.	$(t + 1)x^2 + (2t + 3)x + (t + 2) = 0$		
6.	$x^2 + 2px + p^2 = 0$		
7.	$x^2 + qx + q^2 = 0$		
8.	$x^2 - 3x + (2 - k^2) = 0$		
9.	$x^2 + 2(k - 1)x + (k - 1)^2 = 0$		
10.	$px^2 + (p + 1)x + 1 = 0$		

11. Find the value(s), or range of values, of k for which each of the following equations has:

    (a) equal roots   **(b)** real roots   **(c)** no real roots

    (i) $x^2 - kx + 1 = 0$
    (ii) $8x^2 - kx + 2 = 0$

    (iii) $kx^2 + (2k + 1)x + k = 0$
    (iv) $(k + 3)x^2 + (6 - 2k)x + (k - 1) = 0$

    (v) $kx^2 + kx + (k - 1) = 0$
    (vi) $4x^2 + 2(k + 1)x + k^2 = 0$

12. Verify that the roots of the equation $x^2 - 3x = q^2 - 2$ are real for all $q \in \mathbf{R}$.

13. Verify that the roots of the equation $x^2 - (a + b)x + (ab - c^2) = 0$ are real for all $a, b, c \in \mathbf{R}$.

14. Show that the roots of the equation $x^2 - (2p + 5)x + 2(2p + 3) = 0$ are real for all values of $p \in \mathbf{R}$. Verify that one of the roots is independent of p and the other is not.

Inequality Proofs

In this section we deal with inequalities which hold for all real values of the variables involved. We can start with what we are given and by using reversible steps arrive at an algebraic statement that is true or vice versa. We can only square both sides of an inequality when we are sure both sides are non-negative. For example, $-5 < 2$: squaring both sides gives $25 < 4$, which is not true. Many of the inequalities in this section are established using the fact that:

$$\text{(any real number)}^2 \geqslant 0$$

For example, $(a - b)^2 \geqslant 0$ or $(a^2 - b^2)^2 \geqslant 0$.

Example ▼

Prove   **(i)** $a^2 + b^2 \geqslant 2ab$ for all real values of a and b.

and   **(ii)** hence, prove that $a^2 + b^2 + c^2 \geqslant ab + bc + ca$ for all real values of a, b and c.

Solution:

(i)   **Method 1**
$$a^2 + b^2 \geqslant 2ab$$
$$a^2 - 2ab + b^2 \geqslant 0$$
$$(a - b)^2 \geqslant 0 \quad \text{true}$$
$$\therefore \quad a^2 + b^2 \geqslant 2ab$$

Method 2
$$\text{(any real number)}^2 \geqslant 0$$
Thus, $(a - b)^2 \geqslant 0$
$$a^2 - 2ab + b^2 \geqslant 0$$
$$\therefore \ a^2 + b^2 \geqslant 2ab$$

(ii) From **(i)**
$$a^2 + b^2 \geqslant 2ab$$
$$b^2 + c^2 \geqslant 2bc$$
$$c^2 + a^2 \geqslant 2ca$$
$$\underline{2a^2 + 2b^2 + 2c^2 \geqslant 2ab + 2bc + 2ca} \quad \text{(add)}$$
$$\therefore \ a^2 + b^2 + c^2 \geqslant ab + bc + ca \quad \text{(divide both sides by 2)}$$

If $a, b > 0$, prove $\dfrac{1}{b} + \dfrac{1}{a} \geqslant \dfrac{4}{a+b}$.

Solution:

$$\frac{1}{b} + \frac{1}{a} \geqslant \frac{4}{a+b}$$

$$ab \cdot \frac{1}{b} + ab \cdot \frac{1}{b} \geqslant ab \cdot \frac{4}{a+b} \qquad \text{[multiply each part by } ab \text{, which is positive]}$$

$$a + b \geqslant \frac{4ab}{a+b}$$

$$(a+b)(a+b) \geqslant (a+b) \cdot \frac{4ab}{a+b} \qquad \text{[multiply both sides by } (a+b) \text{, which is positive]}$$

$$a^2 + 2ab + b^2 \geqslant 4ab$$

$$a^2 - 2ab + b^2 \geqslant 0$$

$$(a-b)^2 \geqslant 0 \qquad \text{[true]}$$

Thus, $\dfrac{1}{b} + \dfrac{1}{a} \geqslant \dfrac{4}{a+b}$ for $a, b > 0$

Exercise 3.3 ▼

1. If $a, b \in \mathbf{R}$ prove:

   (i) $a^2 + 2ab + b^2 \geqslant 0$ **(ii)** $(a+b)^2 \geqslant 4ab$ **(iii)** $2(a^2 + b^2) \geqslant (a+b)^2$

   (iv) $\dfrac{a^2 + 4b^2}{4} \geqslant ab$ **(v)** $a^2 + 2ab + 3b^2 \geqslant 0$ **(vi)** $a^2 - 8a + 16 + b^2 \geqslant 0$

2. If $p, q > 0$, prove:

   (i) $p + \dfrac{1}{p} \geqslant 2$ **(ii)** $\dfrac{p}{q} + \dfrac{q}{p} \geqslant 2$ **(iii)** $(p+q)\left(\dfrac{1}{p} + \dfrac{1}{q}\right) \geqslant 4$

   (iv) $\left(p + \dfrac{1}{q}\right)\left(q + \dfrac{1}{p}\right) \leqslant \left(p + \dfrac{1}{p}\right)\left(q + \dfrac{1}{q}\right)$

3. If $a, b > 0$ and $a \neq b$, prove $\dfrac{a+b}{2} > \sqrt{ab}$.

4. If $a, b > 0$ and $\dfrac{a}{b} = \sqrt{2}$, show that $a - b < b$.

5. If $a, b \in \mathbf{R}$, show that $\left|\dfrac{a}{b} + \dfrac{b}{a}\right| \geqslant 2$.

6. If $a^2 + b^2 = 1 = c^2 + d^2$, $a, b, c, d \in \mathbf{R}$, prove that $ab + cd \leqslant 1$.

7. Let a, b, c be positive unequal real numbers.

   Using results $a^2 + b^2 > 2ab$, $b^2 + c^2 > 2bc$ and $c^2 + a^2 > 2ac$,

   (i)   deduce that $a^2 - ab + b^2 > ab$

   (ii)   deduce that $a^2 + b^2 + c^2 > bc + ca + ab$

   (iii) show that $a^3 + b^3 > ab(a + b)$.

   (iv) show that $3(a^3 + b^3 + c^3) > (a^2 + b^2 + c^2)(a + b + c)$

8. **(a)** Factorise $a^3 + b^3$ and $a^2b - ab^2$.

   (b) If p, $q > 0$ and $p \neq q$, prove that $\dfrac{p^3 - q^3}{p^2q - pq^2} > 3$

9. Prove that $a^2 + b^2 \geqslant 2ab$.

   If a, $b > 0$ and $a + b = 1$, prove that:

   (i) $a^2 + b^2 = 1 - 2ab$ **(ii)** $4ab \leqslant 1$ **(iii)** $a^2 + b^2 \geqslant \frac{1}{2}$

10. If p, q, r, $s \geqslant 0$, prove that:

    (i) $(p + q)(q + r)(r + p) \geqslant 8pqr$ **(ii)** $(pq + rs)(pr + qs) \geqslant 4pqrs$

INDICES

Indices

In the expression a^m, a is the base and m is the index or exponent. a^m is read as 'a to the power of m'.

Rules of indices

1.	$a^m \cdot a^n = a^{m+n}$	**2.**	$\dfrac{a^m}{a^n} = a^{m-n}$
3.	$(a^m)^n = a^{mn}$	**4.**	$(ab)^m = a^m b^m$
5.	$\left(\dfrac{a}{b}\right)^m = \dfrac{a^m}{b^m}$	**6.**	$a^0 = 1$
7.	$a^{-m} = \dfrac{1}{a^m}$	**8.**	$a^{m/n} = (a^{1/n})^m$

$8^{1/3}$ means the number that multiplied by itself three times will equal 8.
Thus, $8^{1/3} = 2$, as $2 \times 2 \times 2 = 8$
Note: $\sqrt{a} = a^{1/2}$
Alternative notation: $a^{1/n} = \sqrt[n]{a}$ and $a^{m/n} = \sqrt[n]{a^m}$

| *Example* ▼ |

Evaluate each of the following, expressing your answers as rational numbers:

(i) $32^{3/5}$ **(ii)** $8^{-2/3}$ **(iii)** $(2\frac{1}{4})^{3/2}$ **(iv)** $4^{1/2} \cdot 27^{-1/3}$ **(v)** $(\frac{16}{25})^{-1/2}$ **(vi)** $(\frac{1}{16})^{3/4}$

Solution:

(i) $\quad 32^{3/5} = (32^{1/5})^3 = (2)^3 = 8$

(ii) $\quad 8^{-2/3} = \dfrac{1}{8^{2/3}} = \dfrac{1}{(8^{1/3})^2} = \dfrac{1}{(2)^2} = \dfrac{1}{4}$

(iii) $(2\frac{1}{4})^{3/2} = \left(\dfrac{9}{4}\right)^{3/2} = \dfrac{9^{3/2}}{4^{3/2}} = \dfrac{(9^{1/2})^3}{(4^{1/2})^3} = \dfrac{(3)^3}{(2)^3} = \dfrac{27}{8}$

(iv) $4^{1/2} \cdot 27^{-1/3} = \dfrac{4^{1/2}}{27^{1/3}} = \dfrac{2}{3}$

(v) $\left(\dfrac{16}{25}\right)^{-1/2} = \dfrac{16^{-1/2}}{25^{-1/2}} = \dfrac{25^{1/2}}{16^{1/2}} = \dfrac{5}{4}$

(vi) $\left(\dfrac{1}{16}\right)^{3/4} = \dfrac{1^{3/4}}{16^{3/4}} = \dfrac{1}{(16^{1/4})^3} = \dfrac{1}{(2)^3} = \dfrac{1}{8}$

If $\dfrac{3(2^{n+1}) - 4(2^{n-1})}{2^{n+1} - 2^n} = k$, find the value of $\sqrt{k}$.

Solution:

$\dfrac{3(2^{n+1}) - 4(2^{n-1})}{2^{n+1} - 2^n}$

$= \dfrac{3(2^2 . 2^{n-1}) - 4(2^{n-1})}{2^2 . 2^{n-1} - 2^1 . 2^{n-1}}$

$= \dfrac{3 . 2^2(2^{n-1}) - 4(2^{n-1})}{2^2(2^{n-1}) - 2^1(2^{n-1})}$

$= \dfrac{3 . 2^2 - 4}{2^2 - 2}$

$= \dfrac{3(4) - 4}{4 - 2} = \dfrac{8}{2} = 4$

Thus, $\sqrt{k} = \sqrt{4} = 2$

The basic idea is to have the lowest power of 2, 2^{n-1}, present in every term, then divide each term by 2^{n-1}.

$n + 1 = 2 + n - 1 = 2 + (n - 1)$
$\therefore \quad 2^{n+1} = 2^{2 + (n-1)} = 2^2 . 2^{n-1}$

$n = 1 + n - 1 = 1 + (n - 1)$
$\therefore \quad 2^n = 2^{1 + (n-1)} = 2^1 . 2^{n-1}$

(divide each term by 2^{n-1})

Exercise 4.1 ▼

Evaluate each of the following, expressing your answers as rational numbers:

1. $27^{2/3}$ **2.** $16^{5/4}$ **3.** $128^{4/7}$ **4.** $49^{-1/2}$ **5.** $32^{-2/5}$

6. $10,000^{3/4}$ **7.** $(12\tfrac{1}{4})^{1/2}$ **8.** $(\tfrac{16}{81})^{-3/4}$ **9.** $(27^{-1/3})^2$ **10.** $(32^{-1/5})^3$

11. $\left(\dfrac{4}{9}\right)^{-1/2} . \left(\dfrac{1}{27}\right)^{1/3}$ **12.** $\dfrac{16^{-3/4}}{81^{-1/2}}$ **13.** $\dfrac{27^{-1/3}}{8^{-2/3}}$ **14.** $\dfrac{4^{-1/2}}{64^{2/3}}$ **15.** $(64^{5/12})^2$

Find the value of n if:

16. $\dfrac{8^{-2/3}}{4^{-5/2}} = 2^n$ **17.** $\dfrac{27^{2/3} \times 81^{-1/2}}{9^{-1}} = 3^n$ **18.** $\dfrac{16^{1/3} \times 4^{1/3}}{8} = 2^n$

19. If $\sqrt{\dfrac{9^{1/2} - 2^{-1}}{32^{-3/5}}} = a\sqrt{b}$, where b is prime, find the value of a and the value of b.

Simplify each of the following:

20. $\dfrac{x^{3/2} - x^{-1/2}}{x^{1/2} - x^{-1/2}}$ **21.** $\dfrac{(x - 1)^{1/2} + (x - 1)^{-1/2}}{(x - 1)^{-1/2}}$

Evaluate each of the following:

22. $5.4^{3n+1} - 20.8^{2n}$ **23.** $7.3^{2n+1} - 21.9^n$ **24.** $\dfrac{3.2^{n+2} - 4.2^n}{2^{n+2} - 2^{n+1}}$ **25.** $\dfrac{9^{n+2} - 2.3^{2n+3}}{3^{2n+1} - 9^n}$

26. $f(x) = 2^x$. If $f(x + 3) - f(x + 1) = kf(x)$, find the value of k.

Exponential Equations

Exponent is another name for power or index.

An equation involving the variable in the power is called an '**exponential equation**'.

For example, $3^{2x+3} = 9$ is an exponential equation.

Exponential equations are solved with the following steps:

1. Write all the numbers as powers of the same number (usually a prime number).
2. Write both sides as one power of the same number, using the laws of indices.
3. Equate these powers and solve this equation.

Example ▼

Solve for x: (i) $9^{x^2+2} = 27^{x+3}$ (ii) $2^{3x-1} = \dfrac{\sqrt{2}}{8}$

Solution:

Write each side as a power of 3

(i)
$$9^{x^2+2} = 27^{x+3}$$
$$(3^2)^{x^2+2} = (3^3)^{x+3}$$
$$3^{2(x^2+2)} = 3^{3(x+3)}$$
$$3^{2x^2+4} = 3^{3x+9}$$
$$\therefore \quad 2x^2 + 4 = 3x + 9 \quad \text{(equate powers)}$$
$$2x^2 - 3x - 5 = 0$$
$$(2x - 5)(x + 1) = 0$$
$$2x - 5 = 0 \quad \text{or} \quad x + 1 = 0$$
$$x = \tfrac{5}{2} \quad \text{or} \quad x = -1$$

Write each side as a power of 2

(ii)
$$2^{3x-1} = \frac{\sqrt{2}}{8}$$
$$2^{3x-1} = \frac{2^{1/2}}{2^3}$$
$$2^{3x-1} = 2^{1/2-3}$$
$$2^{3x-1} = 2^{-5/2}$$
$$\therefore \quad 3x - 1 = -\tfrac{5}{2} \quad \text{(equate powers)}$$
$$6x - 2 = -5$$
$$6x = -3$$
$$x = -\tfrac{1}{2}$$

Sometimes exponential equations lead to simultaneous equations.

Example ▼

Solve for x and y: $2^{x+y} = 8$ and $9^x \cdot 3^{-y} = 27$

Solution:

Write each side as a power of 2
$$2^{x+y} = 8$$
$$2^{x+y} = 2^3$$
$$\therefore \quad x + y = 3 \quad \text{① (equate powers)}$$

Write each side as a power of 3
$$9^x \cdot 3^{-y} = 27$$
$$(3^2)^x \cdot 3^{-y} = 3^3$$
$$3^{2x} \cdot 3^{-y} = 3^3$$
$$3^{2x-y} = 3^3$$
$$\therefore \quad 2x - y = 3 \quad \text{② (equate powers)}$$

By solving the simultaneous equations ① and ② we get $x = 2$ and $y = 1$.

Often a substitution of the form $y = a^x$ is required to obtain an equation in y.

Example ▼

If $y = 2^x$, express **(i)** 2^{2x} and **(ii)** 2^{x+1} in terms of y.
Hence, solve the equation $2^{2x+1} - 15.2^x - 8 = 0$.

Solution:

(i) $\quad 2^{2x} = (2^x)^2 = y^2$

$$2^{2x+1} - 15.2^x - 8 = 0$$
$$2y^2 - 15y - 8 = 0$$
$$(2y + 1)(y - 8) = 0$$
$$2y + 1 = 0 \quad \text{or} \quad y - 8 = 0$$
$$y = -\tfrac{1}{2} \quad \text{or} \quad y = 8$$

(ii) $\quad 2^{2x+1} = 2^{1+2x} = 2^1 \cdot 2^{2x} = 2y^2$

$y = 8$	$y = -\tfrac{1}{2}$
$2^x = 2^3$	$2^x = -2^{-1}$
$\therefore \quad x = 3$	(no solution)

Thus, $x = 3$ is the solution.

Exercise 4.2 ▼

Solve each of the following equations:

1. $4^{x+1} = 128$

2. $3^{2x-5} = 27$

3. $5^{x^2} = 25^{3x-4}$

4. $7^{2x-1} = \dfrac{49}{\sqrt{7}}$

5. $2^{2x-1} = \left(\dfrac{16}{\sqrt{8}}\right)^2$

6. $\sqrt{3}(3^x) = \left(\dfrac{243}{\sqrt{27}}\right)^2$

7. $8^{4/3} = \dfrac{2^{5x-3}}{\sqrt{2}}$

8. $8(2^{x^2}) = 16^x$

9. $\dfrac{(8^x)^x}{32^x} = 4$

10. Express **(i)** 27 as a power of 3 **(ii)** 32 as a power of 2.
Hence, solve for x and y: $\quad 3^{2x+y} = 27$ and $2^{3x+y} = 32$.

Solve each of the following for x and y:

11. $2^{5x-2y} = 8$
$\ 3^{x+y} = 9$

12. $2^x = 8^{y+1}$
$\ 3^{x-9} = 9^y$

13. $3^x \cdot 9^{-y} = 3$
$\ 2^x \cdot 4^{2y} = 2$

14. Solve each of the following equations and state which ones have no solution, $x \in \mathbf{R}$:

(i) $2^x = 4$ **(ii)** $3^x = 3$ **(iii)** $5^x = 1$ **(iv)** $2^x = \tfrac{1}{4}$

(v) $3^x = \tfrac{1}{3}$ **(vi)** $2^x = -8$ **(vii)** $3^x = -\tfrac{1}{3}$ **(viii)** $5^x = \tfrac{1}{125}$

15. If $y = 2^x$, express **(i)** 2^{2x} **(ii)** 2^{x+1} in terms of y.
Hence, solve the equation $2^{2x} - 5.2^{x+1} + 16 = 0$.

Use the substitution $y = a^x$ to solve each of the following equations:

16. $2^{2x} - 5.2^x + 4 = 0$

17. $3^{2x} - 4.3^x + 3 = 0$

18. $2^{2x} - 6.2^x + 8 = 0$

19. $2^{2x} - 12.2^x + 32 = 0$

20. $3^{2x+1} - 10.3^x + 3 = 0$

21. $3^{2x} - 4.3^{x+1} + 27 = 0$

22. $2^{2x+1} - 3.2^x + 1 = 0$

23. $2^x - 6 + 2^{3-x} = 0$

24. $3^{x+2} - 82 + 3^{2-x} = 0$

25. If $2^x + 2^{x+1} + 2^{x+2} = k2^x$, find the value of k.
Hence, solve the equation $2^x + 2^{x+1} + 2^{x+2} = 224$.

Recurrence Equations

A recurrence equation is a formula which will generate any term in a sequence from previous terms.

For example, $u_{n+1} = 2u_n + 4^n$ is a recurrence equation.

Note: The notation used here is called '**sequence notation**'.

Example

If $u_n = 5^n - 140.2^n$, show that $u_{n+2} - 7u_{n+1} + 10u_n = 0$.

Solution:

The basic idea is to express u_{n+1} and u_{n+2} is terms of 5^n and 2^n, the lowest powers of 5 and 2 and then substitute these into the given expression.
To find u_{n+1} replace n with $(n+1)$, to find u_{n+2} replace n with $(n+2)$.

$$u_n = 5^n - 140.2^n$$
$$u_{n+1} = 5^{n+1} - 140.2^{n+1} = 5^n.5^1 - 140.2^n.2^1 = 5.5^n - 2.140.2^n = 5.5^n - 280.2^n$$
$$u_{n+2} = 5^{n+2} - 140.2^{n+2} = 5^n.5^2 - 140.2^n.2^2 = 5^n.25 - 140.2^n.4 = 25.5^n - 560.2^n$$

$$\underset{u_{n+2}}{\qquad} \quad - \quad \underset{7u_{n+1}}{\qquad} \quad + \quad \underset{10u_n}{\qquad}$$

$$= (25.5^n - 560.2^n) - 7(5.5^n - 280.2^n) + 10(5^n - 140.2^n)$$
$$= 25.5^n - 560.2^n - 35.5^n + 1960.2^n + 10.5^n - 1400.2^n$$
$$= 35.5^n - 35.5^n + 1960.2^n - 1960.2^n$$
$$= 0$$

Thus, u_n satisfies the given equation.

Exercise 4.3 ▼

1. If for all integers n, $u_n = 2^n + 3^n$, show that $u_{n+2} - 5u_{n+1} + 6u_n = 0$.

2. If for all integers n, $u_n = 5.3^n + 4^n$, show that $u_{n+2} - 7u_{n+1} + 12u_n = 0$.

3. If for all $n \geqslant 0$, $n \in \mathbf{N}$, $u_n = 2(3^n) - 5(2^n)$, verify that $u_{n+2} - 5u_{n+1} + 6u_n = 0$.

4. $f(n) = 7(5^n) - 2(3^n)$ for all integers n. Evaluate $f(1)$ and $f(2)$.
   Verify that $f(n+2) - 8f(n+1) + 15f(n) = 0$.

5. If for all integers n, $u_n = (n-20)2^n$, verify that $u_{n+2} - 4u_{n+1} + 4u_n = 0$.
   Find the values of n for which $u_{n+1} > 3u_n$.

6. If for all integers n, $u_n = (n+4)3^n$, show that $u_{n+2} - 6u_{n+1} + 9u_n = 0$.
   For what values of $n > 0$ is $u_{n+2} > 4(u_{n+1} - 6.3^n)$?

7. If for all integers n, $u_n = n(n-1)^2 + 3$, show that $u_{n+1} - u_n = 3n^2 - n$.

8. If for all integers n, $u_n = (5n-3)2^n$, verify that $u_{n+1} - 2u_n = 5(2^{n+1})$.

9. If for all integers n, $u_n = 2^{2n-1} + 2^{n-1}$, show that $u_{n+1} - 2u_n - 2^{2n} = 0$.

10. If $u_n = p(3^n) + q(4^n)$ for all integers n, verify that $u_{n+2} - 7u_{n+1} + 12u_n = 0$.

LOGARITHMS

Logarithms

A **logarithm** ('log' for short) is an index (exponent).
Given any two positive numbers a and b, there exists a third number c such that $a = b^c$.
The number c is said to be the log of a to the base b.

Thus,
$$a = b^c \Leftrightarrow \log_b a = c$$

Any statement in index form has an equivalent log form, for example:

$$100 = 10^2 \quad \text{(index form)}$$
$$\log_{10} 100 = 2 \quad \text{(log form)}$$

$$8 = 2^3 \quad \text{(index form)}$$
$$\log_2 8 = 3 \quad \text{(log form)}$$

It is very important to be able to change from '**index form**' to '**log form**' and vice versa.

Note: $\log_3 81 = 4$ is read 'the log of 81 to the base 3 is 4', i.e. $81 = 3^4$.

Laws of Logarithms

As logs are indices, the laws of logs are directly related to the laws of indices.

	Laws of Logs		Numerical Example	
L1.	$\log_b mn = \log_b m + \log_b n$	$\log_2 32 = 5$	$\log_2 32 = \log_2 4 \times 8 = \log_2 4 + \log_2 8 = 2 + 3 = 5$	
L2.	$\log_b \dfrac{m}{n} = \log_b m - \log_b n$	$\log_3 27 = 3$	$\log_3 27 = \log\left(\frac{81}{3}\right) = \log_3 81 - \log_3 3 = 4 - 1 = 3$	
L3.	$\log_b m^n = n \log_b m$	$\log_2 8 = 3$	$\log_2 8 = \log_2 2^3 = 3 \log_2 2 = 3(1) = 3$	
L4.	$\log_n m = \dfrac{\log_b m}{\log_b n}$ (change of base)	$\log_4 64 = 3$	$\log_4 64 = \dfrac{\log_2 64}{\log_2 4} = \frac{6}{2} = 3$	
L5.	$\log_b b = 1$	$\log_2 2 = 1$	$b = b^1$ thus $\log_b b = 1$	
L6.	$\log_b 1 = 0$	$\log_5 1 = 0$	$1 = b^0$ thus $\log_b 1 = 0$	

Natural Logs

Logs to the base 10, i.e. $\log_{10} x$, are called '**common logs**'.

Logs to the base e, i.e. $\log_e x$, are called '**natural logs**'.

$\log_e x$ is written $\ln x$. The number $e = 2.71828$ (correct to 5 decimal places) is an irrational number, just like π.

It is very important to remember that natural logs obey the same rules as logs to any other base.

Example ▾

Evaluate:

(i) $\log_{10} 2 + \log_{10} 500$ (ii) $\log_5 \frac{1}{5}$ (iii) $\log_8 16$

(iv) $\log_9 3$ (v) $\ln e^2$ (vi) $\ln\left(\frac{1}{e}\right)$

(i) $\log_{10} 2 + \log_{10} 500$
$= \log_{10}(2 \times 500)$ (L1)
$= \log_{10} 1000$
$= 3$

(ii) $\log_5(\frac{1}{5})$
$= \log_5 1 - \log_5 5$ (L2)
$= 0 - 1$ (L5 and L6)
$= -1$

(iii) $\log_8 16$
$= \dfrac{\log_2 16}{\log_2 8}$ (L4)
(16 and 8 can be written as powers of 2)
$= \frac{4}{3}$

(iv) $\log_9 3$
$= \dfrac{\log_3 3}{\log_3 9}$ (L4)
(3 and 9 can be written as powers of 3)
$= \frac{1}{2}$
Alternatively, $\log_9 3$
$= \log_9 9^{1/2} = \frac{1}{2} \log_9 9$
$= \frac{1}{2}(1) = \frac{1}{2}$

(v) $\ln e^2$
$= 2 \ln e$ (L3)
$= 2(1)$
$= 2$

($\ln e = \log_e e = 1$)

(vi) $\ln(\frac{1}{e})$
$\ln 1 - \ln e$ (L2)
$= 0 - 1$
$= -1$

Example ▾

(i) If $\log_x 125 = 3$ find the value of x (ii) Evaluate: $2 \log_2 2 + \log_2 12 - \log_2 6$.

Solution:

(i) $\log_x 125 = 3$
$\quad 125 = x^3$
$\quad 5^3 = x^3$
$\quad \therefore x = 5$

(ii) $2 \log_2 2 + \log_2 12 - \log_2 6$
$= \log_2 2^2 + \log_2 12 - \log_2 6$
$= \log_2 4 + \log_2 12 - \log_2 6$
$= \log_2 \dfrac{4 \times 12}{6}$
$\left(\log a + \log b - \log c = \log \dfrac{a \times b}{c}\right)$
$= \log_2 8 = 3$

1. Write each of the following in the form $a = b^c$:
   (i) $\log_2 16 = 4$ (ii) $\log_3 81 = 4$ (iii) $\log_{10} 10,000 = 4$ (iv) $\log_5 125 = 3$
   (v) $\log_6 36 = 2$ (vi) $\log_4 2 = \frac{1}{2}$ (vii) $\log_{27} 3 = \frac{1}{3}$ (viii) $\log_4 8 = \frac{3}{2}$

2. Write each of the following in the form $\log_b a = c$:
   (i) $100 = 10^2$ (ii) $8 = 2^3$ (iii) $27 = 3^3$ (iv) $49 = 7^2$
   (v) $4 = 16^{1/2}$ (vi) $9 = 27^{2/3}$ (vii) $4 = 4$ (viii) $1 = 8^0$

3. Evaluate each of the following:
   (i) $\log_2 8$ (ii) $\log_4 16$ (iii) $\log_3 81$ (iv) $\log_5 125$
   (v) $\log_{10} 10,000$ (vi) $\log_2 32$ (vii) $\log_5 5$ (viii) $\log_4 1$
   (ix) $\log_2 \frac{1}{2}$ (x) $\log_7 \frac{1}{49}$ (xi) $\log_4 32$ (xii) $\log_{16} 8$
   (xiii) $\log_9 27$ (xiv) $\frac{1}{3}\log_2 8$ (xv) $\log_{27} \frac{1}{3}$ (xvi) $\log_2 2\sqrt{2}$

4. Evaluate each of the following:
   (i) $\log_a a^2$ (ii) $\log_a a^3$ (iii) $(\log_6 4 + \log_6 9)^2$
   (iv) $(\log_5 25 + \log_5 15 - \log_5 3)^4$ (v) $\log 3 + \log 16 - \log 4 - \log 12$

5. (a) $f(x) = 2\log_5 x$. Evaluate   (i) $f(5)$ (ii) $f(25)$ (iii) $f(\frac{1}{5})$ (iv) $f(\sqrt{5})$
   (b) If $\log_4 x = 1 - p$ and $\log_4 y = 1 + p$, evaluate xy.

6. Evaluate $\log \dfrac{p}{q} + \log \dfrac{q}{r} + \log \dfrac{r}{p}$.

7. (a) Use the fact that $\log_b a = \dfrac{\log_c a}{\log_c b}$ to evaluate   (i) $\log_{27} 81$ (ii) $\log_{32} 8$.
   (b) Evaluate $\log_b a \cdot \log_c b \cdot \log_a c$.
   (c) Show that $\log_b a = \dfrac{1}{\log_a b}$.
   (d) If $x > 0$ and $x \neq 1$, show that $\dfrac{1}{\log_2 x} + \dfrac{1}{\log_3 x} + \dfrac{1}{\log_5 x} = \dfrac{1}{\log_{30} x}$.

8. If $\log_r p = \log_r 2 + 3\log_r q$, express p in terms of q.

9. If $\log_a y = 2\log_a x - \log_a 5$, express y in terms of x.

10. If $3\log_2 y = 3 + \log_2(x + 4)$, show that $y^3 = 8(x + 4)$.

Logarithm Equations

There are two methods for solving an equation involving logs.

Method 1:

> Get a single log on **both** sides in the equation, equate the expressions and solve,
> i.e. write the equation in the form $\log_b x = \log_b y$, $\Rightarrow x = y$ and solve.

Method 2:

> Get a single log in the equation and then change from log form to index form,
> i.e. write the equation in the form $\log_b a = c$, $\Rightarrow a = b^c$.

Note: **1.** Make sure that all logs have the same base. If necessary, use the 'change of base' law, L4, to write all logs to the same base.
2. Logs are defined only for positive numbers. Therefore, reject any solutions that give rise to log (negative number) in the **original** equation.

Example ▼

Solve for x: $\quad \log_2 x = 3 - \log_2(x - 2), \quad x \in \mathbf{R}$.

Solution:

Method 1	**Method 2**
$\log_2 x = 3 - \log_2 (x - 2)$	$\log_2 x = 3 - \log_2(x - 2)$
$\log_2 x + \log_2(x - 2) = 3$	$\log_2 x + \log_2(x - 2) = 3$
$\log_2 x(x - 2) = \log_2 8$	$\log_2 x(x - 2) = 3$
$\log_2 (x^2 - 2x) = \log_2 8$	$\log_2(x^2 - 2x) = 3$
$x^2 - 2x = 8$	$x^2 - 2x = 2^3$
$x^2 - 2x - 8 = 0$	$x^2 - 2x = 8$
$(x - 4)(x + 2) = 0$	$x^2 - 2x - 8 = 0$
$x - 4 = 0 \quad$ or $\quad x + 2 = 0$	$(x - 4)(x + 2) = 0$
$x = 4 \quad$ or $\quad x = -2$	$x - 4 = 0 \quad$ or $\quad x + 2 = 0$
	$x = 4 \quad$ or $\quad x = -2$

Reject $x = -2$, as substitution into the **original** equation yields $\log_2(-2)$ or $\log_2(-4)$, which is not defined.

$\therefore x = 4$ is the solution (which can be checked in the original equation).

Sometimes a change of base is required.

Example ▼

Solve for x: $\quad \log_2 x + 4 \log_x 2 = 5$

Solution:

First write the equation in terms of one base only.

$\log_2 x + 4 \log_x 2 = 5$

$\log_2 x + 4\left(\dfrac{1}{\log_2 x}\right) = 5$

$\log_2 x + \dfrac{4}{\log_2 x} = 5$

Let $\log_2 x = y$ (using a substitution)

$y + \dfrac{4}{y} = 5$

$y^2 + 4 = 5y$

$y^2 - 5y + 4 = 0$

$(y - 4)(y - 1) = 0$

$y = 4 \quad$ or $\quad y = 1$

$$\boxed{\begin{aligned} \log_x 2 &= \frac{\log_2 2}{\log_2 x} \\ &= \frac{1}{\log_2 x} \end{aligned}}$$

Change both to the base of the constant 2

$y = 4$	or	$y = 1$
$\log_2 x = 4$		$\log_2 x = 1$
$x = 2^4$		$x = 2^1$
$x = 16$		$x = 2$

Sometimes we have to solve simultaneous equations.

Solve the simultaneous equations:
$2 \log x = \log(x + y)$ and $\log y = \log 2 + \log(x - 1)$, $\qquad x > 1, y > 0$.

Solution:

$$2 \log x = \log(x + y)$$
$$\log x^2 = \log(x + y)$$
$$x^2 = x + y \qquad ①$$

$$\log y = \log 2 + \log(x - 1)$$
$$\log y = \log 2(x - 1)$$
$$y = 2(x - 1) \qquad ②$$

From ② $y = 2(x - 1)$, put this into ①
$$x^2 = y + x \qquad ①$$
$$x^2 = 2(x - 1) + x \qquad \text{(replace } y \text{ with } 2(x - 1))$$
$$x^2 = 2x - 2 + x$$
$$x^2 - 3x + 2 = 0$$
$$(x - 2)(x - 1) = 0$$
$$x = 2 \quad \text{or} \quad x = 1$$

$x = 2:\qquad y = 2(x - 1) = 2(2 - 1) = 2(1) = 2$
$x = 1:\qquad y = 2(x - 1) = 2(1 - 1) = 2(0) = 0$

Thus, $x = 2$ and $y = 2$ or $x = 1$ and $y = 0$.

However, we are given $x > 1$ and $y > 0$

$\therefore \quad x = 2$ and $y = 2$ is the solution.

Sometimes we have to use a calculator.

If $5^n = 3000$, find the value of n, correct to 4 significant figures.

Solution:

$$5^n = 3000$$
$$\log_{10} 5^n = \log_{10} 3000 \qquad \text{(take the log of both sides)}$$
$$n \log_{10} 5 = \log_{10} 3000 \qquad \text{(use law 3)}$$
$$n = \frac{\log_{10} 3000}{\log_{10} 5} \qquad \text{(divide both sides by } \log_{10} 5)$$
$$n = 4.974635869 \qquad (\boxed{} \; \boxed{\log} \; 3000 \; \boxed{\div} \; \boxed{\log} \; 5 \; \boxed{=} \;)$$
$$n = 4.975 \qquad \text{(correct to 4 significant figures)}$$

(check: $5^{4.975} = 30001.758655$, $\qquad \boxed{} \; 5 \; \boxed{x^y} \; 4.975 \; \boxed{=} \;$)

Note: Using natural logs to the base e would have given the same answer, i.e. $\dfrac{\ln 3000}{\ln 5} = 4.974635869$.

Solve each of the following equations, $x \in \mathbf{R}$:

1. $\log_2 3 + \log_2 x = \log_2 12$

2. $\log_3 x - \log_3 4 = \log_3 2$

3. $\log_{10} x^2 + \log_{10} 2 = \log_{10} 50$

4. $\log_5(x + 1) + \log_5(x - 1) = \log_5 8$

5. $\log_a(x - 6) + \log_a(x - 4) = \log_a x$

6. $\log_3(x^2 - 10) - \log_3 x = 2 \log_3 3$

7. $\log_2(x + 2) + \log_2(x - 2) = 5$

8. $\log_5(x - 2) = 1 - \log_5(x - 6)$

9. $\log_2(x + 2) - \log_2 x = 3$

10. $\log_{10}(x^2 + 24) - \log_{10} x = 1$

11. $2 \log_9 x = \frac{1}{2} + \log_9(5x + 18)$

12. $\log_7(x^2 + 4) - \log_7(x - 1) = \log_7(3x + 2)$

13. $\log_5 x = 1 + \log_5\left(\dfrac{3}{2x - 1}\right)$

14. $2 \log_3(x + 2) - \log_3(x + 1) = \log_3(x + 5)$

Solve each of the following simultaneous equations, x, $y \in \mathbf{R}$:

15. $\log(5x - y) = \log 9$ and $\log(3x + 2y) = \log 8$

16. $\log_2(2x + y) = 3$ and $\log_2(3x - 4y) = 0$

17. $\log_3(3x - y) = \log_3(y + 1)$ and $\log_3 2 + \log_3(x + y) = 2$

18. $\log x^2 = \log y$ and $\log(2x + y) - \log 3 = 0$

19. $\log_2 2 + \log_2(x + 1) = \log_2 y$ and $\log_2 x + \log_2 y = 2$, $\quad x > 0, y > 0$.

20. $\log_2 x - \log_2 2 = \log_2(1 - y)$ and $\log_2 x + \log_2(x + 2y) = 3$

Questions 21 to 26 require changing the base.
Solve each of the following equations, $x \in \mathbf{R}$:

21. $\log_2 x = \log_4(x + 6)$

22. $\log_2(x - 1) = \log_4(4x - 7)$

23. $\log_3 x + 3 \log_x 3 = 4$

24. $\log_4 x + 2 \log_x 4 = 3$

25. $\log_5 x - 1 = 6 \log_x 5$

26. $4 \log_x 2 = \log_2 x + 3$

27. If $\log_4\left(\dfrac{x}{y}\right) = 5$, $\quad x, y > 0$, find the value of $\log_2 x - \log_2 y$.

28. The point $a(p, k)$ lies on the curve with equation $y = \log_2 x$.
The point $b(q, k)$ lies on the curve with equation $y = \log_4 x$.
Find a relationship between p and q and hence evaluate p when $q = \frac{9}{16}$.

29. $\log_a 2 + 2 \log_a x = \log_a(5x - 2a) + 1$.
Write a quadratic equation in terms of x and find, in terms of a, the values of x.

30. If $\log_4 xy = 2$, prove that $\log_2 x + \log_2 y = 4$.
Solve the simultaneous equations $\log_4 xy = 2$ and $\log_2 x . \log_2 y = 3$.
(Hint: let $\log_2 x = p$ and $\log_2 y = q$)

31. If $\log_4 a = k$, express in terms of k:

    (i) $\log_4 a^2$ (ii) $\log_4 4a^2$ (iii) $\log_{16} a$ (iv) $\log_a 4$ (v) $\log_a \frac{1}{4}$

Questions 32 to 39 require using a calculator.

Solve each of the following for n, correct to 4 significant figures:

32. $3^n = 2500$ **33.** $5^n = 680$ **34.** $4^n = 20$ **35.** $2^n = 31$

36. $4^{n+2} = 3460$ **37.** $3^{2n-1} = 4800$ **38.** $5^{n-1} = 2^n$ **39.** $5^{2n-1} = 4^{n+1}$

Questions 40 to 45 involve using natural logarithms.

40. Evaluate each of the following:

    (i) $\ln e$ (ii) $\ln e^3$ (iii) $\ln\left(\dfrac{1}{e^2}\right)$ (iv) $\ln \sqrt{e}$

41. By taking the log of both sides, verify that if:

    (i) $e^x = a$, then $x = \ln a$ (ii) $e^{\ln x} = y$, then $x = y$

42. Solve each of the following:

    (i) $e^x = 2$ (ii) $e^x = 5$ (iii) $e^x = -4$ (iv) $e^x = \frac{1}{3}$

    (v) $e^x = -1$ (vi) $e^{2x} = 3$ (vii) $\ln x = 1$ (viii) $\ln x = 2$

    (ix) $\ln x = \frac{1}{2}$ (x) $\ln x = -1$ (xi) $\ln x = -3$ (xii) $\ln x = -\frac{1}{2}$

43. By writing $e^x = y$, or otherwise, solve each of the following equations:

    (i) $e^x - 5 + 6e^{-x} = 0$

    (ii) $e^{2x} - 8e^x + 15 = 0$

    (iii) $e^{2x} - 3e^x - 4 = 0$

    (iv) $3e^x - 7 + 2e^{-x} = 0$

44. By letting $e^x = y$, write $e^{2x} + (k-2)e^x + (-3k-2) = 0$ as a quadratic equation in y, $k \in \mathbf{R}$. Find the values of k for which this equation has equal roots.

Assuming these values of k, solve the equation $e^{2x} + (k-2)e^x + (-3k-2) = 0$.

45. Solve: (i) $(\ln x)^2 - 3\ln x + 2 = 0$ (ii) $2(\ln x)^2 - 7\ln x + 3 = 0$

COORDINATE GEOMETRY
THE LINE AND LINEAR TRANSFORMATIONS

Revision

In all cases (x_1, y_1) and (x_2, y_2) represent points.

1. **Distance between two points.**

$$\sqrt{(x_2 - x_1)^2 + (y_2 - y_1)^2}$$

2. **Midpoint of a line segment.**

$$\left(\frac{x_1 + x_2}{2}, \frac{y_1 + y_2}{2} \right)$$

3. **Slope of a line, m, given two points.**

$$m = \frac{y_2 - y_1}{x_2 - x_1}$$

4. **Parallel lines have equal slopes (and vice versa).**

$$\text{If } L_1 \parallel L_2, \text{ then } m_1 = m_2$$

5. **If two lines are perpendicular, when we multiply their slopes we always get –1 (and vice versa).**

$$\text{If } L_1 \perp L_2, \text{ then } m_1 \cdot m_2 = -1$$

(In 4 and 5 above, m_1 = the slope of the line L_1 and m_2 = the slope of the line L_2).

Note: If we know the slope of a line and we need to find the slope of a line perpendicular to it, simply do the following:

> Turn the known slope upside down and change its sign.

For example, if a line has a slope of $-\frac{3}{5}$, then the slope of a line perpendicular to it has a slope of $\frac{5}{3}$ (turn upside down and change its sign), because $-\frac{3}{5} \times \frac{5}{3} = -1$.

6. **Equation of a line**

> To find the equation of a line we need:
> 1. The slope of line, m
>   Then use the formula.
> 2. A point on the line, (x_1, y_1)
> $(y - y_1) = m(x - x_1)$.

In short: we need the **slope** and a **point** on the line.

7. **Slope of a line when given its equation.**

To find the slope of a line when given its equation, do the following:

Method 1:

> Get y on its own and the number in front of x is the slope.

Note: The number in front of x is called the **coefficient** of x.
In short, write the line in the form:

$$y = mx + c$$

$$y = (\text{slope})x + (\text{where the line cuts the } y\text{-axis})$$

Method 2:

> If the line is in the form $ax + by + c = 0$, then $-\dfrac{a}{b}$ is the slope.

In words: slope $= -\dfrac{\text{number in front of } x}{\text{number in front of } y}$

Note: When using this method, make sure every term is on the left-hand side in the given equation of the line.

8. **Proving lines are parallel or perpendicular.**

To prove whether or not two lines are parallel, do the following:

> 1. Find the slope of each line.
> 2. (a) If the slopes are the same, the lines are parallel.
>   (b) If the slopes are different, the lines are **not** parallel.

To prove whether or not two lines are perpendicular, do the following:

> 1. Find the slope of each line.
> 2. Multiply both slopes.
> 3. (a) If the answer in step 2 is -1, the lines are perpendicular.
>   (b) If the answer in step 2 is **not** -1, the lines are **not** perpendicular.

Note: $ax + by + k = 0$ is a line parallel to the line $ax + by + c = 0$.
$bx - ay + k = 0$ or $-bx + ay + k = 0$ is a line perpendicular to the line $ax + by + c = 0$.

9. **Verify that a point belongs to a line.**

Substitute the coordinates of the point into the equation of the line. If the coordinates satisfy the equation, then the point is on the line. Otherwise, the point is not on the line.

10. Point of intersection of two lines.

Use the method of solving simultaneous equations to find the point of intersection of two lines.

11. Graphing lines.

To draw a line only two points are needed. The easiest points to find are where lines cut the x and y axes. This is known as the **intercept method**.

> **Note:** On the x-axis $y = 0$.　　On the y-axis $x = 0$.

To draw a line do the following:

> **1.** Let $y = 0$ and find x.
> **2.** Let $x = 0$ and find y.
> **3.** Plot these two points.
> **4.** Draw the line through these points.

If the constant in the equation of a line is zero, e.g. $3x - 5y = 0$, or $4x = 3y$, then the line will pass through the origin, $(0, 0)$. In this case the **intercept method** will not work.

To draw a line that contains the origin, $(0, 0)$, do the following:

> **1.** Choose a suitable value for x and find the corresponding value for y (or vice versa).
> **2.** Plot this point.
> **3.** A line drawn through this point and the origin is the required line.

Note: A very suitable value is to let x equal the number in front of y and then find the corresponding value for y (or vice versa).

12. Lines parallel to the axes.

$x = 2$ is a line parallel to the y-axis through 2 on the x-axis.

$y = -1$ is a line parallel to the x-axis through -1 on the y-axis.

> **Note:** $y = 0$ is the equation of the x-axis.
> $x = 0$ is the equation of the y-axis.

13. Transformations of the Plane.

(i) **Translation**: A translation moves a point in a straight line.
(ii) **Central symmetry**: Central symmetry is a reflection in a point.
(iii) **Axial symmetry**: Axial symmetry is a reflection in a line.

(iv) Axial symmetry in the axes or central symmetry in the origin.

> The following three patterns emerge and it is worth memorising them:
> **1.** Axial symmetry in the x-axis $\rightarrow$ **change the sign of y**
> **2.** Axial symmetry in the y-axis $\rightarrow$ **change the sign of x**
> **3.** Central symmetry in the origin, $(0, 0) \rightarrow$ **change the sign of both x and y**

Note: Under a translation, or central symmetry, a line is mapped onto a parallel line.

Exercise 6.1 ▼

1. $a(2, -2)$ and $b(4, 4)$ are two points.
   - **(i)** Find $|ab|$ **(ii)** find the coordinates of m, the midpoint of $[ab]$.
   - **(iii)** Find the slope and equation of the line ab.
   - **(iv)** The point $(-2, r)$ is on the line ab; find the value of r.
   - **(v)** The perpendicular bisector of the line segment $[ab]$ cuts the x-axis at the point $p(h, 0)$ and the y-axis at $q(0, k)$. Find the value of h and the value of k.
   - **(vi)** Find the image of the point a under a central symmetry in b.
   - **(vii)** Find the image of the point $c(-1, 5)$ under the translation $\vec{ab}$.
   - **(viii)** Find the equation of the image of the line ab under a central symmetry in the point $s(-1, 1)$.

2. $L: 3x - 2y + 8 = 0$ and $K: 2x + 3y - 1 = 0$ are two lines. Prove $L \perp K$.

3. $L: px + qy + r = 0$ and $N: qx - py + 5 = 0$ are two lines. Prove $L \perp N$.

4. $L: ax + 3y = 0$ and $K: 3x - 5y - 4 = 0$ are two lines. If $L \perp K$, find the value of a.

5. $p(2, -3)$, $q(3, 1)$ and $r(-1, k)$ are three points. If $pq \perp qr$, find the value of k.

6. $L: 2x - 5y - 9 = 0$ and $K: 3x - 2y - 8 = 0$ are two lines. L intersects K at the point q. Find the coordinates of q. Find the equation of the line M such that $L \perp M$ and $q \in M$. Show that the point $r(4, -6)$ is on M. Find the coordinates of the image of the point r under an axial symmetry in L.

7. Find the equation of the line through the point $(2, -3)$ which makes an angle of
   - **(i)** 45°   **(ii)** 135° with the positive sense of the x-axis.

8. Show that the points $p(2, -3)$, $q(3, 1)$ and $r(5, 9)$ are collinear.

9. Show that the lines $L: x + y + 4 = 0$, $K: 9x - 5y - 20 = 0$ and $M: 5x - 9y + 20 = 0$ form an isosceles triangle.

10. The point $m(-2, -1)$ is the midpoint of $[pq]$.
    If the coordinates of p are $(4, -5)$, find the coordinates of q.

11. $p(-1, -2)$, $q(5, k)$, $r(8, 2)$ and $s(h, 1)$ are the four vertices of the parallelogram $pqrs$.
    Find the value of h and the value of k.

12. $p(-1, 5)$, $q(-2, 1)$, $r(3, -2)$ and $s(a, b)$ are the four vertices of a parallelogram, with $pq \parallel rs$.
    Find two pairs of coordinates of the point s.

13. $L: 3x + 2y - 5 = 0$, $K: 4x - y - 14 = 0$ and $M: 2x + 5y - 1 = 0$ are the equations of three lines.
    Find the equation of the line containing the point of intersection of L and K and perpendicular to M.

14. Show that the point $(2, -5)$ is on the line L: $3x - 2y - 16 = 0$. Find the equation of the image of L
under **(i)** the translation $(2, -5) \rightarrow (4, -6)$ **(ii)** the central symmetry in the point $(-1, -1)$.

15. Find the image of the point $(-4, -5)$ under the axial symmetry in the line $3x + 2y - 4 = 0$.

16. Find the equations of the two lines which contain the point $(4, 2)$ and cut equal intercepts on the x
and y axes.

17. $a(2t, 0)$ and $b(0, -t)$ are two points. If $|ab| = \sqrt{20}$. Find the two values of t.

18. $p(1, 6)$, $q(-3, -1)$ and $r(2, k)$ are three points. If $|pq| = |pr|$, find the two values of k.

19. $a(5, 2)$, $b(2, -1)$, $c(x, 4)$ and $d(4, x)$ are four points and $|ab| = |cd|$.
Show that $(x - 4)^2 = 9$ and solve for x.

20. $a(0, 5)$, $b(x, 10)$ and $c(2x, x)$ are three points. If $|ab| = |bc|$, find the two values of x.

21. Calculate the area of the triangle formed by the x-axis, the y-axis and the line $3x - y - 6 = 0$.

22. $pqrs$ is a parallelogram in which the opposite vertices are $p(2, 1)$ and $r(4, 4)$.
If the slope of pq is $\frac{1}{3}$ and the slope of $ps = -2$, find:
(i) the equation of pq
(ii) the equation of qr
(iii) hence, or otherwise, find the coordinates of q and s.

23. The equation of the line L is $ax + by + c = 0$. L cuts the x-axis at p and the y-axis at q.
Find **(i)** the coordinates of p and the coordinates of q **(ii)** $|pq|$.
Calculate the area of the triangle formed by the x-axis, the y-axis and the line $ax + by + c = 0$.
Give each answer in terms of a, b and c.

24. Find the equation of the line parallel to $ax + \dfrac{y}{a} = b$ containing the point $\left(\dfrac{b}{a}, ab\right)$.

25. The line $\dfrac{x}{a} + \dfrac{y}{b} = 1$, $a, b > 0$, intersects the x-axis at p and the y-axis at q.
If the slope of the line pq is -2 and $|pq| = 4\sqrt{5}$, find the value of a and the value of b.

26. Let $f(x) = \dfrac{1}{x}$ for all $x \in \mathbf{R}$ and $x \neq 0$.
Points a and b have coordinates $(p, f(p))$ and $(q, f(q))$, respectively, for $0 < p < q$.
Show that the equation of the line ab can be written as $y = g(x) = \dfrac{1}{p} - \dfrac{1}{pq}(x - p)$.

Area of a Triangle

Area of a Triangle

The area of a triangle with vertices $(0, 0)$, (x_1, y_1) and (x_2, y_2) is given by the formula: Area of triangle $= \frac{1}{2}|x_1 y_2 - x_2 y_1|$

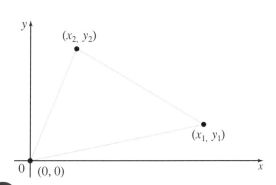

Notes:

1. The modulus symbol, $| \ \ |$, is included to make sure your answer is positive.
   Therefore, if the above formula gives a negative answer, simply ignore the negative sign,
   e.g. $\frac{1}{2}|-10| = \frac{1}{2} . 10 = 5$

2. If none of the vertices is at the origin, simply select one of the vertices and map (move) it to the point $(0, 0)$ by a translation. Then apply the same translation to the other two vertices to get (x_1, y_1) and (x_2, y_2).

3. To find the area of a quadrilateral (4-sided figure), divide it into two triangles.
   The **diagonal** of a **parallelogram** bisects its area.

Example ▼

Find the area of the triangle with vertices $(-2, 1)$, $(-4, 9)$ and $(3, -6)$.

Solution:

Area of triangle	Map the point $(-2, 1)$ on to $(0, 0)$.
$= \frac{1}{2}\|x_1 y_2 - x_2 y_1\|$	$\quad(-2, 1) \quad\quad (-4, 9) \quad\quad (3, -6)$
$= \frac{1}{2}\|(-2)(-7) - (5)(8)\|$	$\quad\quad\downarrow\quad\quad\quad\quad\downarrow\quad\quad\quad\quad\downarrow$
$= \frac{1}{2}\|14 - 40\|$	$\quad(0, 0) \quad\quad (-2, 8) \quad\quad (5, -7)$
$= \frac{1}{2}\|-26\| = \frac{1}{2}\|26\| = 13$ square units	$\quad\quad\quad\quad\quad\quad x_1, y_1 \quad\quad\quad x_2, y_2$
	(**Rule**: add 2 to x, subtract 1 from y)

Sometimes we are given the area of a triangle and asked to find the unknown values of missing coordinates. We are given an equation in disguise and we solve this equation to find the unknown values of the missing coordinates.

Note: If we need to map one of the points to $(0, 0)$, it is good practice to choose one of the **known** coordinates.

Example ▼

$a(3k, 5)$, $b(-2, 3)$ and $c(-k, 4))$ are vertices of the triangle abc.
If the area of triangle abc is 4 square units, find the values of k.

Solution:

Area of triangle abc	Map the point $(-2, 3)$ on to $(0, 0)$.
$= \frac{1}{2}\|x_1 y_2 - x_2 y_1\|$	$\quad(3k, 5) \quad\quad (-2, 3) \quad\quad (-k, 4)$
$= \frac{1}{2}\|(3k + 2)(1) - (-k + 2)(2)\|$	$\quad\quad\downarrow\quad\quad\quad\quad\downarrow\quad\quad\quad\quad\downarrow$
$= \frac{1}{2}\|3k + 2 + 2k - 4\|$	$\quad(3k + 2, 2) \quad (0, 0) \quad\quad (-k + 2, 1)$
$= \frac{1}{2}\|5k - 2\|$	$\quad\quad x_1, y_1 \quad\quad\quad\quad\quad\quad x_2, y_2$
	(Rule: add 2 to x, subtract 3 from y.)

Given:

Area of $\triangle abc = 4$	(equation given in disguise)
$\frac{1}{2}\lvert 5k - 2 \rvert = 4$	(area of triangle $= \frac{1}{2}\lvert 5k - 2 \rvert$)
$\lvert 5k - 2 \rvert = 8$	(multiply both sides by 2)
$5k - 2 = \pm 8$	(must include both positive and negative solutions)
$5k - 2 = 8$ or $5k - 2 = -8$	
$5k = 10$ or $5k = -6$	
$k = 2$ or $k = -\frac{6}{5}$	

Exercise 6.2 ▼

Find the area of each of the following triangles whose vertices are:

1. $(0, 0), (5, 2), (3, 4)$

2. $(10, 8), (0, 0), (3, 5)$

3. $(1, 5), (-5, -3), (4, 1)$

4. $(7, -1), (-5, 6), (3, -2)$

5. $(-4, -8), (4, -5), (3, -2)$

6. $(-1, -4), (2, -1), (-2, 3)$

Find the area of the parallelogram whose vertices are:

7. $(0, 0), (1, 3), (5, 5), (4, 2)$

8. $(-2, 4), (2, 4), (2, 7), (-2, 7)$

9. $(5, 1), (3, 1), (5, 4), (7, 4)$

10. $(-1, 3), (0, 2), (5, 4), (4, 5)$

Find the area of the quadrilateral whose vertices are:

11. $(1, 1), (1, 2), (9, 3), (6, 1)$

12. $(5, -6), (5, -4), (0, 1), (-2, -9)$

13. $(2, -4), (-1, -4), (-2, 2), (5, 5)$

14. $(-2, 2), (-5, -6), (8, -4), (9, 0)$

15. $a(-1, -3), b(2, -1)$ and $c(5, 1)$ are the vertices of triangle abc. By finding the area of triangle abc, show that a, b and c are collinear.

16. $a(-1, -3), b(4, 1)$ are $c(3, k)$ are the vertices of triangle abc.
If the area of triangle abc is 12 square units, find the two values of k.

17. The area of the triangle with vertices $(0, 0), (5t, 3t)$ and $(t, 2t)$ is 14 square units.
Find the two possible values of $t \in \mathbf{R}$.

18. The area of the triangle with vertices $p(-k, 1), q(0, 3)$ and $r(2k, -1)$ is 4 square units.
Find the two values of k.

19. $a(1, 3), b(-3, 1), c(5, -2), p(-1, 1), q(9, 7), r(1, k), k > 0$, are six points.
If the area of triangle abc = area of triangle pqr, find the value of k.

20. $p(h, k), q(1, -2)$ and $r(8, -3)$ are the vertices of the triangle pqr.
Calculate the coordinates of p if p is a point on the x-axis and area of triangle pqr is 8 square units.

21. $a(2, -1), b(1, -3), c(-1, 1)$ are three points. Show that the area of $\triangle abc$ is 4.
$k_1(\alpha_1, 0)$ and $k_2(0, \alpha_2)$ are two points such that:
area of $\triangle k_1 ac$ = area of $\triangle k_2 ac = 4$.
Find α_1 and α_2.

Division of a Line Segment in a Given Ratio

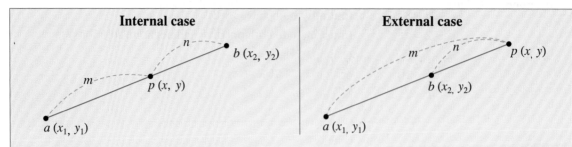

Internal case	External case

The coordinates of the point p which divides the line segment $a(x_1, y_1)$ and $b(x_2, y_2)$ in the ratio $m:n$ are given by:

internal divisor	external divisor
$p = \left(\dfrac{mx_2 + nx_1}{m+n}, \dfrac{my_2 + ny_1}{m+n} \right)$	$p = \left(\dfrac{mx_2 - nx_1}{m-n}, \dfrac{my_2 - ny_1}{m-n} \right)$

Note: The coordinates of p can also be found using similar triangles.

Example ▼

Find the coordinates of the point that divides the line segment $(-4, 3)$ and $(6, -12)$ in the ratio $3:2$ **(i)** internally **(ii)** externally.

Solution:

Method 1: Using the formula

(i) internal divisor

$$(x, y) = \left(\frac{mx_2 + nx_1}{m+n}, \frac{my_2 + ny_1}{m+n} \right)$$

$$= \left(\frac{3(6) + 2(-4)}{3+2}, \frac{3(-12) + 2(3)}{3+2} \right)$$

$$= \left(\frac{18 - 8}{5}, \frac{-36 + 6}{5} \right)$$

$$= (2, -6)$$

(ii) external divisor

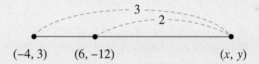

$$(x, y) = \left(\frac{mx_2 - nx_1}{m-n}, \frac{my_2 - ny_1}{m-n} \right)$$

$$= \left(\frac{3(6) - 2(-4)}{3-2}, \frac{3(-12) - 2(3)}{3-2} \right)$$

$$= \left(\frac{18 + 8}{1}, \frac{-36 - 6}{1} \right)$$

$$= (26, -42)$$

Method 2: Using similar triangles

(i) internal divisor

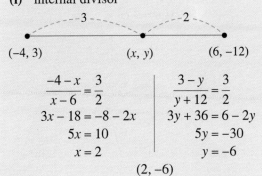

$$\frac{-4-x}{x-6}=\frac{3}{2}$$ $$\qquad$$ $$\frac{3-y}{y+12}=\frac{3}{2}$$

$$3x-18=-8-2x \qquad 3y+36=6-2y$$

$$5x=10 \qquad\qquad 5y=-30$$

$$x=2 \qquad\qquad\quad y=-6$$

$$(2,-6)$$

(ii) external divisor

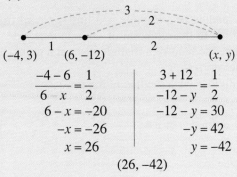

$$\frac{-4-6}{6\ \ x}=\frac{1}{2}$$ $$\qquad$$ $$\frac{3+12}{-12-y}=\frac{1}{2}$$

$$6-x=-20 \qquad -12-y=30$$

$$-x=-26 \qquad\quad -12-y=30$$

$$x=26 \qquad\qquad -y=42$$

$$\qquad\qquad\qquad\qquad\quad y=-42$$

$$(26,-42)$$

Exercise 6.3 ▼

Complete the following table, by dividing the line segment [a, b] in the given ratio:

	a	*b*	**Ratio**	**Internally**	**Externally**
1.	(3, 1)	(9, 4)	2 : 1		
2.	(−5, 3)	(10, −7)	3 : 2		
3.	(−4, 3)	(12, −6)	1 : 3		
4.	(1, −2)	(−20, 12)	4 : 3		
5.	(−3, −7)	(9, −17)	5 : 1		
6.	(−2, 5)	(14, −19)	5 : 3		

7. $a(-1, 3)$ and $b(6, -11)$ are two points. p is a point on [ab] such that $|ap|:|pb|=3:4$.
Find the coordinates of p.

8. $p(-2, 5)$ and $q(1, 3)$ are two points. The point r is on [pq] produced, such that $|pq|:|qr|=1:2$.
Find the coordinates of r.

9. The point $p(-1, 8)$ divides the line segment [ab] internally such that $|ap|:|pb|=3:1$.
If the coordinates of a are $(5, -1)$, find the coordinates of b.

10. $a(3, 2)$ and $b(18, 12)$ are two points.
[ab] is produced to c such that $|ac|:|bc|=7:2$. Find the coordinates of c.

11. a is a point on the x-axis and b is a point on the y-axis.
p is $(9, -8)$ and p divides [ab] internally in the ratio $4:3$.
Find the coordinates of a and b.

12. Find the coordinates of the point that divides the segment $(2h, 3k)$ to $(12h, -17k)$ in the ratio $3:2$
(i) internally   **(ii)** externally.

Concurrencies of a Triangle

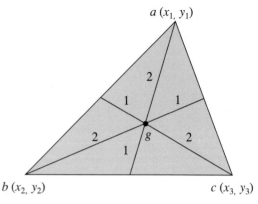

1. **Centroid g**
   A median of a triangle is a line segment from a vertex to the midpoint of the opposite side. The three medians of a triangle meet at a point called the centroid, g.
   g divides each median in the ratio $2 : 1$.

   Coordinates of $g = \left(\dfrac{x_1 + x_2 + x_3}{3}, \dfrac{y_1 + y_2 + y_3}{3} \right)$

2. **Circumcentre o**
   The circumcentre of a triangle is the point of intersection of the perpendicular bisectors of the sides.

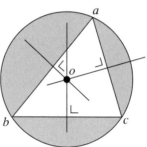

3. **Orthocentre h**
   The orthocentre is the point of intersection of the perpendicular lines from the vertices to the opposite sides.

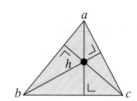

Example ▼

$a(-2, 7)$, $b(p, -4)$ and $c(4, q)$ are the coordinates of the vertices of the triangle abc. If the coordinates of the centroid of triangle abc are $(-1, 3)$, find the value of p and the value of q.

Solution:

The coordinates of the centroid, (x, y), are given by $\left(\dfrac{x_1 + x_2 + x_3}{3}, \dfrac{y_1 + y_2 + y_3}{3} \right)$.

Thus, $\dfrac{x_1 + x_2 + x_3}{3} = x$ and $\dfrac{y_1 + y_2 + y_3}{3} = y$

$\therefore \dfrac{-2 + p + 4}{3} = -1$ $\qquad \therefore \dfrac{7 - 4 + q}{3} = 3$

$\dfrac{p + 2}{3} = -1$ $\qquad\qquad \dfrac{q + 3}{3} = 3$

$p + 2 = -3$ $\qquad\qquad q + 3 = 9$

$p = -5$ $\qquad\qquad\qquad q = 6$

Find the coordinates of the centroid of each of the following triangles, whose vertices are:

1. $(0, -1), (2, -1), (7, 8)$ **2.** $(5, -2), (1, 3), (6, 2)$

3. $(4, 3), (3, 5), (-4, -8)$ **4.** $(3, -2), (-5, 6), (-4, -1)$

5. $a(2, -3), b(p, 0)$ and $c(-3, q)$ are the coordinates of the vertices of triangle abc.
If the coordinates of the centroid of triangle abc are $(1, 2)$, find the value of p and the value of q.

6. $p(h, k), q(7, 2)$ and $r(-3, 10)$ are the coordinates of the vertices of the triangle pqr.
If the coordinates of the centroid of triangle are $(-7, -13)$, find the value of h and the value of k.

Find the coordinates of the circumcentre of each of the triangles, whose vertices are:

7. $(5, -3), (3, -1), (-1, 5)$ **8.** $(-3, -3), (5, 1), (11, -1)$

9. $(4, 6), (-4, -2), (10, 0)$ **10.** $(-2, 2), (-4, -2), (5, -5)$

Find the coordinates of the orthocentre of each of the triangles, whose vertices are:

11. $(0, 3), (7, 4), (4, -5)$ **12.** $(2, 2), (4, 1), (1, 5)$

13. $(-6, 3), (-2, 5), (1, 4)$ **14.** $(3, 15), (10, -2), (-15, 3)$

15. $a(-2, 2), b(2, -6)$, and $c(5, 3)$ are the coordinates of the vertices of triangle abc.
Find the coordinates of **(i)** the centroid **(ii)** the circumcentre **(iii)** the orthocentre.
Find the equation of the line containing the circumcentre and the orthocentre and show that the
centroid is also on this line.

Note: The circumcentre, orthocentre and centroid in a triangle all lie on a straight line called 'Euler's
line'.

Perpendicular Distance from a Point to a Line

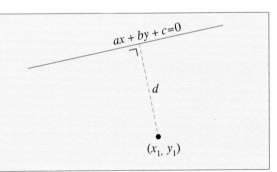

The perpendicular distance, d, from the point
(x_1, y_1) to the line $ax + by + c = 0$, is given by:

$$d = \frac{|ax_1 + by_1 + c|}{\sqrt{a^2 + b^2}}$$

Example ▼

Find the perpendicular distance from the point $(-2, 4)$ to the line $3x + y - 8 = 0$.

Solution:

Point $(-2, 4)$; line $3x + y - 8 = 0$.

$$\text{distance} = \frac{|ax_1 + by_1 + c|}{\sqrt{a^2 + b^2}}$$

$$= \frac{|3(-2) + 1(4) - 8|}{\sqrt{3^2 + 1^2}}$$

$$= \frac{|-6 + 4 - 8|}{\sqrt{9 + 1}} = \frac{|-10|}{\sqrt{10}} = \frac{10}{\sqrt{10}} = \sqrt{10}$$

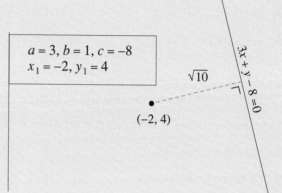

$a = 3, b = 1, c = -8$
$x_1 = -2, y_1 = 4$

$\sqrt{10}$

$(-2, 4)$

$3x + y - 8 = 0$

Example ▼

Find the slopes of the two lines through the point $(-3, 2)$ which are at a distance $2\sqrt{2}$ from the point $(-6, 1)$.

Solution:

We have a point $(-3, 2)$ and we need the slopes.

Equation:

$$(y - y_1) = m(x - x_1)$$
$$(y - 2) = m(x + 3)$$
$$y - 2 = mx + 3m$$
$$mx - y + (3m + 2) = 0$$

$2\sqrt{2}$

$(-6, 1)$ •   • $(-3, 2)$

$2\sqrt{2}$

Given: The distance from $(-6, 1)$ to this line is $2\sqrt{2}$.

Thus,

$$\frac{|m(-6) - 1(1) + (3m + 2)|}{\sqrt{m^2 + (-1)^2}} = 2\sqrt{2} \qquad \text{(distance formula)}$$

$$\frac{|1 - 3m|}{\sqrt{m^2 + 1}} = 2\sqrt{2}$$

$$\frac{1 - 6m + 9m^2}{m^2 + 1} = 8 \qquad \text{(square both sides)}$$

$$1 - 6m + 9m^2 = 8m^2 + 8 \qquad \text{(multiply both sides by } m^2 + 1\text{)}$$

$$m^2 - 6m - 7 = 0$$

$$(m - 7)(m + 1) = 0$$

$$m = 7 \qquad \text{or} \qquad m = -1$$

Distance between parallel lines

To find the distance between two parallel lines, do the following:
Find one point on one of the lines and find the distance from this point to the other line.

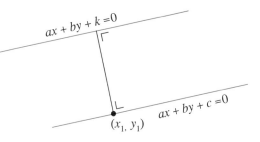

Points on the same side or opposite sides of a line

> **1.** Substitute the coordinates of the points into the equation of the line.
> **2.** Two possibilities arise:
>   **(i)** same signs, then same side of the line
>   **(ii)** opposite signs, then opposite sides of the line.

Note: The formula for the perpendicular distance from a point to a line, without the modulus bars, can also be used with the same results as above.

Example ▼

Investigate if the points $(101, 34)$ and $(58, 18)$ are on the same side of the line $5x - 13y - 60 = 0$.

Solution:

$(101, 34) : 5(101) - 13(34) - 60 = 505 - 442 - 60 = 3$
$(58, 18) : 5(58) - 13(18) - 60 = 290 - 234 - 60 = -4$

Opposite signs, therefore the points are on **opposite** sides of the line.

Exercise 6.5 ▼

In each case, find the perpendicular distance from the point $p(x_1, y_1)$ to the line $L : ax + by + c = 0$:

1. $p(1, 3)$; $L : 3x + 4y + 10 = 0$.   **2.** $p(8, 3)$; $L : 5x - 12y + 9 = 0$.

3. $p(-1, 3)$; $L : 15x - 8y + 5 = 0$.   **4.** $p(3, 2)$; $L : 24x - 7y - 8 = 0$.

5. $p(3, 2)$; $L : 2x - y + 1 = 0$.   **6.** $p(4, 3)$; $L : x + y + 1 = 0$.

7. Show that the point $(2, -1)$ is equidistant from the lines with equations $4x + 3y - 20 = 0$ and $12x - 5y + 10 = 0$.

8. Show that the point $(4, -\frac{1}{2})$ is on the line $3x + 4y - 10 = 0$ and, hence, find the distance between the parallel lines $3x + 4y - 10 = 0$ and $3x + 4y - 15 = 0$.

Find the distance between each pair of parallel lines, L and K:

9. $L : 4x - 3y + 10 = 0$ and $K : 4x - 3y + 15 = 0$.

10. $L : 5x + 12y - 5 = 0$ and $K : 5x + 12y + 10 = 0$.

11. $L : 3x + 4y - 12 = 0$ and $K : 6x + 8y - 9 = 0$.

12. $L : 2x + y + 5 = 0$ and $K : 2x + y = 0$.

13. (i) Show that the points $(100, 72)$ and $(59, 27)$ lie on opposite sides of the line $x + y - 120 = 0$.
   (ii) Are the points $(-20, 10)$ and $(35, -40)$ on the same side of the line $3x - 2y + 50 = 0$?
   (iii) Investigate whether the points $(30, 16)$ and $(-19, -11)$ are on the same side of the line $10x - 20y - 1 = 0$ as the origin $(0, 0)$.

14. Find the values of a, if the point $(4, 1)$ is 2 units from the line $ax + 3y - 9 = 0$.

15. Find the values of k if the distance from the point $(3, -1)$ to the line $3x + 4y - k = 0$ is 6 units.

16. Find the equations of the two lines parallel to $3x - 4y + 1 = 0$ and two units from it.

17. $L : 4x - 3y - 1 = 0$ and $K : 3x - 4y + 1 = 0$ are the equations of two lines.
Find the locus of the point $p(x, y)$ such that p is equidistant from L and K.

18. A line, with slope m, contains the point $(-2, 1)$. Write its equation in the form $ax + by + c = 0$.
Hence, find the equations of the two lines through the point $(-2, 1)$ and whose distance from the origin is 1 unit.

19. Find the equations of the two lines which contain the point $(4, 1)$ and are a distance $2\sqrt{2}$ units from $(1, 2)$.

20. Find the equations of the two lines which are perpendicular to the line $2x + 3y - 6 = 0$ and which are a distance $\sqrt{13}$ units from $(3, 2)$.

Angle Between Two Lines

If two lines, L_1 and L_2, have slopes m_1 and m_2, respectively, and θ is the angle between them, then:

$$\tan \theta = \pm \frac{m_1 - m_2}{1 + m_1 m_2}$$

In practice the best approach is to find the acute angle θ, by using $\tan \theta = \left| \dfrac{m_1 - m_2}{1 + m_1 m_2} \right|$.

The obtuse angle is obtained by finding $180° - \theta$.
The formula has the variables, θ, m_1 and m_2. In the question we are usually given two of these variables and we use the formula to find the third variable.

Find the measure of the obtuse angle between the lines $3x - 5y + 2 = 0$ and $x + 4y + 5 = 0$.

Solution:

Let θ be the acute angle between the lines.
Let the slope of $3x - 5y + 2 = 0$ be m_1. Thus $m_1 = -\frac{3}{-5} = \frac{3}{5}$.
Let the slope of $x + 4y + 5 = 0$ be m_2. Thus $m_2 = -\frac{1}{4}$.

(multiply each part by 20)

$$\tan\theta = \left|\frac{m_1 - m_2}{1 + m_1 m_2}\right| = \left|\frac{\frac{3}{5} - (-\frac{1}{4})}{1 + (\frac{3}{5})(-\frac{1}{4})}\right| = \left|\frac{\frac{3}{5} + \frac{1}{4}}{1 - \frac{3}{20}}\right| = \left|\frac{12 + 5}{20 - 3}\right| = \left|\frac{17}{17}\right| = |1| = 1$$

$\therefore \quad \theta = \tan^{-1} 1 = 45°$

Thus, the obtuse angle $= 180° - 45° = 135°$

$L : tx - y - 3 = 0$ and $K : x - 2y - 1 = 0, \quad t \in \mathbf{R}$, are the equations of two lines.
Given that the angle between L and K is $45°$, find the two possible values of t.

Solution:

Let the slope of $tx - y - 3 = 0$ be m_1. Thus $m_1 = -\dfrac{t}{-1} = t$.

Let the slope of $x - 2y - 1 = 0$ be m_2. Thus $m_2 = -\dfrac{1}{-2} = \dfrac{1}{2}$.

$$\tan\theta = \left|\frac{m_1 - m_2}{1 + m_1 m_2}\right|$$

$$\tan 45° = \left|\frac{t - \frac{1}{2}}{1 + (t)(\frac{1}{2})}\right|$$

$$1 = \left|\frac{t - \frac{1}{2}}{1 + \frac{1}{2}t}\right|$$

$$1 = \left|\frac{2t - 1}{2 + t}\right|$$

(multiply each part by 2)

$\dfrac{2t - 1}{2 + t} = 1$ or $\dfrac{2t - 1}{2 + t} = -1$

(take + and − separately)

$2t - 1 = 2 + t$ or $2t - 1 = -2 - t$

$t = 3$ or $3t = -1$

$t = 3$ or $t = -\frac{1}{3}$

Find, to the nearest degree, the measures of the angles between the following lines:

1. $2x - y - 3 = 0$ and $x - 3y + 2 = 0$.

2. $5x - 2y - 1 = 0$ and $x - 2y + 4 = 0$.

3. $x + y - 5 = 0$ and $2x + y + 3 = 0$.

4. $3x + 2y - 6 = 0$ and $4x - 3y + 8 = 0$.

5. If θ is the acute angle between the lines $x + y - 3 = 0$ and $2x - y + 6 = 0$, find the value of $\tan\theta$.

6. Find the measure of the acute angle between the lines $2x - y + 3 = 0$ and $3x + y - 6 = 0$.

7. Find the measure of the obtuse angle between the lines $3x - y + 2 = 0$ and $x - 2y + 7 = 0$.

8. $p(2, 3)$, $q(4, -3)$ and $r(6, 1)$ are three points.
   Find the acute angle between the lines pq and pr.

9. Show that the line $6x - 2y + 5 = 0$ makes the same angle with each of the lines $2x - 4y - 1 = 0$ and $2x + y + 3 = 0$.

10. A line, with slope m, contains the point $(2, 3)$. Write its equation in the form $ax + by + c = 0$.

11. Find the equations of the lines through the point $(2, 3)$ which make angles of $45°$ with the line $x - 2y - 1 = 0$.

12. Find the equations of the lines through the point $(4, 3)$ which make an angle of $45°$ with the line $6x + y - 5 = 0$.

13. **(i)** Find the measure of the acute angle between the lines $\sqrt{3}x + y + 5 = 0$ and $x - \sqrt{3}y - 2 = 0$.
    (ii) Find the measure of the acute angle between the lines $ax - by + c = 0$ and $(b - a)x + (a + b)y + d = 0$.

14. A line L, with slope m, contains the point $(0, 1)$.
    K is the line $2x - y + 3 = 0$. θ is the acute angle between L and K.
    If $\sin\theta = \frac{3}{5}$, find the two possible equations for L.

15. $p(2, 6)$ and $r(4, 0)$ are two vertices of a square $pqrs$, where $[pr]$ is a diagonal.
    (i) Find the slope of pr.
    (ii) Write down the acute angle between pq and pr.
    (iii) Find the slope of pq and ps.
    (iv) Find the coordinates of q and s.

Concurrent Lines

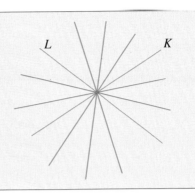

The equation of a line through the point of intersection
of the lines,

$L : ax + by + c = 0$ and $K : px + qy + r = 0$ is given by:

$\mu(ax + by + c) + \lambda(px + qy + r) = 0$.

In practice we usually let $\mu = 1$,

giving $ax + by + c + \lambda(px + qy + r) = 0$.

By varying μ or λ, or both, we get the equations of lines of different slopes, all of which contain the
point of intersection of L and K.

In practice, we are often given one piece of information, or one condition. What we do here is let $\mu = 1$
and consider the equation $ax + by + c + \lambda(px + qy + r) = 0$.

This represents all the lines which contain the point of intersection of L and K, except K itself.

Example ▼

Find the value of λ if the line $3x + y + 12 + \lambda(x + 2y - 5) = 0$,

(i) has slope 2   **(ii)** contains the point $(3, -1)$.

Solution:

$$3x + y + 12 + \lambda(x + 2y - 5) = 0$$
$$3x + y + 12 + \lambda x + 2\lambda y - 5\lambda = 0$$
$$(3 + \lambda)x + (1 + 2\lambda)y + (12 - 5\lambda) = 0$$

(i)   has slope 2

$$\text{Slope} = -\frac{3 + \lambda}{1 + 2\lambda}$$

$$\therefore \quad 2 = -\frac{3 + \lambda}{1 + 2\lambda}$$

$$2(1 + 2\lambda) = -(3 + \lambda)$$
$$2 + 4\lambda = -3 - \lambda$$
$$5\lambda = -5$$
$$\lambda = -1$$

(ii)   contains the point $(3, -1)$

$$\therefore \quad (3 + \lambda)(3) + (1 + 2\lambda)(-1) + (12 - 5\lambda) = 0$$
$$9 + 3\lambda - 1 - 2\lambda + 12 - 5\lambda = 0$$
$$-4\lambda + 20 = 0$$
$$-4\lambda = -20$$
$$\lambda = 5$$

(i) Verify that $L : \lambda(3x - 2y + 5) + \mu(5x - 4y - 3) = 0$ is a line.

(ii) If $K : 6x + 5y - 1 = 0$ is a line such that $L \perp K$, find a relationship between the real numbers λ and μ.

Solution:

(i)

$$\lambda(3x - 2y + 5) + \mu(5x - 4y - 3) = 0$$
$$3\lambda x - 2\lambda y + 5\lambda + 5\mu x - 4\mu y - 3\mu = 0$$
$$(3\lambda + 5\mu)x + (-2\lambda - 4\mu)y + (5\lambda - 3\mu) = 0$$

This is in the form $ax + by + c = 0$.

∴ L is a line.

(ii) Slope of $L = -\dfrac{(3\lambda + 5\mu)}{(-2\lambda - 4\mu)} = \dfrac{3\lambda + 5\mu}{2\lambda + 4\mu}$ 　　　　Slope of $K = -\dfrac{6}{5}$

As $L \perp K$, Slope of $L = \frac{5}{6}$ 　　　　　　　　　　(turn upside down and change sign)

∴ $\dfrac{3\lambda + 5\mu}{2\lambda + 4\mu} = \dfrac{5}{6}$

$$18\lambda + 30\mu = 10\lambda + 20\mu$$
$$8\lambda + 10\mu = 0$$
$$4\lambda + 5\mu = 0$$ 　　　　　　　　(this is the relationship)

Exercise 6.7 ▼

1. Find the equation of the line through the point of intersection of the lines $x + 2y - 5 = 0$ and $2x - 3y + 4 = 0$ and which contains the point $(3, 8)$.

2. Find the equation of the line through the point of intersection of the lines $x - 2y + 6 = 0$ and $3x + 10y - 2 = 0$ and which contains the point $(\frac{1}{4}, 0)$.

3. Find the equation of the line through the point of intersection of the lines $3x - 5y + 6 = 0$ and $5x - 7y + 4 = 0$ and which is parallel to the line $x - 3y - 3 = 0$.

4. Find the equation of the line through the point of intersection of the lines $2x - 3y + 2 = 0$ and $4x - y - 2 = 0$ and which is perpendicular to $3x + 5y + 11 = 0$.

5. (i) Find the coordinates of p, the point of intersection of the lines $3x + 2y - 7 = 0$ and $x - y + 6 = 0$.

(ii) Show that p is on the line $L : 3x + 2y - 7 + \lambda(x - y + 6) = 0$.

(ii) Find the value of λ if 　　**(a)** the point $(1, 2)$ is on L 　　**(b)** the slope of L is 2.

6. Find the value of λ if the line $12x - 5y + 14 + \lambda(3x - 4y + 7) = 0$
   (i) has slope $\frac{5}{3}$
   (ii) contains the origin, $(0, 0)$.

7. Find the value of λ if the line $3x + y - 7 + \lambda(x + 2y - 8) = 0$ is perpendicular to the line $x - y - 2 = 0$.

8. The equation of the line L is $x - 2y + 4 + \lambda(4x - y - 4) = 0$.
  (i) Find the value of λ if L contains the origin, $(0, 0)$.
  (ii) Find the values of λ if L cuts off equal intercepts on the axes.

9. Find the coordinates of the point which is on the line $\mu(x + 5y - 13) + \lambda(2x - y + 7) = 0$, for all $\mu, \lambda \in \mathbf{R}$.

10. Find the relationship between the parameters μ and λ, where $\mu, \lambda \neq 0$, for which the line $\mu(3x - 2y + 3) + \lambda(x - 2y - 5) = 0$
  (i) makes an angle measuring $45°$ with the positive sense of the x-axis
  (ii) contains the origin $(0, 0)$.

11. $L : \mu(5x - 4y + 3) + \lambda(15x - 8y + 9) = 0$ and $K : 4x - 5y - 3 = 0$ are two lines.
  If $L \perp K$, find a relationship between the real numbers μ and λ.

12. Prove that $\mu(ax + by + c) + \lambda(px + qy + r) = 0$
  (i) represents a line
  (ii) contains the point of intersection of the lines $ax + by + c = 0$ and $px + qy + r = 0$.

Parametric Equations of a Line

The Cartesian equation of a line is usually given in the form $ax + by + c = 0$, which links the variables x and y. However, it can sometimes to useful to involve a third variable, say t, and to express x and y each as a function of t. These two equations, $x = f(t)$ and $y = g(t)$ are said to be the '**parametric equations**' of the line and t is called the '**parameter**'.

Note: Any other parameter, say θ, could also be used.
If we are given a pair of parametric equations, we find the corresponding Cartesian equation by eliminating the parameter, which then gives an equation that links x and y.

To express parametric equations in Cartesian form do the following:

> **Method 1:**
> **1.** Express t in terms of x and t in terms of y
>   (get t on its own from both parametric equations).
> **2.** Equate these two expressions for t and write your answer in the form $ax + by + c = 0$.
>
> **Method 2:**
> **1.** Pick two values for t and find two points on the line.
> **2.** Use these two points to find the equation of the line in the form $ax + by + c = 0$.

Note: Method 2 is '**not acceptable**' if the equation says 'prove', 'verify', 'show' or 'investigate' if the parametric equations represent a straight line.

In general, any parametric equations of the form $x = \dfrac{a + bt}{c + dt}$, $y = \dfrac{p + qt}{r + st}$, represent a straight line, where a, b, c, d, p, q, r and s are constants.

The denominators must be the same in both equations, or a linear multiple of each other, e.g. $2 + t$; $4 + 2t$. We assume that the values of t that would make the denominators equal to zero are excluded.

The parametric equations $x = \dfrac{1 + 3t}{1 + t}$ and $y = \dfrac{2 - t}{1 + t}$ represent a line, $\quad t \in \mathbf{R}, t \neq -1$.

Find the Cartesian equation of the line, in the form $ax + by + c = 0$.

Solution:

Method 1: Express t in terms of x and t in terms of y and equate both expressions of t.

$$x = \dfrac{1 + 3t}{1 + t} \qquad\qquad y = \dfrac{2 - t}{1 + t}$$

$$x + tx = 1 + 3t \qquad\qquad y + ty = 2 - t$$

$$tx - 3t = 1 - x \qquad\qquad ty + t = 2 - y$$

$$t(x - 3) = 1 - x \qquad\qquad t(y + 1) = 2 - y$$

$$t = \dfrac{1 - x}{x - 3} \qquad\qquad t = \dfrac{2 - y}{y + 1}$$

$$t = t$$

$$\dfrac{1 - x}{x - 3} = \dfrac{2 - y}{y + 1}$$

$$(1 - x)(y + 1) = (x - 3)(2 - y)$$

$$y + 1 - xy - x = 2x - xy - 6 + 3y$$

$$y + 1 - x = 2x - 6 + 3y$$

$$3x + 2y - 7 = 0$$

Method 2: Put in two values of t and find two points on the line.

$$x = \dfrac{1 + 3t}{1 + t} \qquad y = \dfrac{2 - t}{1 + t}$$

$t = 0 : x = 1, y = 2$, thus one point on the line is $(1, 2)$.

$t = 1 : x = 2, y = \frac{1}{2}$, thus another point on the line is $(2, \frac{1}{2})$.

Thus, we have two points on the line and we need the slope.

$$\text{Slope} = \dfrac{y_2 - y_1}{x_2 - x_1} \qquad\qquad \text{Equation: } (y - y_1) = m(x - x_1)$$

$$= \dfrac{\frac{1}{2} - 2}{2 - 1} \qquad\qquad (y - 2) = -\tfrac{3}{2}(x - 1)$$

$$= \dfrac{-\frac{3}{2}}{1} = -\dfrac{3}{2} \qquad\qquad 2y - 4 = -3x + 3$$

$$\qquad\qquad\qquad\qquad 3x + 2y - 7 = 0$$

Express each of the following pairs of parametric equations in Cartesian form:

1. $x = t + 1$ and $y = t - 1$

2. $x = 3t - 1$ and $y = 1 - 2t$

3. $x = \dfrac{t + 1}{t - 1}$ and $y = \dfrac{t + 2}{t - 1}$

4. $x = \dfrac{t - 1}{t + 1}$ and $y = \dfrac{2t + 5}{t + 1}$

5. $x = \dfrac{3t + 5}{t - 3}$ and $y = \dfrac{t - 2}{t - 3}$

6. $x = \dfrac{2t - 1}{t + 1}$ and $y = \dfrac{t + 2}{t + 1}$

7. $x = \dfrac{3t + 2}{t - 4}$ and $y = \dfrac{3t - 1}{t - 4}$

8. $x = \dfrac{3 - t}{1 + t}$ and $y = \dfrac{5t}{1 + t}$

9. Find the area of the triangle formed by the line $x = \dfrac{2t - 1}{t - 1}$, $y = \dfrac{2t}{t - 1}$, the x-axis and the y-axis.

10. Find the obtuse angle between the two lines whose parametric equations are:

$x = t + 2, \ y = 3 - 3t$ and $x = \dfrac{2t - 1}{t - 1}, \ y = \dfrac{2t}{t - 1}$.

11. Investigate if the parametric equations $x = 1 - \dfrac{1}{t}$ and $y = 1 + \dfrac{1}{t}$, $t \neq 0$, represent a line.

12. L and K are two lines whose parametric equations are:

$L : x = \dfrac{2t + 1}{t + 1}, \ y = \dfrac{t}{t + 1}$ $K : x = \dfrac{1 + t}{1 - t}, \ y = \dfrac{3t}{1 - t}$.

Find the point of intersection of L and K.
Find the tangent of the acute angle between L and K.
Find the equation of the line through the point of intersection of L and K and containing the point $(-2, 3)$.

13. If $a = (1, -3)$ and $b = (2, -1)$, show that
$x = t + 1, y = 2t - 3, 0 \leqslant t \leqslant 1$, are parametric equations of the line segment $[ab]$.

14. Show that the point $p(2t + 3, t + 1)$ is on the line $x - 2y - 1 = 0$, for all $t \in \mathbf{R}$.
If $a = (1, 0)$ and $b = (7, 3)$, find the values of t for which $p \in [ab]$.

Linear Transformations

A linear combination of x and y is a combination of the type $ax + by$, $a, b \in \mathbf{R}$.
Examples are $3x + 4y$ and $2x - 5y$.
A linear transformation is a transformation of the form

$f(x, y) = (ax + by, cx + dy)$, $a, b, c, d \in \mathbf{R}$ and $ad - bc \neq 0$

This is often written:

$f(x, y) = (x', y')$

where

$x' = ax + by$
$y' = cx + dy$.

Notice that x' and y' are linear combinations of x and y.

Properties of a Linear Transformation

> **1.** The origin $(0, 0)$ is mapped onto the origin.
> **2.** A line is mapped onto a line.
> **3.** A line segment is mapped onto a line segment.
> **4.** Pairs of parallel lines are mapped onto pairs of parallel lines.
> **5.** Parallelograms are mapped onto parallelograms.

Notes:

(a) In general, pairs of perpendicular lines are **not** mapped onto pairs of perpendicular lines.

(b) In general, distances and area are not invariant (not preserved), i.e. in general, distances and areas are not invariant under a linear transformation.

Example ▼

$a(2, -2), b(4, 1), c(-2, -1)$ and $d(2, 5)$ are four points.

A transformation f is given by

$$f(x, y) \rightarrow (x', y')$$

where

$x' = x + 2y$
$y' = -x + y.$

(a) Find $f(a), f(b), f(c)$ and $f(d)$.

(b) Verify: **(i)** $|ab| \neq |f(a)f(b)|$

            (ii)   area of $\triangle abc = \frac{1}{3}$ area of $\triangle f(a)f(b)f(c)$

            (iii) $\dfrac{|ab|}{|cd|} = \dfrac{|f(a)f(b)|}{|f(c(f(d)|}$

(c) p is the midpoint of $[bc]$, q is the midpoint of $[f(b)f(c)]$,
g is the centroid of $\triangle abc$, h is the centroid of $\triangle f(a)f(b)f(c)$.

Investigate if **(i)** $f(p) = q$ **(ii)** $f(g) = h$.

(d) $s(7, 8)$ is the image of $r(x, y)$ under f. Find the coordinates r.

Solution:

(a) $(x, y) \rightarrow (x + 2y, -x + y)$

$a(2, -2) \rightarrow (2 + 2(-2), -2 - 2) = (2 - 4, -2 - 2) = (-2, -4) = f(a)$

$b(4, 1) \rightarrow (4 + 2(1), -4 + 1) = (4 + 2, -4 + 1) = (6, -3) = f(b)$

$c(-2, -1) \rightarrow (-2 + 2(-1), 2 - 1) = (-2 - 2, 2 - 1) = (-4, 1) = f(c)$

$d(2, 5) \rightarrow (2 + 2(5), -2 + 5) = (2 + 10, -2 + 5) = (12, 3) = f(d)$

(b) (i) $a(2, -2), b(4, 1)$

$|ab| = \sqrt{(4 - 2)^2 + (1 + 2)^2}$

$\quad = \sqrt{2^2 + 3^2}$

$\quad = \sqrt{4 + 9}$

$\quad = \sqrt{13}$

$f(a) = (-2, -4), \quad f(b) = (6, -3)$

$|f(a)f(b)| = \sqrt{(6 + 2)^2 + (-3 + 4)^2}$

$\quad = \sqrt{8^2 + 1^2}$

$\quad = \sqrt{64 + 1}$

$\quad = \sqrt{65}$

Thus, $|ab| \neq |f(a)f(b)|$.

(ii) $a(2, -2), b(4, 1), c(-2, -1)$

$(2, -2) \qquad (4, 1) \qquad (-2, -1)$

$\downarrow \qquad\quad \downarrow \qquad\quad \downarrow$

$(0, 0) \qquad (2, 3) \qquad (-4, 1)$

area $= \frac{1}{2}|(2)(1) - (-4)(3)|$

$\quad = \frac{1}{2}|2 + 12|$

$\quad = \frac{1}{2}|14| = 7$

$f(a) = (-2, -4), f(b) = (6, -3), f(c) = (-4, 1)$

$(-2, -4) \qquad (6, -3) \qquad (-4, 1)$

$\downarrow \qquad\qquad \downarrow \qquad\qquad \downarrow$

$(0, 0) \qquad (8, 1) \qquad (-2, 5)$

area $= \frac{1}{2}|(8)(5) - (-2)(1)|$

$\quad = \frac{1}{2}|40 + 2|$

$\quad = \frac{1}{2}|42| = 21$

Thus, area of $\Delta abc = \frac{1}{3}$ area of $\Delta f(a)f(b)f(c)$

i.e. $7 = \frac{1}{3}(21)$

(iii) $|ab| = \sqrt{13}$ (from **(i)**)

$c(-2, -1), d(2, 5)$

$|cd| = \sqrt{(2 + 2)^2 + (5 + 1)^2}$

$\quad = \sqrt{4^2 + 6^2}$

$\quad = \sqrt{16 + 36} = \sqrt{52}$

$\dfrac{|ab|}{|dc|} = \dfrac{\sqrt{13}}{\sqrt{52}}$

$\quad = \sqrt{\dfrac{13}{52}} = \sqrt{\dfrac{1}{4}} = \dfrac{1}{2}$

$|f(a)f(b)| = \sqrt{65}$ (from **(i)**)

$f(c) = (-4, 1), f(d) = (12, 3)$

$|f(c)f(d)| = \sqrt{(12 + 4)^2 + (3 - 1)^2}$

$\quad = \sqrt{16^2 + 2^2}$

$\quad = \sqrt{256 + 4} = \sqrt{260}$

$\dfrac{|f(a)f(b)|}{|f(c)f(d)|} = \dfrac{\sqrt{65}}{\sqrt{260}}$

$\quad = \sqrt{\dfrac{65}{260}} = \sqrt{\dfrac{1}{4}} = \dfrac{1}{2}$

Thus, $\dfrac{|ab|}{|cd|} = \dfrac{|f(a)f(b)|}{|f(c)f(d)|}$.

(c) (i) $b(4, 1)$ $c(-2, -1)$

p is the midpoint of $[bc]$

Thus, $p = (1, 0)$

$$f(p) = f(1, 0)$$
$$= (1 + 2(0), -1 + 0) = (1, -1)$$

Thus, $f(p) = q$

i.e., the midpoint of $[bc]$ is mapped onto the midpoint of $[f(b)f(c)]$.

$f(b) = (6, -3)$ $f(c) = (-4, 1)$

q is the midpoint of $[f(b)f(c)]$

Thus, $q = (1, -1)$

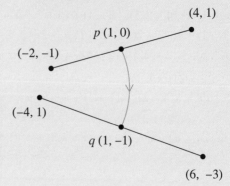

(ii) $a(2, -2)$, $b(4, 1)$, $c(-2, -1)$

g is the centroid of $\triangle abc$.

Thus,

$$g = \left(\frac{2 + 4 - 2}{3}, \frac{-2 + 1 - 1}{3}\right)$$

$$g = \left(\tfrac{4}{3}, -\tfrac{2}{3}\right)$$

$$f(g) = f\left(\tfrac{4}{3}, -\tfrac{2}{3}\right)$$
$$= \left(\tfrac{4}{3} + 2\left(-\tfrac{2}{3}\right), -\tfrac{4}{3} - \tfrac{2}{3}\right)$$
$$= \left(\tfrac{4}{3} - \tfrac{4}{3}, -\tfrac{6}{3}\right)$$
$$= (0, -2)$$

Thus, $f(g) = h$, i.e., the centroid of $\triangle abc$ is mapped onto the centroid of $\triangle f(a)f(b)f(c)$.

$f(a) = (-2, -4)$, $f(b) = (6, -3)$, $f(c) = (-4, 1)$

h is the centroid of $\triangle f(a)f(b)f(c)$

Thus,

$$h = \left(\frac{-2 + 6 - 4}{3}, \frac{-4 - 3 + 1}{3}\right)$$

$$h = (0, -2)$$

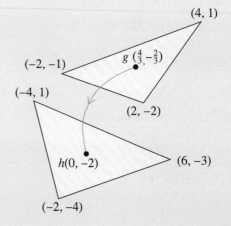

(d) Given: $(x', y') = (7, 8)$

Thus, $(x + 2y, -x + y) = (7, 8)$

$x + 2y = 7$ ① and $-x + y = 8$ ②

Solving ① and ② simultaneously gives

$x = -3, y = 5$

Thus, the coordinates of r are $(-3, 5)$.

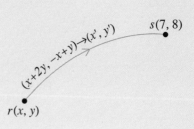

f is a transformation $(x, y) \rightarrow (x', y')$, where

$$x' = 3x + 2y$$
$$y' = 5x + 3y.$$

(i) $L: x - 2y - 3 = 0$ and $K: 2x + y = 0$ are two lines. Verify that $L \perp K$.

(ii) Express x and y in terms of x' and y'.

(iii) Find the equation of $f(L)$ and $f(K)$ and investigate if $f(L) \perp f(K)$.

Solution

(i) $L: x - 2y - 3 = 0$. Thus, slope of $L = -\frac{1}{-2} = \frac{1}{2}$.

$K: 2x + y = 0$. Thus, slope of $K = -\frac{2}{1} = -2$.

(Slope of L) . (Slope of K) $= \frac{1}{2} \times -2 = -1$ $\therefore$ $L \perp K$

(ii) Solve as a pair of simultaneous equations.

Remove the y's			Remove the x's	
$3x + 2y = x'$	①		$3x + 2y = x'$	①
$5x + 3y = y'$	②		$5x + 3y = y'$	②
$9x + 6y = 3x'$	① × 3		$15x + 10y = 5x'$	① × 5
$-10x - 6y = -2y'$	② × -2		$-15x - 9y = -3y'$	② × -3
$-x = 3x' - 2y'$	(add)		$y = 5x' - 3y'$	(add)
$x = -3x' + 2y'$				

Thus,

$$x = -3x' + 2y', \qquad y = 5x' - 3y'$$

(iii) To find the equation of $f(L)$ and $f(K)$ we substitute these expressions for x and y into the equations of L and K, and simplify.

$$L: x - 2y - 3 = 0$$

$$f(L): (-3x' + 2y') - 2(5x' - 3y') - 3 = 0$$
$$-3x' + 2y' - 10x' + 6y' - 3 = 0$$
$$-13x' + 8y' - 3 = 0$$
$$13x' - 8y' + 3 = 0$$

$$K: 2x + y = 0$$

$$f(K): 2(-3x' + 2y') + (5x' - 3y') = 0$$
$$-6x' + 4y' + 5x' - 3y' = 0$$
$$-x' + y' = 0$$
$$x' - y' = 0$$

Thus, $13x' - 8y' + 3 = 0$ is the equation of $f(L)$ and $x' - y' = 0$ is the equation of $f(K)$.

$$\text{Slope of } f(L) = -\frac{13}{-8} = \frac{13}{8}, \qquad \text{Slope of } f(K) = -\frac{1}{-1} = 1$$

$$(\text{Slope of } f(L)) \cdot (\text{Slope of } f(K)) = \frac{13}{8} \times 1 = \frac{13}{8} \neq -1$$

Thus, $f(L) \not\perp f(K)$.

Example ▼

$a(-5, 0)$ and $b(1, 3)$ are two points. Find the equation of the line ab.

Show that $x = 2t - 1$ and $y = t + 2$, $\quad -2 \leqslant t \leqslant 1$, are parametric equations of the line segment $[ab]$.

Find the image of this line segment under the transformation f:

$$x' = 3x - y$$
$$y' = x - y$$

(i) in parametric form $\qquad$ **(ii)** in Cartesian form.

Solution:

$a(-5, 0), \quad b(1, 3)$

$\text{Slope} = \dfrac{3 - 0}{1 + 5}$

$\qquad = \dfrac{3}{6} = \dfrac{1}{2}$

Equation: $\quad (y - 0) = \frac{1}{2}(x + 5)$

$$2y = x + 5$$
$$x - 2y + 5 = 0$$

We first verify that $x = 2t - 1$ and $y = t + 2$ are parametric equations of $x - 2y + 5 = 0$.

Method: Replace x with $2t - 1$ and y with $t + 2$.

$$x - 2y + 5 = 0$$

$$(2t - 1) - 2(t + 2) + 5 = 2t - 1 - 2t - 4 + 5 = 0$$

Thus, $x = 2t - 1$ and $y = t + 2$ are parametric equations of $x - 2y + 5 = 0$.

$a(-5, 0), x = 2t - 1, y = t + 2$

$\qquad 2t - 1 = -5 \quad$ and $\quad t + 2 = 0$

$\qquad \quad 2t = -4 \quad$ and $\qquad t = -2$

$\qquad \quad t = -2 \quad$ and $\qquad t = -2$

$b(1, 3), x = 2t - 1, y = t + 2$

$\qquad 2t - 1 = 1 \quad$ and $\quad t + 2 = 3$

$\qquad \quad 2t = 2 \quad$ and $\qquad t = 3 - 2$

$\qquad \quad t = 1 \quad$ and $\qquad t = 1$

$$-2 \leqslant t \leqslant 1$$

Thus, when $-2 \leqslant t \leqslant 1$, $x = 2t - 1$ and $y = t + 2$ are parametric equations of the line segment $[ab]$.

(i) Parametric form

To find the image, we substitute $x = 2t - 1$, $y = t + 2$ into the transformation.

$$x' = 3x - y \qquad\qquad\text{and}\qquad\qquad y' = x - y$$
$$x' = 3(2t - 1) - (t + 2) \qquad\qquad\qquad y' = (2t - 1) - (t + 2)$$
$$x' = 6t - 3 - t - 2 \qquad\qquad\qquad\qquad y' = 2t - 1 - t - 2$$
$$x' = 5t - 5 \qquad\qquad\qquad\qquad\qquad y' = t - 3$$

Thus, $x = 5t - 5$ and $y = t - 3$, $-2 \leqslant t \leqslant 1$, are parametric equations for the image of the line segment [ab].

(ii) Cartesian form

$a(-5, 0), \qquad b(1, 3)$

$$(x', y') \rightarrow (3x - y, x - y)$$
$$a(-5, 0) \rightarrow (3(-5) - 0, -5 - 0) = (-15, -5)$$
$$b(1, 3) \rightarrow (3(1) - 3, 1 - 3) = (0, 2)$$

We need the equation of the line through $(-15, -5)$ and $(0, -2)$.

Slope $= \dfrac{-5 + 2}{-15 - 0} = \dfrac{-3}{-15} = \dfrac{1}{5}$

Equation: $(y' + 2) = \frac{1}{5}(x' - 0)$

$$5y' + 10 = x'$$
$$x' - 5y' - 10 = 0$$

$(-15, -5) \qquad (0, -2)$

Thus, $x' - 5y' - 10 = 0$

where $-15 \leqslant x \leqslant 0$ or $-5 \leqslant y \leqslant -2$

is the Cartesian equation for the image of the line segment [ab].

Exercise 6.9 ▼

1. $a(0, 0)$, $b(1, 2)$, $c(3, -2)$ and $d(2, 3)$ are four points.
A transformation f is given by $f(x, y) = (x', y')$ where $x' = 2x + y$ and $y' = x + y$.
  (i)   Find $f(a), f(b), f(c)$ and $f(d)$
  (ii)   Verify that:
      (a) $|ab| \neq |f(a)f(b)|$ **(b)** Area of $\Delta abc = \Delta f(a)f(b)f(c)$ **(c)** $\dfrac{|ab|}{|cd|} \neq \dfrac{|f(a)f(b)|}{|f(c)f(d)|}$
  (iii) p is the midpoint of [bc], q is the midpoint of [f(b)f(c)],
      g is the centroid of Δbcd, h is the centroid of $\Delta f(b)f(c)f(d)$.
      Investigate if   **(a)** $f(p) = q$ **(b)** $f(g) = h$.
  (iv) $s(8, 5)$ is the image of $r(x, y)$ under f. Find the coordinates r.

2. f is the transformation $(x, y) \rightarrow (x', y')$, where $x' = -2x + y$, $y' = x$.
$p(-5, 5)$, $q(1, 2)$, $r(3, 1)$, and $o(0, 0)$ are four points.
  (i)   Show that:
      (a) p, q and r are collinear   **(b)** $pq \perp qo$ **(c)** $|pq| : |qr| = 3 : 1$.
  (ii)   Investigate if:
      (a) $f(p), f(q)$ and $f(r)$ are collinear
      (b) $f(p)f(q) \perp f(q)f(o)$
      (c) $|f(p)f(q)| : |f(q)f(r)| = 3 : 1$.
  (iii)   Investigate if: $\dfrac{\text{Area } \Delta opr}{\text{Area } \Delta oqr} = \dfrac{\text{Area } \Delta f(o)f(p)f(r)}{\text{Area } \Delta f(o)f(q)f(r)}$.

3. f is the transformation $(x, y) \rightarrow (x', y')$ where $x' = -3x + y$, $y' = 2x + 3y$.
   $o(0, 0)$, $p(4, 3)$, $q(2, 4)$ and $r(-4, 2)$ are four points.
   (i)   Find $f(o), f(p), f(q), f(r)$.
   (ii) Investigate if:
         (a) $|pq| = |f(p)f(q)|$ (b) $|or| : |pq| = |f(o)f(r)| : |f(p)f(q)|$.
         (c) Area of $\Delta pqr = \frac{1}{11}$ area of $\Delta f(p)f(q)f(r)$
   (iii) Verify that $|\angle qor| = 90°$. Investigate if $|\angle f(q)f(o)f(r)| = 90°$.
   (iv) If $f(k)$ is $(-1, 19)$, find the coordinates of k.

4. f is the transformation $(x, y) \rightarrow (x', y')$ where $x' = 3x - y$, $y' = 2x + y$.
   $L: 2x - 5y + 7 = 0$ and $K: 3x + 4y - 1 = 0$ are two lines.
   (i)   Find the point of intersection of L and K.
   (ii) Express x and y in terms of x' and y'.
   (iii) Hence, or otherwise, find $f(L)$ and $f(K)$, the image of L and K under f.
   (iv) Show that $f(L \cap K) = f(L) \cap f(K)$.
   (v)   Show that $f^{-1} f(K) = K$.
   (vi) If M is a line such that $f(M) = x - 2y + 2 = 0$, find the equation of M.

5. f is the transformation $(x, y) \rightarrow (x', y')$, where $x' = 2x + y$, $y' = -4x + 3y$.
   (i)   Show that the points $a(1, -2)$, $b(0, -4)$ and $c(3, 2)$ are collinear.
   (ii) Investigate if the points $f(a), f(b)$ and $f(c)$ are collinear.
   (iii) $L: x - y - 4 = 0$ and $K: x - y + 1 = 0$ are two lines. Verify that $L || K$.
   (iv) Express x and y in terms of x' and y'.
   (v)   Hence, or otherwise, find $f(L)$ and $f(K)$, the image of L and K under f.
   (vi) Show that $f(L) || f(K)$.
   (vii) Show that $f^{-1} f(L) = L$.

6. f is the transformation $(x, y) \rightarrow (x', y')$, where $x' = x + 3y$, $y' = 2x - y$.
   $L: 3x - y - 4 = 0$ and $K: x + 3y + 2 = 0$ are two lines.
   $a(2, -2)$, $b(3, -5)$ and $c(-2, 4)$ are three points.
   (i)   Verify that $L \perp K$.
   (ii) Show that the centroid of Δabc is the point of intersection of L and K.
   (iii) Express x and y in terms of x' and y'.
   (iv) Find $f(a), f(b), f(c), f(L)$ and $f(K)$.
   (v)   Investigate if the centroid of $\Delta f(a)f(b)f(c)$ is the point of intersection of $f(L)$ and $f(K)$.
   (vi) M is a line containing the point $(k, 1)$, where $k \in \mathbf{Z}$.
         Given that $f(M)$ is $5x' + y' - 9k = 0$, find the the value of k.

7. f is the transformation $(x, y) \rightarrow (x', y')$ where $x' = x - 2y$, $y' = 3x + 2y$.
   $L: px - y + q = 0$ and $K: x + py + r = 0$, $p, q, r \in \mathbf{R}$, are two lines.
   (i)   Verify that $L \perp K$.
   (ii) Verify that $f(L)$ and $f(K)$ cannot be parallel.

8. f is the transformation $(x, y) \rightarrow (x', y')$, where $x' = 3x + 2y$, $y' = 5x + 3y$.
   (i)   Express x and y in terms of x' and y'.
   (ii) $P: ax + by + c = 0$ and $Q: ax + by + d = 0$ are two parallel lines, $c \neq d$.
         Find $f(P)$ and $f(Q)$ and investigate if $f(P) || f(Q)$.

9. f is the transformation $(x, y) \rightarrow (x', y')$, where $x' = 3x + y$, $y' = x - 3y$.
   $L: ax + by + c = 0$ is a line and K is a line such that $L \perp K$.
   (i)   Write down an equation for K.
   (ii) Investigate if $f(L) \perp f(K)$.
   (iii) If the slope of $f(L)$ is 1, express b in terms of a.

10. f is the transformation $(x, y) \rightarrow (x', y')$ where $x' = px + qy$, $y' = rx + sy$.
    If $f(1, 2) = (8, -6)$ and $f(-3, -1) = (-9, -7)$, find the values of p, q, r and s.

    $L: 2x + 3y - 7 = 0$ and $K: 3x - 2y - 4 = 0$.
    Verify that $L \perp K$. Investigate if $f(L) \perp f(K)$.

11. If $p = (2, -1)$ and $q = (-3, 2)$, show that $x = 2 - 5t$, $y = 3t - 1$, $0 \leqslant t \leqslant 1$, $t \in \mathbf{R}$, are parametric equations of the line segment $[pq]$.

    f is the transformation $(x, y) \rightarrow (x', y')$, where $x' = 3x - 4y$, $y' = x - y$.
    (i)   Find the parametric equations of the image of the line segment $[pq]$ under f.
    (ii) Find the coordinates of the end point of the line segment $f([pq])$.

12. $x = 2t + 1$, $y = 1 - t$, $0 \leqslant t \leqslant 3$, $t \in \mathbf{R}$ are the parametric equations of the line segment $[pq]$.
    (i)   Find the coordinates of p and the coordinates of q.
          f is the transformation $(x, y) \rightarrow (x', y')$ where $x' = x - 2y$, $y' = 2x + y$.
    (ii) Find the image of $[pq]$ under f, giving your answers in:
          (a) parametric form   (b) Cartesian form,
          stating the range of values of t, x' and y' for which the line segment exists.

TRIGONOMETRY I

Radian Measure

In more advanced trigonometry, and always in calculus, angles are measured in radians.

One radian is the measure of the angle at the centre of a circle subtended by an arc equal in length to the radius of the circle.

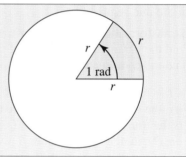

Note: Radians are often called '**circular measure**' and are denoted by rads.

The number of radians in one complete revolution is given by the ratio:

$$\frac{\text{circumference of a circle}}{\text{length of its radius}} = \frac{2\pi r}{r} = 2\pi \text{ radians}$$

Relationship between radians and degrees

One complete revolution = 2π radians = 360°, thus:

$$2\pi \text{ radians} = 360° \qquad \text{or} \qquad \pi \text{ radians} = 180°$$

Note: Very often the word radian is not used, thus we can write $\pi = 180°$, where π means 'π radians' ($\pi \neq 180°$).

The more common angles used are given in the following table:

Degrees	0°	30°	45°	60°	90°	120°	150°	180°	270°	360°
Radians	0	$\dfrac{\pi}{6}$	$\dfrac{\pi}{4}$	$\dfrac{\pi}{3}$	$\dfrac{\pi}{2}$	$\dfrac{2\pi}{3}$	$\dfrac{5\pi}{6}$	π	$\dfrac{3\pi}{2}$	2π

These can be calculated from the equation π radians = 180°.

Note: 1 radian = $\dfrac{180°}{\pi} \approx 57.3°$ (correct to one decimal places).

Convert: **(i)** 225° to radians   **(ii)** $\dfrac{5\pi}{3}$ radians to degrees.

Solution:

(i) $180° = \pi$ radians

$1° = \dfrac{\pi}{180}$ radians

$225° = 225 \times \dfrac{\pi}{180}$ radians

$225° = \dfrac{5\pi}{4}$ radians

(ii) $\dfrac{5\pi}{3}$ radians

$= \dfrac{5(180°)}{3}$

(put in $\pi = 180°$)

$= 300°$

The diagram shows a sector of a circle of radius r, angle θ, arc length l and area A.
The length of the arc l and the area of the sector A may be found by multiplying the length of the circumference and the area of the circle by $\dfrac{\theta}{2\pi}$.

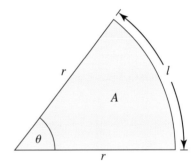

Note: $\dfrac{\theta}{2\pi}$ is the fraction of the circle required.

Length of arc, $l = \dfrac{\theta}{2\pi} \times 2\pi r = r\theta$

Area of sector, $A = \dfrac{\theta}{2\pi} \times \pi r^2 = \tfrac{1}{2}r^2\theta$

Arc length, $l = r\theta$

Area of sector, $A = \tfrac{1}{2}r^2\theta$

(θ in radians)

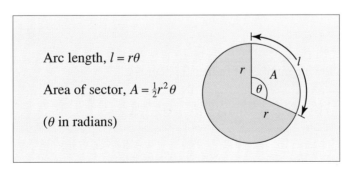

These formulas are on page 9 of the tables.
Each formula contains three variables and we are usually given two of these variables and asked to find the third one.

(i) The radius of a circle is 20 cm. Find the angle subtended at the centre by an arc of length 8π cm.

(ii) The area of a sector of a circle of radius r is 30 cm². If the angle subtended at the centre of the circle by this sector is $\frac{5}{3}$ radians, calculate r.

Solution:

(i) **Given:** $r = 20$, $l = 8\pi$, find θ.

$$l = r\theta$$
$$8\pi = 20\theta$$
$$2\pi = 5\theta$$
$$\frac{2\pi}{5} = \theta$$

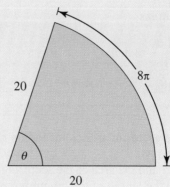

(ii) **Given:** $A = 30$, $\theta = \frac{5}{3}$ radians, find r.

$$A = \tfrac{1}{2}r^2\theta$$
$$30 = \tfrac{1}{2}r^2 \times \tfrac{5}{3}$$
$$30 = \tfrac{5}{6}r^2$$
$$180 = 5r^2$$
$$36 = r^2$$
$$6 = r$$
$$\therefore \quad r = 6 \text{ cm}$$

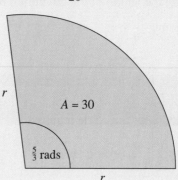

Exercise 7.1 ▼

Express each of the following number of radians in degrees:

1. π **2.** $\dfrac{\pi}{6}$ **3.** $\dfrac{\pi}{4}$ **4.** $\dfrac{2\pi}{3}$ **5.** $\dfrac{3\pi}{5}$

6. $\dfrac{4\pi}{3}$ **7.** $\dfrac{5\pi}{4}$ **8.** $\dfrac{4\pi}{9}$ **9.** $\dfrac{5\pi}{18}$ **10.** $\dfrac{11\pi}{6}$

Express each of the following angles in radians, leaving π in your answers:

11. 30°   **12.** 45°   **13.** 60°   **14.** 90°   **15.** 120°

16. 150°   **17.** 210°   **18.** 240°   **19.** 135°   **20.** 450°

21. 390°   **22.** 72°   **23.** 288°   **24.** 105°   **25.** $22\frac{1}{2}°$

In each of the following find:

(i) the length of the minor arc *pq*   **(ii)** the area of the corresponding minor sector *opq*

26.
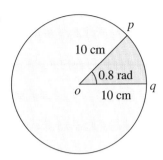

27.
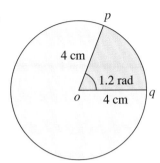

28.
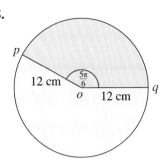

In each case below, find:

(i) the area of the shaded region
(ii) the perimeter of the shaded region.

29.
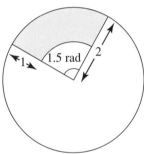

30.
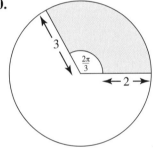

31. The radius of a circle is 12 cm. Find the angle subtended at the centre by an arc of length 16π cm.

32. Find the area of a sector of a circle of radius 20 cm if the arc of the sector subtends an angle of $\dfrac{2\pi}{5}$ at the centre.

33. The area of a sector of a circle, of radius r, is 24π cm^2. If the angle subtended at the centre of the circle by this sector is $\dfrac{3\pi}{4}$, calculate r, the radius of the circle.

Trigonometric Ratios

The six basic trigonometric ratios (or fractions) for a right-angled triangle are defined as follows for all angles $0° < \theta < 90°$, $\left(\text{or } 0 < \theta < \dfrac{\pi}{2}\right)$.

$$\sin \theta = \frac{O}{H} \qquad \operatorname{cosec} \theta = \frac{H}{O}$$

$$\cos \theta = \frac{A}{H} \qquad \sec \theta = \frac{H}{A}$$

$$\tan \theta = \frac{O}{A} \qquad \cot = \frac{A}{O}$$

From this we can see that:

$$\operatorname{cosec} \theta = \frac{1}{\sin \theta} \qquad\qquad \sec \theta = \frac{1}{\cos \theta}$$

$$\tan \theta = \frac{\sin \theta}{\cos \theta} \qquad\qquad \cot \theta = \frac{1}{\tan \theta} = \frac{\cos \theta}{\sin \theta}$$

$$\sin(90° - \theta) = \frac{A}{H} = \cos \theta \qquad \cos(90° - \theta) = \frac{O}{H} = \sin \theta \qquad \tan(90° - \theta) = \cot \theta$$

Note: These ratios hold for all values of $\theta \in \mathbf{R}$, not just for $0 < \theta < 90°$.

sec, cosec, cot are short for secant, cosecant and cotangent, respectively.

Special Angles: $45°\left(\dfrac{\pi}{4}\right)$, $60°\left(\dfrac{\pi}{3}\right)$, $30°\left(\dfrac{\pi}{6}\right)$

There are three special angles whose sine, cosine and tangent ratios can be expressed as simple fractions or surds.

$$\sin 45° = \frac{1}{\sqrt{2}}$$

$$\cos 45° = \frac{1}{\sqrt{2}}$$

$$\tan 45° = 1$$

$$\sin 60° = \frac{\sqrt{3}}{2} \qquad\qquad \sin 30° = \frac{1}{2}$$

$$\cos 60° = \frac{1}{2} \qquad\qquad \cos 30° = \frac{\sqrt{3}}{2}$$

$$\tan 60° = \sqrt{3} \qquad\qquad \tan 30° = \frac{1}{\sqrt{3}}$$

These ratios can be used instead of a calculator.

Trigonometric Ratios for Any Angle
The Unit Circle

The unit circle has its centre at the origin (0, 0) and
the length of the radius is 1.
Take any point $p(x, y)$ on the circle, making an angle
of θ, from the centre.

$$\cos \theta = \frac{x}{1} = x$$

$$\sin \theta = \frac{y}{1} = y$$

$$\tan \theta = \frac{y}{x} = \frac{\sin \theta}{\cos \theta}$$

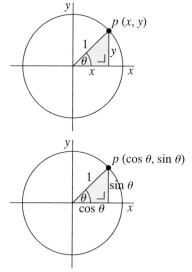

This very important result indicates that the coordinates of any point on the unit circle can be repre-
sented by $p(\cos \theta, \sin \theta)$, where θ is any angle.

As the point p rotates, θ changes. These definitions of cos θ and sin θ in terms of the coordinates of a
point rotating around the unit circle apply for **all** values of the angle $\theta°$.
Memory Aid: (christian name, surname) = (cos θ, sin θ) = (x, y)

Note: Using Pythagoras's theorem: $\cos^2 \theta + \sin^2 \theta = 1$

Values of sin, cos and tan for 0°, 90°, 180°, 270° and 360°

Both diagrams below represent the unit circle but using two different notations to describe any point p
on the circle.

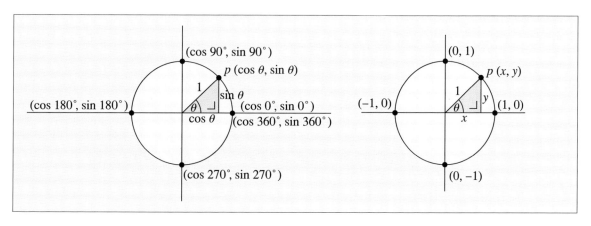

By comparing corresponding points on both unit circles, the values of sin, cos and tan for 0°, 90°, 180°,
270° and 360°, can be read directly.

$(\cos 0°, \sin 0°) = (\cos 360°, \sin 360°) = (1, 0)$ $\cos 0° = \cos 360° = 1$ $\sin 0° = \sin 360° = 0$ $\tan 0° = \tan 360° = \frac{0}{1} = 0$	$(\cos 90°, \sin 90°) = (0, 1)$ $\cos 90° = 0$ $\sin 90° = 1$ $\tan 90° = \frac{1}{0}$ (undefined)
$(\cos 180°, \sin 180°) = (-1, 0)$ $\cos 180° = -1$ $\sin 180° = 0$ $\tan 180° = \frac{0}{-1} = 0$	$(\cos 270°, \sin 270°) = (0, -1)$ $\cos 270° = 0$ $\sin 270° = -1$ $\tan 270° = \frac{-1}{0}$ (undefined)

Note: Division by zero is undefined.

The x and y axes divide the plane into four quadrants.
Consider the unit circle on the right:

$\cos \theta = x \qquad \sin \theta = y$

$\tan \theta = \dfrac{\sin \theta}{\cos \theta} = \dfrac{y}{x}$

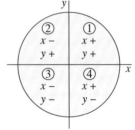

By examining the signs of x and y in the four quadrants, the signs of $\sin \theta$, $\cos \theta$, and $\tan \theta$ for any value of θ can be found.

Summary of signs

1st quadrant: sin, cos and tan are all positive.
2nd quadrant: sin is positive, cos and tan are negative.
3rd quadrant: tan is positive, sin and cos are negative.
4th quadrant: cos is positive, sin and tan are negative.
A very useful memory aid, *CAST*, in the diagram on the right, show the ratios that are positive for the angles between 0° and 360°.

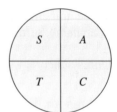

Negative angles

Consider the unit circle showing angles θ and $-\theta$.

$\cos \theta = x \qquad \sin \theta = y \qquad \tan \theta = \dfrac{y}{x}$

$\cos (-\theta) = x \qquad \sin (-\theta) = -y \qquad \tan(-\theta) = -\dfrac{y}{x}$

Thus,

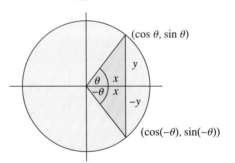

$\cos(-\theta) = \cos \theta$	$\sin(-\theta) = -\sin \theta$	$\tan(-\theta) = -\tan \theta$

Method for finding the trigonometric ratio for any angle between 0° and 360°:

1. Draw a rough diagram of the angle.
2. Determine in which quadrant the angle lies and use 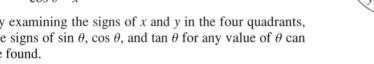 to find its sign.

3. Find its **related** angle (acute angle to nearest horizontal).
4. Use the trigonometric ratio of the related angle with the sign in step 2.

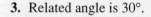

Example ▼

Find cos 210°, leaving your answer in surd form.

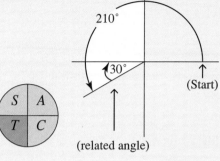

Solution:

Surd form, ∴ cannot use calculator.

1. The diagram shows the angle 210°.

2. 210° is in the 3rd quadrant.
cos is negative in the 3rd quadrant.

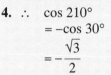

3. Related angle is 30°.

4. ∴ $\quad$ cos 210°
$\qquad = -\cos 30°$
$\qquad = -\dfrac{\sqrt{3}}{2}$
(or use tables page 9)

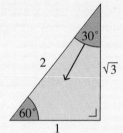

Note: $\sin^2 A = (\sin A)^2$, $\cot^2 A = (\cot A)^2$, etc.

Exercise 7.2 ▼

Evaluate each of the following, answering in·surd form where necessary:

1. $\cos^2 45° + \sin 30°$ $\qquad$ **2.** $1 - \cos^2 \dfrac{\pi}{6}$ $\qquad$ **3.** $\sin^2 60° + \cos^2 45°$ $\qquad$ **4.** $\tan^2 30° \sin^2 60°$

5. $\tan \dfrac{4\pi}{3} \tan \dfrac{\pi}{6}$ $\qquad$ **6.** $\sin \dfrac{5\pi}{4} \cos \dfrac{3\pi}{4}$ $\qquad$ **7.** $\dfrac{\sin^2 270° + \cos^2 180°}{2 \cos 0°}$ $\qquad$ **8.** $\dfrac{1 + \tan 60° \tan 30°}{\cos^2 45°}$

9. $\tan 315° - \sin 330°$ $\qquad$ **10.** $\tan^2 225° - 2 \cos 240°$

11. $\sin 315°$ $\qquad$ **12.** $\tan 120°$ $\qquad$ **13.** $\cos 150°$ $\qquad$ **14.** $\sin 135°$

15. $\cos 330°$ $\qquad$ **16.** $\tan 300°$ $\qquad$ **17.** $\cos \dfrac{3\pi}{4}$ $\qquad$ **18.** $\cos(-120°)$

19. $\sin\left(-\dfrac{7\pi}{6}\right)$ $\qquad$ **20.** $\tan(-150°)$ $\qquad$ **21.** $\cot \dfrac{\pi}{4}$ $\qquad$ **22.** $\sec \dfrac{7\pi}{6}$

23. $\csc 330°$ $\qquad$ **24.** $\cot 150°$ $\qquad$ **25.** $\csc 120°$

26. (i) $\quad$ Find the value of A for which $\cos A = -1$, $\quad 0° \leqslant A \leqslant 360°$.
$\quad$ **(ii)** $\quad$ If $0° \leqslant A \leqslant 360°$, find the value of A for which $\sin A = 1$.
$\quad$ **(iii)** $\quad$ If $0° \leqslant A \leqslant 360°$, find the values of A for which $\cos A = 0$.

Solution of Triangles

Notation

The diagram shows the **usual notation** for a triangle in trigonometry:

Vertices: a, b, c
Angles: A, B, C
Length of sides: a, b, c

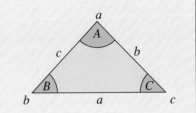

The lengths of the sides are denoted by a lower case letter, and named after the angle they are opposite, i.e., a is opposite angle A, b is opposite angle B, and c is opposite angle C.

Using the same terminology we also have the following:

$$A = |\angle bac|, \qquad B = |\angle abc|, \qquad C = |\angle acb|$$
$$a = |bc|, \qquad b = |ac|, \qquad c = |ab|$$

Sine and Cosine Rule, Area of a Triangle

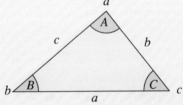

Sine Rule: $\qquad \dfrac{a}{\sin A} = \dfrac{b}{\sin B} = \dfrac{c}{\sin C}$

or $\qquad \dfrac{\sin A}{a} = \dfrac{\sin B}{b} = \dfrac{\sin C}{c}$

Cosine Rule:

$$a^2 = b^2 + c^2 - 2bc \cos A \qquad b^2 = a^2 + c^2 - 2ac \cos B \qquad c^2 = a^2 + b^2 - 2ab \cos C$$

or

$$\cos A = \frac{b^2 + c^2 - a^2}{2bc} \qquad \cos B = \frac{a^2 + c^2 - b^2}{2ac} \qquad \cos C = \frac{a^2 + b^2 - c^2}{2ab}$$

Area of $\triangle abc = \frac{1}{2}ab \sin C = \frac{1}{2}ac \sin B = \frac{1}{2}bc \sin A$

Use the sine rule if you know:

1. Two angles and one side.
2. Two sides and an angle opposite one of these sides.

Use the cosine rule if you know:

> **1.** Two sides and the included angle.
> **2.** The lengths of the three sides.

Notes: As a general rule, if you cannot use the sine rule then use the cosine rule.
If two angles are given we can work out the third angle straight away, as the three angles in a triangle add up to 180°.
The sine and cosine rules and the area of a triangle formulas also apply to a right-angled triangle, but with right-angled triangles we usually use the basic trigonometric definitions.
The largest angle of a triangle is opposite the largest side and the smallest angle is opposite the shortest side. There can be only one obtuse angle in a triangle.

Tackling problems in Trigonometry:

> **1.** If not given, draw a diagram, and put in as much information as possible.
> **2.** If two, or more, triangles are linked redraw the triangles separately.
> **3.** Watch for common sides which link the triangles
>   (i.e. we can carry common values from one triangle to another triangle).
> **4.** Use the sine or cosine rule as needed.

Example ▼

In $\triangle abc$, $|ab| = 3$, $|ac| = 5$ and $|bc| = 7$.
Calculate:

(i) the measure of the greatest angle of the triangle

(ii) the area of $\triangle abc$, giving your answer in the form $\dfrac{a\sqrt{b}}{c}$, where b is prime.

Solution:

(i) The largest angle is opposite the largest side. Using the cosine rule:

$$a^2 = b^2 + c^2 - 2bc \cos A$$
$$7^2 = 5^2 + 3^2 - 2(5)(3) \cos A$$
$$49 = 25 + 9 - 30 \cos A$$
$$30 \cos A = 25 + 9 - 49$$
$$30 \cos A = -15$$
$$\cos A = \tfrac{1}{2}$$
$$A = \cos^{-1}\left(-\tfrac{1}{2}\right) = 120°$$

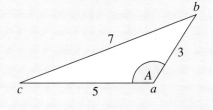

(ii) Area of $\triangle abc = \tfrac{1}{2}bc \sin A = \tfrac{1}{2}(5)(3)\sin 120° = \tfrac{1}{2}(5)(3)\left(\dfrac{\sqrt{3}}{2}\right) = \dfrac{15\sqrt{3}}{4}$

In the diagram, $|pq| = 4$ cm, $|pr| = 5$ cm,

$|qr| = 6$ cm and $|\angle psr| = 22°$.

Find $|ps|$, correct to two places of decimals.

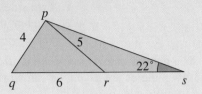

Solution:

Two triangles are linked and we need to work on them separately to find $|ps|$.

1. Consider Δpqr:

We need to use the cosine rule to find $|\angle prq|$, as
we are given three sides.

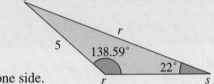

$$\cos R = \frac{p^2 + q^2 - r^2}{2pq} \quad \text{(cosine rule)}$$

$$\cos R = \frac{6^2 + 5^2 - 4^2}{2(6)(5)}$$

$$\cos R = \frac{45}{60} = \frac{3}{4}$$

$$R = \cos^{-1} \tfrac{3}{4} = 41.41°$$

(correct to two places of decimals)

$$\therefore \quad |\angle prs| = 180° - 41.41° = 138.59°$$

2. Consider Δprs:

We now use the sine rule to find $|ps|$,
(from diagram $|ps| = r$), as we have two angles and one side.

$$\frac{r}{\sin R} = \frac{s}{\sin S} \qquad \text{(sine rule, } r \text{ missing so put that first)}$$

$$\frac{r}{\sin 138.59°} = \frac{5}{\sin 22°} \qquad \text{(put in known values)}$$

$$r = \frac{5 \sin 138.59°}{\sin 22°} \qquad \text{(multiply both sides by } \sin 138.59°\text{)}$$

$$r = 8.82849883$$

Thus $|ps| = 8.83$ cm (correct to two places of decimals).

Ambiguous case:

If $\sin A = \dfrac{\sqrt{3}}{2}$, then $A = 60°$ or $120°$: two possible solutions. Thus, we have to be very careful when
using the sine rule to calculate an angle, as there may be two possible answers. Whenever we are given
two sides and a non-included angle, there is a risk of having two triangles that satisfy the given conditions. However, it should not be assumed that there will always be two triangles satisfying the given
conditions. For example, we might find that if we use the larger angle the sum of the three angles in
the triangle is greater than $180°$. The ambiguous case arises only when the smaller of the two given
sides is opposite the known angle.

In a triangle, $a = 8$, $b = 9$ and $A = 60°$. Find the possible values of B and C, correct to the nearest degree, and sketch the triangles.

Solution:

$$\frac{\sin B}{b} = \frac{\sin A}{a}$$

$$\frac{\sin B}{9} = \frac{\sin 60°}{8}$$

$$\sin B = \frac{9 \sin 60°}{8}$$

$$B = \sin^{-1}\left(\frac{9 \sin 60°}{8}\right)$$

$$B = 77°$$

(correct to the nearest degree)

or $B = 180° - 77° = 103°$

$A = 60°$, $B = 77°$, $C = 180° - 60° - 77° = 43°$

$A = 60°$, $B = 103°$, $C = 180° - 60° - 103 = 17°$

Two possible triangles

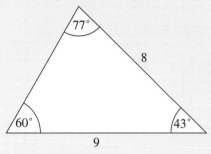

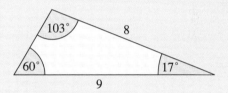

There is no ambiguity when using the cosine rule. This is because cosine is positive in the first quadrant (giving an acute angle), but negative in the second quadrant (giving an obtuse angle).

A vertical flagpole stands on horizontal ground. The angle of elevation of the top of the pole from a certain point on the ground is θ. From a point on the ground 10 metres closer to the pole the angle of elevation is β. Show that the height of the pole is

$$\frac{10 \sin \theta \sin \beta}{\sin(\beta - \theta)}.$$

Solution:

Represent the situation with a diagram, then redraw the two triangles separately.
Put in known length.
Let x m = the length of the common side of both triangles.

$\alpha + \theta = \beta$ (exterior angle of a triangle)

$\alpha = (\beta - \theta)$

From the right-angled triangle,

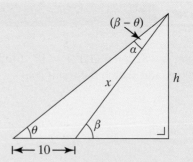

$$\sin \beta = \frac{h}{x} \quad (h = \text{height of flagpole})$$

$$x = \frac{h}{\sin \beta} \quad ①$$

Using the sine rule on the other triangle,

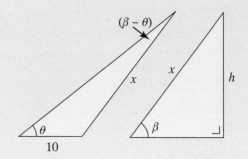

$$\frac{x}{\sin \theta} = \frac{10}{\sin(\beta - \theta)}$$

$$x = \frac{10 \sin \theta}{\sin(\beta - \theta)} \quad ②$$

We now equate the two different expressions for x, the common side of both triangles.

$$x = x$$

$$\frac{h}{\sin \beta} = \frac{10 \sin \theta}{\sin(\beta - \theta)}$$

$$h = \frac{10 \sin \theta \sin \beta}{\sin(\beta - \theta)}$$

Exercise 7.3 ▼

Unless otherwise stated, where necessary give the lengths of sides and areas correct to two decimal places and give angles correct to one place of decimals.

1. In $\triangle pqr$, $p = 7$ cm, $P = 30°$, $Q = 84°$. Find R, q and r.

2. In $\triangle abc$, $b = 8$ cm, $c = 10$ cm, $A = 60°$. Find a.

3. Find the area of these triangles, without using a calculator.

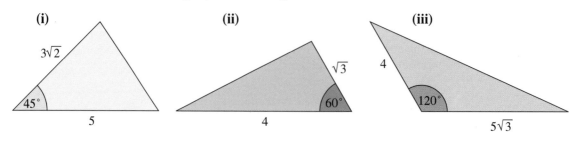

(i) $3\sqrt{2}$ $45°$ 5

(ii) $\sqrt{3}$ $60°$ 4

(iii) 4 $120°$ $5\sqrt{3}$

4. In $\triangle pqr$, $|pr| = \sqrt{8}$ m, $|\angle rpq| = 30°$ and $|\angle pqr| = 45°$. Show that the area of $\triangle pqr = 2.7$ m^2, correct to one place of decimals.

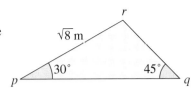

5. In the given triangle, $\cos A = \frac{4}{5}$. Without using tables or a calculator, find the area of the triangle.

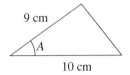

6. The area of the triangle shown on the right is 6 cm^2. Find the value of x.

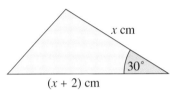

7. Calculate the three angles in triangle pqr, correct to two places of decimals.

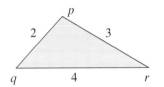

8. The area of the triangle shown is 12 square units. Find two different values of A, and make a sketch of both triangles.

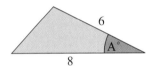

9. In triangle pqr, $|pq| = 13$, $|qr| = 15$ and $|pr| = x$. Find two possible values for x.

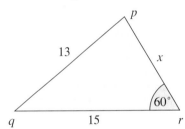

10. In triangle abc, $|ab| = 3\sqrt{3}$, $|bc| = 3\sqrt{2}$ and $|\angle bac| = \frac{\pi}{4}$. Find two possible values for $|\angle acb|$ and the corresponding two possible values of $|\angle abc|$, giving your answers in radians.

11. In the diagram, $|pq| = 5$ cm, $|pr| = 6$ cm, $|qr| = 7$ cm and $|\angle psr| = 25°$. Find $|ps|$, correct to one place of decimals.

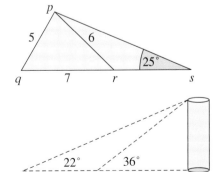

12. A surveyor wishes to measure the height of a round tower. Measuring the angle of elevation, he finds that the angle increases from 22° to 36° after walking 25 m towards the base of the tower. Calculate the height of the tower, correct to the nearest m.

13. $pqrs$ is a quadrilateral. $|pq| = 7$, $|qs| = 8$, $|ps| = 13$.

    (i) Show $|\angle pqs| = 120°$.

    (ii) Given that the quadrilateral $pqrs$ has area $\dfrac{35\sqrt{3}}{2}$ find the ratio, area Δpqs : area Δqrs.

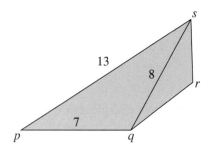

14. In triangle pqr, $|pr| = 5$, $|qr| = 4$ and $|\angle qpr| = 37°$. Find two possible values of $|\angle pqr|$, correct to the nearest degree.

15. In the diagram, $ab \perp bd$, $|ab| = y$, $|bc| = x$ and $|cd| = 80$.

    (i) Using Δabc, express x in terms of y

    (ii) Using Δabd, express x in terms of y.

    Hence, or otherwise, find y, expressing your answer in the form $a\sqrt{b}$, where b is prime.

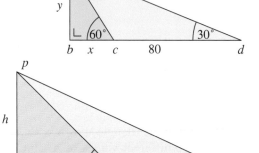

16. In the given diagram, $pq \perp qs$, $|pq| = h$ and $|rs| = x$.

    Show that $x = \dfrac{h \sin(\alpha - \beta)}{\sin \alpha \sin \beta}$.

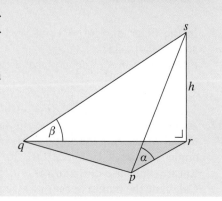

Three-dimensional Problems

When tackling problems in three dimensions it is good practice to redraw each triangle separately and apply the sine and cosine rule to these triangles. Watch for common sides which link the triangles. We can carry common values from one triangle to another triangle.

Example ▼

p, q and r are points on level ground. $[sr]$ is a vertical tower of height h. The angles of elevation of the top of the tower from p and q are α and β, respectively.

    (i) If $|\alpha| = 60°$ and $|\beta| = 30°$, express $|pr|$ and $|qr|$ in terms of h.

    (ii) Find $|qp|$ in terms of h, if $\tan \angle qrp = \sqrt{8}$.

Solution:
Redraw right-angled triangles *prs* and *qrs* separately.

(i)

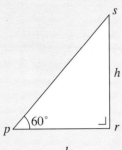

$$\tan 60° = \frac{h}{|pr|}$$
$$\sqrt{3} = \frac{h}{|pr|}$$
$$\sqrt{3}\,|pr| = h$$
$$|pr| = \frac{h}{\sqrt{3}}$$

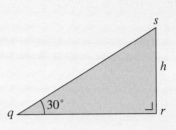

$$\tan 30° = \frac{h}{|qr|}$$
$$\frac{1}{\sqrt{3}} = \frac{h}{|qr|}$$
$$|qr| = \sqrt{3}h$$

(ii) Redraw triangle *qpr* separately.
Using the cosine rule on triangle *qpr*:

$$|qp|^2 = |qr|^2 + |pr|^2 - 2\,|qr|\,.\,|pr|\cos\angle qrp$$

$$|qp|^2 = (\sqrt{3}h)^2 + \left(\frac{h}{\sqrt{3}}\right)^2 - 2(\sqrt{3}h)\left(\frac{h}{\sqrt{3}}\right)\left(\frac{1}{3}\right)$$

$$|qp|^2 = 3h^2 + \frac{h^2}{3} - \frac{2}{3}h$$

$$|qp|^2 = \frac{9h^2 + h^2 - 2h^2}{3}$$

$$|qp|^2 = \frac{8h^2}{3}$$

$$|qp| = \sqrt{\frac{8h^2}{3}} = \sqrt{\frac{8}{3}}\,h$$

Draw a right angle to get $\cos\angle qrp$.

Given: $\tan\angle qrp = \sqrt{8} = \frac{\sqrt{8}}{1}$

Using Pythagoras's theorem, $|qr| = 3$

∴ $\cos\angle qrp = \frac{1}{3}$

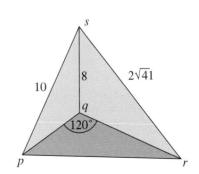

Exercise 7.4 ▼

1. *p*, *q* and *r* are points on horizontal ground.
[*qs*] represents a vertical pole of height 8 m.

If $|\angle pqr| = 120°$, $|ps| = 10$ m and $|rs| = 2\sqrt{41}m$, find:

(i) $|pq|$ **(ii)** $|qr|$ **(iii)** $|pr|$

Calculate the area of triangle *pqr*. Express your answer in the
form $a\sqrt{b}$ m², where *b* is prime.

2. Points *a*, *b* and *c* are on horizontal ground.
[*ad*] represents a vertical pole.

$|ac| = 15$ m, $|bc| = 8$ m, $|\angle acb| = 60°$ and $|\angle abd| = 30°$.

Calculate:

(i) $|ab|$

(ii) $|ad|$, giving your answer in the form $\dfrac{a\sqrt{b}}{b}$.

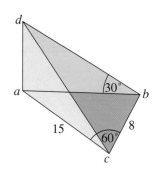

3. The diagram shows a river with parallel banks, *r* metres apart.
A tree, of height *h* metres, is directly opposite from a point *p*, as shown.
A woman wants to measure the height of the tree. From *p* the angle of elevation of the top of the tree is 45°. She then walks to a point *q*, 50 metres downstream, so that the horizontal distance from *q* to the base of the tree is *t* metres. From *q* the angle of elevation of the top of the tree is 30°.

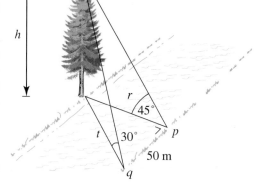

(i)   Express *r* and *t* in terms of *h*.
(ii) Write down an equation involving *r* and *t*.
(iii) Hence, calculate **(a)** *h* **(b)** *t*, correct to one place of decimals.

4. *a*, *b* and *c* are points on level ground.
[*ad*] represents a vertical pole.

$|ab| = x,\ |ac| = \dfrac{\sqrt{3}}{2}x$ and $|\angle abd| = \dfrac{\pi}{3}$.

(i)   Express $|ad|$ in terms of *x*.

(ii) If $\angle acd = \tan^{-1} k,\ k \in \mathbf{N}$,
find the value of *k*.

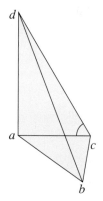

5. Points *p*, *q*, *r* are on the horizontal.

$|pq| = 5,\ |qr| = 3$ and $|pqr| = \dfrac{2\pi}{3}$.

(i)   Calculate $|pr|$.

(ii) [*pd*] represents a vertical mast. The angle of elevation of *d* from *r* is $\frac{\pi}{3}$. Find $|dq|$, giving your answer in the form $2\sqrt{a}$ and calculate the measure of $\angle pqd$, correct to one place of decimals.

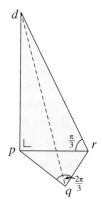

6. $[sp]$, $[tq]$ are vertical poles each of height 10 m, p, q, r are points on level ground. Two wires of equal length join s and t to r, i.e. $|sr| = |tr|$.

If $|pr| = 8$ m and $|\angle prq| = 120°$, calculate:

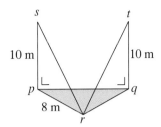

   (i) $|pr|$ in the form $a\sqrt{b}$, where b is prime.

   (ii) $|sr|$ in the form $\sqrt{c}$.

   (iii) $|\angle srt|$ to the nearest degree.

Identities involving the Sine and Cosine Rules

We often have to prove identities involving the usual notation for a triangle using the sine and cosine rules. This usually involves rearranging the sine or cosine rule and substituting the rearranged expression to prove the required identity.

Cosine rule	**Sine rule**
$a^2 = b^2 + c^2 - 2bc \cos A$	$\dfrac{\sin A}{a} = \dfrac{\sin B}{b}$
then $\cos A = \dfrac{b^2 + c^2 - a^2}{2bc}$	then $\sin A = \dfrac{a \sin B}{b}$
Similarly for B and C.	or $\sin B = \dfrac{b \sin A}{a}$

Example ▼

Using the usual notation for a triangle, prove that $c(b \cos A - a \cos B) = b^2 - a^2$.

Solution:

From the cosine rule,

$$\cos A = \frac{b^2 + c^2 - a^2}{2bc} \quad \text{and} \quad \cos B = \frac{a^2 + c^2 - b^2}{2ac}$$

$c(b \cos A - a \cos B)$

$= bc \cos A - ac \cos B$

$= bc\left(\dfrac{b^2 + c^2 - a^2}{2bc}\right) - ac\left(\dfrac{a^2 + c^2 - b^2}{2ac}\right)$ [this is the substitution]

$= \dfrac{(b^2 + c^2 - a^2)}{2} - \dfrac{(a^2 + c^2 - b^2)}{2}$

$= \dfrac{(b^2 + c^2 - a^2) - (a^2 + c^2 - b^2)}{2}$ [same denominator]

$= \dfrac{b^2 + c^2 - a^2 - a^2 - c^2 + b^2}{2}$

$= \dfrac{2b^2 - 2a^2}{2}$

$= b^2 - a^2$

Exercise 7.5 ▼

Prove each of the following identities using the usual notation for a triangle:

1. $b \sin C = c \sin B$

2. $b \cos C + c \cos B = a$

3. $bc \cos A + ac \cos B = c^2$

4. $a(b \cos C - c \cos B) = b^2 - c^2$

5. $\dfrac{1}{c \cos B - b \cos C} = \dfrac{a}{c^2 - b^2}$

6. $\dfrac{\cos A}{a} + \dfrac{\cos B}{b} + \dfrac{\cos C}{c} = \dfrac{a^2 + b^2 + c^2}{2abc}$

7. $a(\sin B - \sin C) + b(\sin C - \sin A) + c(\sin A - \sin B) = 0$

8. $\tan A = \dfrac{a \sin C}{b - a \cos C}$

9. $\dfrac{b - c}{b + c} = \dfrac{\sin B - \sin C}{\sin B + \sin C}$

10. **(i)** $c = a \cos B + b \cos A.$

  (ii) $a + b + c = (b + c)\cos A + (a + c)\cos B + (a + b)\cos C$

11. $\dfrac{\cos B}{b} - \dfrac{\cos C}{c} = \dfrac{c^2 - b^2}{abc}$

12. $a^2 + b^2 + c^2 = 2(bc \cos A + ac \cos B + ab \cos C)$

13. What can you deduce about angle A in triangle abc, using the usual notation? – if:

  (i) $a^2 > b^2 + c^2$

  (ii) $a^2 = b^2 + c^2$

  (iii) $a^2 < b^2 + c^2$

  (iv) $a^2 = b^2 + c^2 - bc$

  (v) $a^2 = b^2 + c^2 + bc$

  (vi) $a^2 = b^2 + c^2 - \sqrt{3}bc$

  If $A = \dfrac{\pi}{4}$ and $B = \dfrac{\pi}{3}$, show that $3a^2 = 2b^2$.

Proving Trigonometric Identities

An identity is an equation that is true for all values of the variable.
Some identities we have met so far are:

$$\tan \theta = \frac{\sin \theta}{\cos \theta}$$

$$\cot \theta = \frac{1}{\tan \theta} = \frac{\cos \theta}{\sin \theta}$$

$$\sec \theta = \frac{1}{\cos \theta}$$

$$\operatorname{cosec} \theta = \frac{1}{\sin \theta}$$

$$\cos(-\theta) = \cos \theta \qquad \sin(-\theta) = -\sin \theta \qquad \tan(-\theta) = -\tan \theta$$

Method for proving trigonometric identities:

> The method is to take one side and convert it into the other side. It is usually easier to start with the side which is more complicated.

Example ▼

Prove that $\cos^2\theta + \sin^2\theta = 1$.
Hence, prove   **(i)** $1 + \tan^2\theta = \sec^2\theta$ **(ii)** $\cot^2\theta + 1 = \text{cosec}^2\theta$.

Solution:

Let θ be any angle as shown in diagram.
The coordinates of p are (x, y) and $|op| = r$.

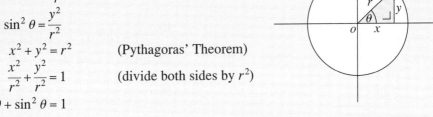

$$\cos\theta = \frac{x}{r} \implies \cos^2\theta = \frac{x^2}{r^2}$$

$$\sin\theta = \frac{y}{r} \implies \sin^2\theta = \frac{y^2}{r^2}$$

$$x^2 + y^2 = r^2 \qquad \text{(Pythagoras' Theorem)}$$

$$\frac{x^2}{r^2} + \frac{y^2}{r^2} = 1 \qquad \text{(divide both sides by } r^2\text{)}$$

$$\cos^2\theta + \sin^2\theta = 1$$

(i) $\qquad \cos^2\theta + \sin^2\theta = 1$

$$\frac{\cos^2\theta}{\cos^2\theta} + \frac{\sin^2\theta}{\cos^2\theta} = \frac{1}{\cos^2\theta}$$

(dividing both sides by $\cos^2\theta$)
$$1 + \tan^2\theta = \sec^2\theta$$

(ii) $\qquad \cos^2\theta + \sin^2\theta = 1$

$$\frac{\cos^2\theta}{\sin^2\theta} + \frac{\sin^2\theta}{\sin^2\theta} = \frac{1}{\sin^2\theta}$$

(dividing both sides by $\sin^2\theta$)
$$\cot^2\theta + 1 = \text{cosec}^2\theta$$

Example ▼

Prove:

(i) $\dfrac{1}{1 - \sin A} + \dfrac{1}{1 + \sin A} = 2\sec^2 A$ **(ii)** $\cot\theta + \dfrac{\sin\theta}{1 + \cos\theta} = \text{cosec}\,\theta$.

Solution:

(i) $\qquad \dfrac{1}{1 - \sin A} + \dfrac{1}{1 + \sin A}$

$= \dfrac{1(1 + \sin A) + 1(1 - \sin A)}{(1 - \sin A)(1 + \sin A)}$

$= \dfrac{1 + \sin A + 1 - \sin A}{1 + \sin A - \sin A - \sin^2 A}$

$= \dfrac{2}{1 - \sin^2 A}$

$= \dfrac{2}{\cos^2 A}$

$= 2\dfrac{1}{\cos^2 A}$

$= 2\sec^2 A$

(ii) $\qquad \cot\theta + \dfrac{\sin\theta}{1 + \cos\theta}$

$= \dfrac{\cos\theta}{\sin\theta} + \dfrac{\sin\theta}{1 + \cos\theta}$

$= \dfrac{\cos\theta(1 + \cos\theta) + \sin\theta(\sin\theta)}{\sin\theta(1 + \cos\theta)}$

$= \dfrac{\cos\theta + \cos^2\theta + \sin^2\theta}{\sin\theta(1 + \cos\theta)}$

$= \dfrac{(1 + \cos\theta)}{\sin\theta(1 + \cos\theta)}$

$= \dfrac{1}{\sin\theta}$

$= \text{cosec}\,\theta$

Exercise 7.6 ▼

Prove each of the following identities:

1. $\sec A \sin A = \tan A$

2. $(1 - \cos A)(1 + \cos A) = \sin^2 A$

3. $\tan \theta \sqrt{1 - \sin^2 \theta} = \sin \theta$

4. $(1 + \tan^2 \theta)(1 - \sin^2 \theta) = 1$

5. $\operatorname{cosec}^2 A = 1 + \cot^2 A$

6. $\sec^2 \theta - \tan^2 \theta = 1$

7. $\dfrac{\tan \theta}{\sqrt{1 + \tan^2 \theta}} = \sin \theta$

8. $\dfrac{\cos A}{1 - \sin A} - \tan A = \sec A$

9. $\dfrac{1 + \tan^2 A}{\sec^3 A} = \cos A$

10. $\dfrac{1}{1 + \tan^2 A} + \dfrac{1}{1 + \cot^2 A} = 1$

11. $(\sin A + \cos A)^2 + (\sin A - \cos A)^2 = 2$

12. $\sin^2 A - \sin^2 B = \cos^2 B - \cos^2 A$

13. $\dfrac{1}{1 + \cos A} + \dfrac{1}{1 - \cos A} = 2 \operatorname{cosec}^2 A$

14. $\dfrac{\cos \theta}{1 + \sin \theta} + \dfrac{1 + \sin \theta}{\cos \theta} = 2 \sec \theta$

15. $(\sin \theta + \cos \theta)(1 - \sin \theta \cos \theta) = \sin^3 \theta + \cos^3 \theta$

16. $(\sec A + \tan A - 1)(\sec A - \tan A + 1) = 2 \tan A$

17. $(1 + \tan \theta)^2 + (1 - \tan \theta)^2 = 2 \sec^2 \theta$

18. $\sec \theta + \operatorname{cosec} \theta \cot \theta = \sec \theta \operatorname{cosec}^2 \theta$

19. $\dfrac{1 - \cos \theta}{\sin \theta} = \dfrac{1}{\operatorname{cosec} \theta + \cot \theta}$

20. $(\tan \theta + \sec \theta)^2 = \dfrac{1 + \sin \theta}{1 - \sin \theta}$

21. $\dfrac{\tan \theta + \cot \theta}{\sec \theta + \operatorname{cosec} \theta} = \dfrac{1}{\sin \theta + \cos \theta}$

22. $\dfrac{\sin A}{\sqrt{1 + \cot^2 A}} + \dfrac{\cos A}{\sqrt{1 + \tan^2 A}} = 1$

TRIGONOMETRY 2

Compound, Multiple and Half-angle Formulas

A **compound angle** is an angle which is written as the sum or difference of two or more angles.

For example, $(A + B)$, $(A - B)$ and $(A - B - C)$ are compound angles.

A **multiple angle** is an angle which is written as a multiple of a single angle.

For example, $2A$, $2B$, 3θ are multiple angles.

A sub-multiple angle is an angle which is written as a fraction of a single angle.

For example, $\dfrac{A}{2}, \dfrac{B}{2}, \dfrac{\theta}{3}$ are sub-multiple angles.

We shall now derive formulas for trigonometric functions of these angles.

In deriving these formulas we make use of the following identities for all $A \in \mathbf{R}$.

---

1. $\cos^2 A + \sin^2 A = 1$ **2.** $\cos(-A) = \cos A$ **3.** $\sin(-A) = -\sin A$

4. $\tan A = \dfrac{\sin A}{\cos A}$ **5.** $\cos(\tfrac{\pi}{2} - A) = \sin A$ **6.** $\sin(\tfrac{\pi}{2} - A) = \cos A$

Example ▼

Given $\cos(A - B) = \cos A \cos B + \sin A \sin B$, prove each of the following:

1. $\cos(A + B) = \cos A \cos B - \sin A \sin B$

2. $\cos 2A = \cos^2 A - \sin^2 A$

3. $\sin(A + B) = \sin A \cos B + \cos A \sin B$

4. $\sin(A - B) = \sin A \cos B - \cos A \sin B$

5. $\sin 2A = 2 \sin A \cos A$

6. $\sin A = 2 \sin \dfrac{A}{2} \cos \dfrac{A}{2}$

7. $\tan(A + B) = \dfrac{\tan A + \tan B}{1 - \tan A \tan B}$

8. $\tan(A - B) = \dfrac{\tan A - \tan B}{1 + \tan A \tan B}$

9. $\tan 2A = \dfrac{2 \tan A}{1 - \tan^2 A}$

10. $\tan 6\theta = \dfrac{2 \tan 3\theta}{1 - \tan^2 3\theta}$

11. $\cos^2 A = \tfrac{1}{2}(1 + \cos 2A)$

12. $\sin^2 A = \tfrac{1}{2}(1 - \cos 2A)$

13. $\cos 2A = \dfrac{1 - \tan^2 A}{1 + \tan^2 A}$

14. $\sin 2A = \dfrac{2 \tan A}{1 + \tan^2 A}$

Solution:

We derive each of these formulas based on the formula:

$\cos(A - B) = \cos A \cos B + \sin A \sin B$.

We then use each new formula to derive another formula.

1. **Prove:** $\cos(A + B) = \cos A \cos B - \sin A \sin B$
   Given: $\cos(A - B) = \cos A \cos B + \sin A \sin B$
   Proof: Replace B with $(-B)$ on both sides.

   $$\cos[A - (-B)] = \cos A \cos(-B) + \sin A \sin(-B)$$
   $$\cos(A + B) = \cos A \cos B + \sin A(-\sin B)$$
   $$\cos(A + B) = \cos A \cos B - \sin A \sin B$$

2. **Prove:** $\cos 2A = \cos^2 A - \sin^2 A$
   Given: $\cos(A + B) = \cos A \cos B - \sin A \sin B$
   Proof: Replace B with A on both sides.

   $$\cos(A + A) = \cos A \cos A - \sin A \sin A$$
   $$\cos 2A = \cos^2 A - \sin^2 A$$

3. **Prove:** $\sin(A + B) = \sin A \cos B + \cos A \sin B$
   Given: $\cos(A - B) = \cos A \cos B + \sin A \sin B$
   Proof: Replace A with $(\frac{\pi}{2} - A)$ on both sides.

   $$\cos[(\tfrac{\pi}{2} - A) - B] = \cos(\tfrac{\pi}{2} - A)\cos B + \sin(\tfrac{\pi}{2} - A)\sin B$$
   $$\cos[\tfrac{\pi}{2} - (A + B)] = \sin A \cos B + \cos A \sin B$$
   $$\sin(A + B) = \sin A \cos B + \cos A \sin B$$

4. **Prove:** $\sin(A - B) = \sin A \cos B - \cos A \sin B$
   Given: $\sin(A + B) = \sin A \cos B + \cos A \sin B$
   Proof: Replace B with $(-B)$ on both sides.

   $$\sin[A + (-B)] = \sin A \cos(-B) + \cos A \sin(-B)$$
   $$\sin(A - B) = \sin A \cos B + \cos A(-\sin B)$$
   $$\sin(A - B) = \sin A \cos B - \cos A \sin B$$

5. **Prove:** $\sin 2A = 2 \sin A \cos A$
   Given: $\sin(A + B) = \sin A \cos B + \cos A \sin B$
   Proof: Replace B with A on both sides.

   $$\sin(A + A) = \sin A \cos A + \cos A \sin A$$
   $$\sin 2A = 2 \sin A \cos A$$

6. Prove: $\sin A = 2 \sin \dfrac{A}{2} \cos \dfrac{A}{2}$

   Given: $\sin 2A = 2 \sin A \cos A$

   Proof: Replace A with $\dfrac{A}{2}$ on both sides.

$$\sin 2\left(\frac{A}{2}\right) = 2 \sin\left(\frac{A}{2}\right)\cos\left(\frac{A}{2}\right)$$

$$\sin A = 2 \sin \frac{A}{2} \cos \frac{A}{2}$$

7. Prove: $\tan(A+B) = \dfrac{\tan A + \tan B}{1 - \tan A \tan B}$

   Given: $\tan A = \dfrac{\sin A}{\cos A}$

   Proof: Replace A with $(A+B)$ on both sides.

$$\tan(A+B) = \frac{\sin(A+B)}{\cos(A+B)}$$

$$\tan(A+B) = \frac{\sin A \cos B + \cos A \sin B}{\cos A \cos B - \cos A \sin B}$$

$$\tan(A+B) = \frac{\dfrac{\sin A \cos B}{\cos A \cos B} + \dfrac{\cos A \sin B}{\cos A \cos B}}{\dfrac{\cos A \cos B}{\cos A \cos B} - \dfrac{\sin A \sin B}{\cos A \cos B}} \quad \left(\begin{matrix}\text{Divide top and bottom} \\ \text{by } \cos A \cos B\end{matrix}\right)$$

$$\tan(A+B) = \frac{\dfrac{\sin A}{\cos A} + \dfrac{\sin B}{\cos B}}{1 - \dfrac{\sin A}{\cos A} \cdot \dfrac{\sin B}{\cos B}}$$

$$\tan(A+B) = \frac{\tan A + \tan B}{1 - \tan A \tan B}$$

8. Prove: $\tan(A-B) = \dfrac{\tan A - \tan B}{1 + \tan A \tan B}$

   Given: $\tan(A+B) = \dfrac{\tan A + \tan B}{1 - \tan A \tan B}$

   Proof: Replace B with $(-B)$ on both sides.

$$\tan(A+(-B)) = \frac{\tan A + \tan(-B)}{1 - \tan A \tan(-B)}$$

$$\tan(A-B) = \frac{\tan A - \tan B}{1 + \tan A \tan B}$$

9. Prove:
$$\tan 2A = \frac{2 \tan A}{1 - \tan^2 A}$$

Given:
$$\tan(A + B) = \frac{\tan A + \tan B}{1 - \tan A \tan B}$$

Proof: Replace B with A on both sides
$$\tan(A + A) = \frac{\tan A + \tan A}{1 - \tan A \tan A}$$
$$\tan 2A = \frac{2 \tan A}{1 - \tan^2 A}$$

10. Prove:
$$\tan 6\theta = \frac{2 \tan 3\theta}{1 - \tan^2 3\theta}$$

Given:
$$\tan 2A = \frac{2 \tan A}{1 - \tan^2 A}$$

Proof: Replace A with 3θ on both sides
$$\tan 2(3\theta) = \frac{2 \tan 3\theta}{1 - \tan^2 3\theta}$$
$$\tan 6\theta = \frac{2 \tan 3\theta}{1 - \tan^2 3\theta}$$

11. Prove: $\cos^2 A = \frac{1}{2}(1 + \cos 2A)$

Given: $\cos 2A = \cos^2 A - \sin^2 A$

Proof:
$$\cos 2A = \cos^2 A - (1 - \cos^2 A)$$
$$\cos 2A = \cos^2 A - 1 + \cos^2 A$$
$$\cos 2A = 2 \cos^2 A - 1$$
$$2 \cos^2 A = 1 + \cos 2A$$
$$\cos^2 A = \frac{1}{2}(1 + \cos 2A)$$

12. Prove: $\sin^2 A = \frac{1}{2}(1 - \cos 2A)$

Given: $\cos 2A = \cos^2 A - \sin^2 A$

Proof:
$$\cos 2A = (1 - \sin^2 A) - \sin^2 A$$
$$\cos 2A = 1 - \sin^2 A - \sin^2 A$$
$$\cos 2A = 1 - 2 \sin^2 A$$
$$2 \sin^2 A = 1 - \cos 2A$$
$$\sin^2 A = \frac{1}{2}(1 - \cos 2A)$$

13. Prove:
$$\cos 2A = \frac{1 - \tan^2 A}{1 + \tan^2 A}$$

Proof:
$$\frac{1 - \tan^2 A}{1 + \tan^2 A} = \frac{1 - \dfrac{\sin^2 A}{\cos^2 A}}{1 + \dfrac{\sin^2 A}{\cos^2 A}}$$

$$= \frac{\cos^2 A - \sin^2 A}{\cos^2 A + \sin^2 A}$$

(multiplying top and bottom by $\cos^2 A$)

$$= \frac{\cos 2A}{1}$$

$$= \cos 2A$$

14. Prove:
$$\sin 2A = \frac{2 \tan A}{1 + \tan^2 A}$$

Proof:
$$\frac{2 \tan A}{1 + \tan^2 A} = \frac{2 \dfrac{\sin A}{\cos A}}{1 + \dfrac{\sin^2 A}{\cos^2 A}}$$

$$= \frac{2 \sin A \cos A}{\cos^2 A + \sin^2 A}$$

(multiplying top and bottom by $\cos^2 A$)

$$= \frac{\sin 2A}{1}$$

$$= \sin 2A$$

Example ▼

Prove that $\sin 3A = 3 \sin A - 4 \sin^3 A$.

Solution:

Proof:
$$\sin 3A$$
$$= \sin(2A + A)$$
$$= \sin 2A \cos A + \cos 2A \sin A$$

$$= (2 \sin A \cos A)\cos A + (\cos^2 A - \sin^2 A)\sin A$$
$$= 2 \sin A \cos^2 A + \sin A \cos^2 A - \sin^3 A$$
$$= 3 \sin A \cos^2 A - \sin^3 A$$

$$= 3 \sin A(1 - \sin^2 A) - \sin^3 A$$
$$= 3 \sin A - 3 \sin^3 A - \sin^3 A$$
$$= 3 \sin A - 4 \sin^3 A$$

Applications

> **Example** ▼

Express **(i)** sin 15° and **(ii)** tan 105° in surd form.

Solution:

First express each angle as a combination of 30°, 45° or 60°.
Then use the compound angle formulas on page 9 of the tables.

(i) $\quad \sin 15°$

$\quad = \sin(45° - 30°)$

$\quad = \sin 45° \cos 30° - \cos 45° \sin 30°$

$\quad = \dfrac{1}{\sqrt{2}} \cdot \dfrac{\sqrt{3}}{2} - \dfrac{1}{\sqrt{2}} \cdot \dfrac{1}{2}$

$\quad = \dfrac{\sqrt{3}}{2\sqrt{2}} - \dfrac{1}{2\sqrt{2}} = \dfrac{\sqrt{3}-1}{2\sqrt{2}}$

(ii) $\quad \tan 105°$

$\quad = \tan(60° + 45°)$

$\quad = \dfrac{\tan 60° + \tan 45°}{1 - \tan 60° \tan 45°}$

$\quad = \dfrac{\sqrt{3}+1}{1 - (\sqrt{3})(1)}$

$\quad = \dfrac{\sqrt{3}+1}{1 - \sqrt{3}}$

> **Example** ▼

If $\tan(A + B) = 3$ and $\tan B = 2$, find the value of $\tan A$.

Solution:

$$\tan(A + B) = \dfrac{\tan A + \tan B}{1 - \tan A \tan B}$$

$$3 = \dfrac{\tan A + 2}{1 - (\tan A)(2)} \qquad \text{[given } \tan(A + B) = 3, \tan B = 2]$$

$$3 = \dfrac{\tan A + 2}{1 - 2\tan A}$$

$$3 - 6\tan A = \tan A + 2 \qquad \text{[multiply both sides by } (1 - 2\tan A)]$$

$$-7\tan A = -1$$

$$7\tan A = 1$$

$$\tan A = \dfrac{1}{7}$$

Alternatively,

$$\tan A = \tan[(A + B) - B] = \dfrac{\tan(A+B) - \tan B}{1 + \tan(A+B)(\tan B)} = \dfrac{3-2}{1 + (3)(2)} = \dfrac{1}{7}$$

If $\sin 2A = \dfrac{7}{25}$, $0 \leqslant A \leqslant \dfrac{\pi}{2}$, find $\tan A$, $\sin A$, and $\cos A$.

Solution:

$$\sin 2A = \frac{2 \tan A}{1 + \tan^2 A}$$

$$\frac{7}{25} = \frac{2 \tan A}{1 + \tan^2 A}$$

(let $t = \tan A$)

$$\frac{7}{25} = \frac{2t}{1 + t^2}$$

$$7 + 7t^2 = 50t$$

$$7t^2 - 50t + 7 = 0$$

$$(7t - 1)(t - 7) = 0$$

$$7t - 1 = 0 \quad \text{or} \quad t - 7 = 0$$

$$t = \frac{1}{7} \quad \text{or} \quad t = 7$$

$$\tan A = \frac{1}{7} \quad \text{or} \quad \tan A = 7$$

1. $\tan A = \dfrac{1}{7}$

$\sin A = \dfrac{1}{\sqrt{50}}$

and $\cos A = \dfrac{7}{\sqrt{50}}$

2. $\tan A = \dfrac{7}{1}$

$\sin A = \dfrac{7}{\sqrt{50}}$

and $\cos A = \dfrac{1}{\sqrt{50}}$

Exercise 8.1 ▼

1. A and B are acute angles such that $\sin A = \dfrac{12}{13}$ and $\cos B = \dfrac{4}{5}$.

Without the use of tables or calculator, find the value of:

    (i) $\cos A$ **(ii)** $\tan A$ **(iii)** $\sin B$ **(iv)** $\tan B$

    (v) $\sin(A + B)$ **(vi)** $\cos(A + B)$ **(vii)** $\tan(A + B)$ **(viii)** $\sin 2A$

2. **(i)** If $\tan \theta = \dfrac{20}{21}$, $0 < \theta < \dfrac{\pi}{2}$, without using tables or calculator find the value of:

      (a) $\sin 2\theta$ **(b)** $\cos 2\theta$ **(c)** $\tan 2\theta$.

  (ii) If $\cos x = \dfrac{1}{\sqrt{5}}$, find the value of $\cos 2x$ without using tables or a calculator.

Express each of the following in surd form:

3. $\cos 75°$ **4.** $\sin 105°$ **5.** $\tan 75°$ **6.** $\cos 15°$

7. $\sin 165°$ **8.** $\cot 15°$ **9.** $\sec 15°$ **10.** $\operatorname{cosec} \dfrac{5\pi}{12}$

11. $\cos 25° \cos 20° - \sin 25° \sin 20°$ **12.** $\sin 70° \cos 10° - \cos 70° \sin 10°$

13. $\dfrac{\tan 80° - \tan 20°}{1 + \tan 80° \tan 20°}$

14. A and B are acute angles such that $\tan A = 4$ and $\tan(A + B) = 5$. Find $\tan B$.

15. A and B are acute angles such that $\tan B = \frac{1}{4}$ and $\tan(A - B) = 2$. Find **(i)** $\tan A$ **(ii)** $\sin 2A$.

16. A and B are acute angles such that $\tan A = \frac{3}{5}$ and $\tan B = \frac{1}{4}$. Find $(A + B)$.

17. $\tan A = \frac{1}{2}$, $180° < A < 360°$, $\tan B = -\frac{1}{3}$, $-90° < B < 90°$. Find $(A - B)$.

Verify each of the following:

18. $\sin(90° - A) = \cos A$ **19.** $\cos(90° + A) = -\sin A$ **20.** $\cos(180° - A) = -\cos A$

21. $\sin(180° - A) = \sin A$ **22.** $\tan(45° + A) = \dfrac{1 + \tan A}{1 - \tan A}$ **23.** $\sin\left(\dfrac{\pi}{2} + \alpha\right) - \sin\left(\dfrac{\pi}{2} - \alpha\right) = 0$

24. If $\cos 2A = \frac{1}{49}$, find the two values of $\cos A$ without using tables or calculator.

25. If $\cos 2A = \frac{12}{13}$, find the two possible values of $\tan A$.

26. A, B, C and D are acute angles such that $\tan A = \frac{1}{3}$, $\tan B = \frac{1}{5}$, $\tan C = \frac{1}{7}$ and $\tan D = \frac{1}{8}$.
     Evaluate   **(a)** $\tan(A + B)$ **(b)** $\tan(C + D)$.
     Hence, or otherwise, find the value of $\tan(A + B + C + D)$.
     Prove that $A + B + C + D = 45°$.

Prove each of the following:

27. $2\cos^2 A - \cos 2A - 1 = 0$ **28.** $\sin(A + B)\sin(A - B) = \cos^2 B + \sin^2 A - 1$

29. $\dfrac{\sin 2A}{1 + \cos 2A} = \tan A$ **30.** $\dfrac{1 - \cos 2A}{1 + \cos 2A} = \tan^2 A$

31. $\cos 3A = 4\cos^3 A - 3\cos A$ **32.** $\tan 3\theta = \dfrac{3\tan\theta - \tan^3\theta}{1 - 3\tan^2\theta}$

33. Use the formula $\cos 2A = 2\cos^2 A - 1$, to write $\cos \dfrac{\pi}{8}$ in surd form.

Sum and Product Formulas

Changing products into sums and differences:

$$2\cos A \cos B = \cos(A + B) + \cos(A - B)$$
$$2\sin A \cos B = \sin(A + B) + \sin(A - B)$$
$$2\sin A \sin B = \cos(A - B) - \cos(A + B)$$
$$2\cos A \sin B = \sin(A + B) - \sin(A - B)$$

Changing sums and differences into products:

$$\cos A + \cos B = 2 \cos \frac{A+B}{2} \cos \frac{A-B}{2}$$

$$\cos A - \cos B = -2 \sin \frac{A+B}{2} \sin \frac{A-B}{2}$$

$$\sin A + \sin B = 2 \sin \frac{A+B}{2} \cos \frac{A-B}{2}$$

$$\sin A - \sin B = 2 \cos \frac{A+B}{2} \sin \frac{A-B}{2}$$

These are given on page 9 of the tables. The proof of these 8 formulas is **not** required.

Example ▼

(i) Express $\cos 3\theta \sin 5\theta$ as a sum or difference of two trigonometric functions.
(ii) Express $\sin 6\theta + \sin 4\theta$ as the product of two trigonometric functions.

Solution:

(i) $\sin 5\theta \cos 3\theta$ (larger angle first)

$A = 5\theta \qquad B = 3\theta$

$\sin A \cos B = \frac{1}{2}[\sin(A+B) + \sin(A-B)]$

$\therefore \ \sin 5\theta \cos 3\theta$

$= \frac{1}{2}[\sin(5\theta + 3\theta) + \sin(5\theta - 3\theta)]$

$= \frac{1}{2}[\sin 8\theta + \sin 2\theta]$

(ii) $\sin 6\theta + \sin 4\theta$

$A = 6\theta \qquad B = 4\theta$

$\sin A + \sin B = 2 \sin\left(\frac{A+B}{2}\right)\cos\left(\frac{A-B}{2}\right)$

$\therefore \ \sin 6\theta + \sin 4\theta$

$= 2 \sin\left(\frac{6\theta + 4\theta}{2}\right)\cos\left(\frac{6\theta - 4\theta}{2}\right)$

$= 2 \sin 5\theta \cos \theta$

Example ▼

(i) Find the exact value of $\sin 105° - \sin 15°$.

(ii) Prove that $\dfrac{\sin \theta - \sin 2\theta + \sin 3\theta}{\cos \theta - \cos 2\theta + \cos 3\theta} = \tan 2\theta$.

Solution:

(i)

$$\sin 105° - \sin 15°$$

$$= 2 \cos\left(\frac{105° + 15°}{2}\right) \sin\left(\frac{105° - 15°}{2}\right) \qquad \left[\,A = 105°, \quad B = 15°\,\right]$$

$$\left[\sin A - \sin B = 2 \cos\left(\frac{A+B}{2}\right)\sin\left(\frac{A-B}{2}\right)\right]$$

$$= 2 \cos 60° \sin 45°$$

$$= 2 \times \frac{1}{2} \times \frac{1}{\sqrt{2}} \qquad \left[\cos 60° = \frac{1}{2}, \quad \sin 45° = \frac{1}{\sqrt{2}}\right]$$

$$= \frac{1}{\sqrt{2}}$$

(ii)

$$\frac{\sin \theta - \sin 2\theta + \sin 3\theta}{\cos \theta - \cos 2\theta + \cos 3\theta}$$

$$= \frac{\sin 3\theta + \sin \theta - \sin 2\theta}{\cos 3\theta + \cos \theta - \cos 2\theta}$$

$\left[\begin{array}{l}\text{linking the odd angles on top and bottom}\\\text{(or even angles if given) and putting the}\\\text{larger angle first in both cases}\end{array}\right]$

$$= \frac{2 \sin\left(\dfrac{3\theta + \theta}{2}\right)\cos\left(\dfrac{3\theta - \theta}{2}\right) - \sin 2\theta}{2 \cos\left(\dfrac{3\theta + \theta}{2}\right)\cos\left(\dfrac{3\theta - \theta}{2}\right) - \cos 2\theta}$$

$\left[\begin{array}{l}\text{using}\\[4pt]\sin A + \sin B = 2 \sin\left(\dfrac{A+B}{2}\right)\cos\left(\dfrac{A-B}{2}\right)\\[4pt]\text{on the top and}\\[4pt]\cos A + \cos B = 2 \cos\left(\dfrac{A+B}{2}\right)\cos\left(\dfrac{A-B}{2}\right)\\[4pt]\text{on the bottom}\end{array}\right]$

$$= \frac{2 \sin 2\theta \cos \theta - \sin 2\theta}{2 \cos 2\theta \cos \theta - \cos 2\theta}$$

$$= \frac{\sin 2\theta(2 \cos \theta - 1)}{\cos 2\theta(2 \cos \theta - 1)} \qquad \text{[factorising top and bottom]}$$

$$= \frac{\sin 2\theta}{\cos 2\theta} \qquad \text{[dividing top and bottom by } (2 \cos \theta - 1)]$$

$$= \tan 2\theta$$

Express each of the following as the product of two trigonometric functions:

1. $\sin 4\theta + \sin 2\theta$

2. $\cos 7\theta + \cos 5\theta$

3. $\cos 8\theta - \cos 2\theta$

4. $\sin 5\theta - \sin 3\theta$

5. $\cos 6\theta - \cos 2\theta$

6. $\cos \theta + \cos 7\theta$

7. $\sin \theta + \sin 3\theta$

8. $\cos \theta + \cos 5\theta$

9. $\sin 2\theta - \sin 8\theta$

Express each of the following as the sum or difference of two trigonometric functions:

10. $2 \sin 6\theta \cos 2\theta$

11. $2 \cos 3\theta \cos \theta$

12. $2 \cos 4\theta \cos \theta$

13. $2 \cos 6\theta \sin 3\theta$

14. $-2 \sin 4\theta \sin \theta$

15. $2 \cos 7\theta \sin 6\theta$

16. $\cos x \sin 5x$

17. $\sin 2A \sin A$

18. $\cos 3A \sin A$

Find the exact value of each of the following:

19. $\sin 75° - \sin 15°$

20. $\cos 105° - \cos 15°$

21. $\sin 255° - \sin 15°$

22. $2 \sin 75° \sin 105°$

23. $2 \cos 75° \cos 15°$

24. $\cos 37\frac{1}{2}° \sin 7\frac{1}{2}°$

Verify:

25. $\dfrac{\cos 80° - \cos 40°}{\sin 80° - \sin 40°} = -\sqrt{3}$

26. $\dfrac{\sin(120° + A) + \sin A}{\cos(60° - A) + \cos A} = \dfrac{1}{\sqrt{3}}$

Prove each of the following identities:

27. $\sin 3\theta + \sin \theta = 4 \sin \theta \cos^2 \theta$

28. $\cos 3\theta + \cos \theta = 4 \cos^3 \theta - 2 \cos \theta$

29. $\dfrac{\cos 5A + \cos 3A}{\sin 5A - \sin 3A} = \cot A$

30. $\dfrac{\cos 5A - \cos 3A}{\sin 3A - \sin A} = -2 \sin 2A$

31. $2 \cos\left(\dfrac{\pi}{4} + \theta\right)\cos\left(\dfrac{\pi}{4} - \theta\right) = \cos 2\theta$

32. $\dfrac{\cos 2\theta \cos \theta - \sin 4\theta \sin 3\theta}{\sin 8\theta \cos \theta - \sin 6\theta \cos 3\theta} = \cot 2\theta$

Trigonometric Equations I

Between 0° and 360° there may be two angles with the same trigonometric ratio.

For example, $\cos 120° = -\frac{1}{2}$ and $\cos 240° = -\frac{1}{2}$.

To solve a trigonometric equation do the following:

1. Ignore the sign and calculate the related angle.

2. From the sign of the given ratio, decide in which quadrants the angles lie.

3. Using a rough diagram, state the angles between 0° and 360°.

If $\sin \theta = k$, then, $-1 \leqslant k \leqslant 1$ min. value $= -1$, max. value $= 1$
If $\cos \theta = k$, then, $-1 \leqslant k \leqslant 1$ min. value $= -1$, max. value $= 1$
If $\tan \theta = k$, then, $k \in \mathbf{R}.$ any value, $-\infty$ to ∞

Example ▼

(i) Solve $\cos \theta = -\dfrac{1}{\sqrt{2}},$ $0 < \theta < 2\pi.$

(ii) Solve $\sin \theta = \dfrac{\sqrt{3}}{2},$ $0 < \theta < 2\pi.$

(iii) Solve $\sin^2 \theta = \frac{1}{2},$ $0 \leqslant \theta \leqslant 360°.$

Solution:

(i) $\cos \theta = -\dfrac{1}{\sqrt{2}}$

related angle (ignore sign) $= 45°$ or $\dfrac{\pi}{4}$

cos is negative in the 2nd and 3rd quadrants.

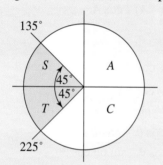

Thus, if $\cos \theta = -\dfrac{1}{\sqrt{2}},$ $0 < \theta < 2\pi,$

$\theta = 135°, 225°$ or $\theta = \dfrac{3\pi}{4}, \dfrac{5\pi}{4}$

(ii) $\sin \theta = \dfrac{\sqrt{3}}{2}$

related angle $= 60°$ or $\dfrac{\pi}{3}$

sin is positive in the 1st and 2nd quadrants.

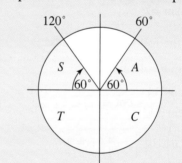

Thus, if $\sin \theta = \dfrac{\sqrt{3}}{2},$ $0 < \theta < 2\pi,$

$\theta = 60°, 120°$ or $\theta = \dfrac{\pi}{3}, \dfrac{2\pi}{3}$

(iii) $\sin^2 \theta = \frac{1}{2},$ $0 \leqslant \theta \leqslant 360°$

$\sin \theta = \pm \dfrac{1}{\sqrt{2}},$ related angle, $\theta = 45°$

$\theta = 45°, 135°, 225°, 315°$

or $\theta = \dfrac{\pi}{4}, \dfrac{3\pi}{4}, \dfrac{5\pi}{4}, \dfrac{7\pi}{4}$

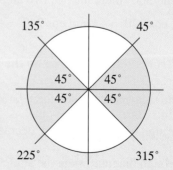

Solve $\sin\left(x + \dfrac{\pi}{6}\right) = -\dfrac{\sqrt{3}}{2}$, $0 \leqslant x \leqslant 2\pi$.

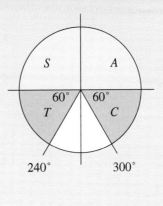

Solution:

$\sin\left(x + \dfrac{\pi}{6}\right) = -\dfrac{\sqrt{3}}{2}$, $0 \leqslant x \leqslant 2\pi$

let $\left(x + \dfrac{\pi}{6}\right) = \theta$

$\sin\theta = -\dfrac{\sqrt{3}}{2}$

    related angle, $\theta = 60°$

$\sin$ is negative in the 3rd and 4th quadrants, thus $\theta = 240°$ or $300°$.

Thus, $x + \dfrac{\pi}{6} = 240°$ or $x + \dfrac{\pi}{6} = 300°$

        $x + 30° = 240°$ $x + 30° = 300°$

            $x = 210°$ $x = 270°$

or $x = \dfrac{7\pi}{6}$ or $x = \dfrac{3\pi}{2}$

We may have to solve equations involving multiple and sub-multiple angles.

Solve $\cos 3A = \frac{1}{2}$, $0 \leqslant A \leqslant 360°$

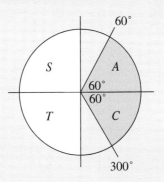

Solution:

$\cos 3A = \frac{1}{2}$
related angle $= 60°$
cos is positive in the 1st and 4th quadrants.
Given: $0 \leqslant A \leqslant 360°$
∴ $0 \leqslant 3A \leqslant 1080°$ (multiply each part by 3)

Thus, we need to go as far as $A + 1080°$

∴ $3A = 60°, 60° + 360°, 60° + 720°,$ or $3A = 300°, 300° + 360°, 300° + 720°,$
        $60° + 1080°$ $300° + 1080°$

    $3A = 60°, 420°, 780°, 1140°$ or $3A = 300°, 660°, 1020°, 1380°$

    $A = 20°, 140°, 260°, 380°$ or $A = 100°, 220°, 340°, 460°$

But we are given $0 \leqslant A \leqslant 360°$
Thus, $A = 20°, 100°, 140°, 220°, 260°, 340°$.

Solve each of the following equations for $0 \leqslant \theta \leqslant 360°$.

1. $\tan \theta = 1$

2. $\cos \theta = \frac{1}{2}$

3. $\sin \theta = \frac{1}{\sqrt{2}}$

4. $\sin \theta = \frac{\sqrt{3}}{2}$

5. $\cos \theta = -\frac{1}{\sqrt{2}}$

6. $\sin \theta = -\frac{\sqrt{3}}{2}$

7. $\tan \theta = \sqrt{3}$

8. $\sin \theta = 0$

9. $\cos \theta = -1$

10. $\operatorname{cosec} \theta = -2$

11. $\cot \theta = -1$

12. $\sec \theta = -\frac{2}{\sqrt{3}}$

13. $\tan^2 \theta = \frac{1}{3}$

14. $4 \cos^2 \theta = 1$

15. $2 \sin^2 \theta - 1 = 0$

16. $\tan 3\theta = 1$

17. $\sin 2\theta = \frac{1}{2}$

18. $\cos \frac{\theta}{2} = -\frac{\sqrt{3}}{2}$

19. $\sin(\theta + 60°) = \frac{1}{2}$

20. $\cos(\theta - 45°) = \frac{\sqrt{3}}{2}$

21. $\tan(\theta + 30°) = -\sqrt{3}$

22. $\sin(2\theta + 30°) = \frac{1}{2}$

23. $\cos(3\theta + 15°) = \frac{1}{2}$

24. $\tan\left(\frac{\theta}{2} + 60°\right) = -\frac{1}{\sqrt{3}}$

In questions 25–27, give your answers correct to one place of decimals:

25. $100 \sin \theta = 43$

26. $4 \tan \theta = 5$

27. $3 \cos \theta = -1$

Trigonometric Equations 2

More complicated trigonometric equations can usually be reduced to one or more simple trigonometric equations by factorising or rearranging.

Example ▼

Solve $\cos 2A + 3 \sin A - 2 = 0$, $0 \leqslant A \leqslant 360°$.

Solution:

$$\cos 2A + 3 \sin A - 2 = 0$$

$$\downarrow$$

$$(1 - 2 \sin^2 A) + 3 \sin A - 2 = 0 \qquad [\cos 2A = 1 - 2 \sin^2 A]$$

$$-2 \sin^2 A + 3 \sin A - 1 = 0$$

$$2 \sin^2 A - 3 \sin A + 1 = 0$$

$$(2 \sin A - 1)(\sin A - 1) = 0 \qquad [\text{factorise}]$$

$$2 \sin A - 1 = 0 \qquad \text{or} \qquad \sin A - 1 = 0$$

$$\sin A = \frac{1}{2} \qquad \text{or} \qquad \sin A = 1$$

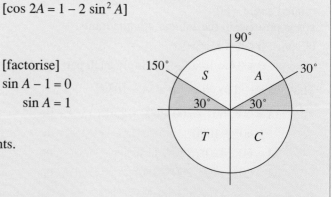

$\sin A = \frac{1}{2}$, related angle $= 30°$
$\sin$ is positive in the 1st and 2nd quadrants.
Thus $A = 30°$ or $150°$.
$\quad \sin A = 1$
$\quad\quad A = 90°$
Thus, $A = 30°, 90°, 150°$

Example ▼

Solve $\sqrt{2} \sin \theta \cos \theta + \cos \theta = 0$, $0 \leqslant \theta \leqslant 360°$.

Solution:

$$\sqrt{2} \sin \theta \cos \theta + \cos \theta = 0$$
$$\cos \theta(\sqrt{2} \sin \theta + 1) = 0 \qquad \text{[take out common factor } \cos \theta]$$
$$\cos \theta = 0 \quad \text{or} \quad \sqrt{2} \sin A + 1 = 0$$
$$\cos \theta = 0 \quad \text{or} \quad \sin A = -\frac{1}{\sqrt{2}}$$
$$\cos \theta = 0$$
$$\theta = 90°, 270°$$

$\sin A = -\dfrac{1}{\sqrt{2}}$, related angle = 45°.

sin is negative in the 3rd and 4th quadrants.

$\quad A = 225°$ or $315°$

Thus, $A = 90°, 225°, 270°, 315°$.

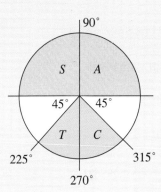

Example ▼

Solve $\sin 5\theta + \sin 3\theta = 0$, $0 \leqslant \theta \leqslant 180°$.

Solution:

$$\sin 5\theta + \sin 3\theta = 0$$
$$2 \sin\left(\frac{5\theta + 3\theta}{2}\right)\cos\left(\frac{5\theta - 3\theta}{2}\right) = 0 \qquad \left[\sin A + \sin B = 2 \sin\left(\frac{A+B}{2}\right)\cos\left(\frac{A-B}{2}\right)\right]$$
$$2 \sin 4\theta \cos \theta = 0$$
$$\sin 4\theta \cos \theta = 0$$

$\sin 4\theta = 0$ or $\cos \theta = 0$

$\quad 4\theta = 0°, 180°, 360°, 540°, 720°$ or $\theta = 90°$

$\quad \theta = 0°, 45°, 90°, 135°, 180°$ or $\theta = 90°$

Thus, $\theta = 0°, 45°, 90°, 135°, 180°$.

Note: As we are given $0 \leqslant \theta \leqslant 180°$, then $0 \leqslant 4\theta \leqslant 720°$.
Thus, we need to go as far as 720° for $\sin 4\theta = 0$.

Exercise 8.4 ▼

Solve each of the following equations for $0 \leqslant \theta \leqslant 360°$:

1. $(2 \cos \theta - 1)(\cos \theta + 1) = 0$

2. $\sin \theta(2 \sin \theta - 1) = 0$

3. $\tan^2 \theta + \tan \theta = 0$

4. $2 \cos^2 \theta - \cos \theta = 0$

5. $2 \sin^2 \theta - \sin \theta - 1 = 0$

6. $\sqrt{3} \sin \theta = 2 \cos^2 \theta - 2$

7. $3 - 3 \cos \theta = 2 \sin^2 \theta$

8. $\sqrt{2} \sin A \cos A - \cos A = 0$

9. $\cos 2\theta + \sin \theta = 0$

10. $\sin 2\theta + \sin \theta = 0$

11. $\cos 4\theta = \cos 2\theta$

12. $\cos 2\theta = 1 - 2 \sin \theta$

13. $\sin^2 \theta + 3 \cos^2 \theta - 2 = 0$

14. $4 \cos^3 \theta - \cos \theta = 0$

15. $\tan^2 \theta = 1 + \sec \theta$

16. $2 \sin \theta + 1 = \mathrm{cosec}\ \theta$

17. Show that $\sin(\theta + 30°) = \frac{1}{2}(\sqrt{3} \sin \theta + \cos \theta)$.
Hence, solve $\sin(\theta + 30°) = 2 \cos \theta$, $0 \leqslant \theta \leqslant 2\pi$.

18. Show that $\sin 3\theta + \sin \theta = 2 \sin 2\theta \cos \theta$.
Hence, show that $\sin 3\theta + \sin \theta + \sin 2\theta = \sin 2\theta(2 \cos \theta + 1)$
Hence, solve $\sin 3\theta + \sin \theta + \sin 2\theta = 0$, $0 < \theta < 180°$.

19. Prove that $\sin 2A = \dfrac{2 \tan A}{1 + \tan^2 A}$ and hence solve $\sin 2A - \tan A = 0$, $0 \leqslant A \leqslant 180°$.

20. Show that $\sin 5x - \sin x = 2 \cos 3x \sin 2x$.
Hence, solve $\sin 5x - \sin x + \sqrt{3} \cos 3x = 0$, $\pi \leqslant x \leqslant 2\pi$.

21. Prove that $\cos 3A = 4 \cos^3 A - 3 \cos A$, and hence solve $\cos 3A + 2 \cos A = 0$, $0 \leqslant A \leqslant 180°$.

22. $x = 0°$ and $x = 60°$ are two solutions of the equation $a \sin^2 x + b \cos x - 3 = 0$, where $a, b \in \mathbf{N}$.
Find the value of a and the value of b.
Using these values of a and b, find all the solutions of the equation where $0° \leqslant x \leqslant 360°$.

23. Solve $\dfrac{1}{\sqrt{3}} \sin x - \cos \dfrac{x}{2} = 0$, $0 \leqslant x \leqslant 2\pi$.

Inverse Trigonometric Functions

We now consider the reverse process of determining an angle given the value of one of the trigonometric ratios.

Consider the right-angled triangle on the right.

Ratio	Angle
$\sin \theta = \dfrac{\sqrt{3}}{2}$	$\theta = \sin^{-1} \dfrac{\sqrt{3}}{2}$
$\cos \theta = \dfrac{1}{2}$	$\theta = \cos^{-1} \dfrac{1}{2}$
$\tan \theta = \sqrt{3}$	$\theta = \tan^{-1} \sqrt{3}$

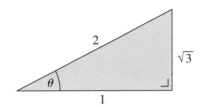

However, a problem arises with the $\sin^{-1} x$, $\cos^{-1} x$ and $\tan^{-1} x$ notation.
Consider the following equations:

If $\sin \theta = \frac{1}{2}$, then $\theta = \sin^{-1} \frac{1}{2} = \dots, -330°, -210°, 30°, 150°, 390°, 510°, \dots$

If $\tan \theta = 1$, then $\theta = \tan^{-1} 1 = \dots, -315°, -135°, 45°, 315°, 405°, 675°, \dots$

From this we can see that if there is no restriction on the value of θ, then the equations $\sin \theta = \frac{1}{2}$ and $\tan \theta = 1$ have an infinite number of solutions.

To overcome this problem, the value of θ is restricted to the range $-90° \leqslant \theta \leqslant 90°$ or $-\dfrac{\pi}{2} \leqslant \theta \leqslant \dfrac{\pi}{2}$.

The angles within this range are often called the '**principal values**'.
Using these restrictions for θ we always obtain a single value for our answer.

Thus, $\sin^{-1} \dfrac{\sqrt{3}}{2} = 60°$, not also $120°$, as $120°$ in not in the range $-90°$ to $90°$.

Note: $\sin^{-1} x$ is pronounced '**inverse sine x**' or '**sine inverse x**' or '**arc sine x**'.

Domain and range of the 'inverse trigonometric functions':

$\sin^{-1} x$:	Domain = $[-1, 1]$,	Range = $\left[-\dfrac{\pi}{2}, \dfrac{\pi}{2} \right]$
$\tan^{-1} x$:	Domain = $[-\infty, \infty]$,	Range = $\left[-\dfrac{\pi}{2}, \dfrac{\pi}{2} \right]$
$\cos^{-1} x$:	Domain = $[-1, 1]$,	Range = $[0, \pi]$

If $f(x) = \sin^{-1} x$, copy and complete the table below giving $\sin^{-1} x$ in terms of π.

x	-1	$-\dfrac{\sqrt{3}}{2}$	$-\dfrac{1}{2}$	0	$\dfrac{1}{2}$	$\dfrac{\sqrt{3}}{2}$	1
$\sin^{-1} x$		$-\dfrac{\pi}{3}$		0			

Draw the graph of this function in the domain $[-1, 1]$.

Solution:

Completed table.

x	-1	$-\dfrac{\sqrt{3}}{2}$	$-\dfrac{1}{2}$	0	$\dfrac{1}{2}$	$\dfrac{\sqrt{3}}{2}$	1
$\sin^{-1} x$	$-\dfrac{\pi}{2}$	$-\dfrac{\pi}{3}$	$-\dfrac{\pi}{6}$	0	$\dfrac{\pi}{6}$	$\dfrac{\pi}{3}$	$\dfrac{\pi}{2}$

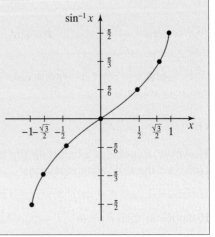

Evaluate: $\sin\left(\cos^{-1} \dfrac{8}{17} - \sin^{-1} \dfrac{12}{13}\right)$

Solution:

$\cos^{-1} \dfrac{8}{17}$ and $\sin^{-1} \dfrac{12}{13}$ are angles.

let $\quad A = \cos^{-1} \dfrac{8}{17}$

$\cos A = \dfrac{8}{17}$

$\sin A = \dfrac{15}{17}$

let $\quad B = \sin^{-1} \dfrac{12}{13}$

$\sin B = \dfrac{12}{13}$

$\cos B = \dfrac{5}{13}$

$\sin\left(\cos^{-1} \dfrac{8}{17} - \sin^{-1} \dfrac{12}{13}\right)$

$= \sin(A - B)$

$= \sin A \cos B - \cos A \sin B$ $\qquad \left(A = \cos^{-1} \dfrac{8}{17}, B = \sin^{-1} \dfrac{12}{13}\right)$

$= \dfrac{15}{16} \cdot \dfrac{5}{13} - \dfrac{8}{17} \cdot \dfrac{12}{13}$

$= \dfrac{75}{221} - \dfrac{96}{221} = -\dfrac{21}{221}$

Find the principal value of each of the following:

1. $\sin^{-1}\dfrac{1}{2}$

2. $\tan^{-1}1$

3. $\cos^{-1}\dfrac{1}{\sqrt{2}}$

4. $\sin^{-1}\left(-\dfrac{1}{\sqrt{2}}\right)$

5. $\tan^{-1}(-\sqrt{3})$

6. $\sin^{-1}0$

7. $\tan^{-1}(-1)$

8. $\sin^{-1}\left(-\dfrac{\sqrt{3}}{2}\right)$

9. $\tan^{-1}\left(-\dfrac{1}{\sqrt{3}}\right)$

10. $\sin^{-1}\left(-\dfrac{1}{2}\right)$

Drawing an appropriate right-angled triangle will help in the following problems.
Evaluate each of the following:

11. $\tan\left(\sin^{-1}\dfrac{3}{5}\right)$

12. $\cos\left(\sin^{-1}\dfrac{5}{13}\right)$

13. $\tan\left(\sin^{-1}\dfrac{\sqrt{3}}{2}\right)$

14. $\sin^{2}\left(\tan^{-1}\dfrac{3}{4}\right)$

15. $\tan^{2}\left(\sin^{-1}\dfrac{15}{17}\right)$

16. $\sin\left(2\cos^{-1}\dfrac{8}{17}\right)$

17. $\sin\left(\sin^{-1}\dfrac{5}{13}+\sin^{-1}\dfrac{4}{5}\right)$

18. $\tan\left(\sin^{-1}\dfrac{3}{5}+\sin^{-1}\dfrac{5}{13}\right)$

19. $\cos\left(\sin^{-1}\dfrac{3}{5}+\cos^{-1}\dfrac{12}{13}\right)$

20. $\sin\left(\sin^{-1}\dfrac{1}{\sqrt{5}}+\sin^{-1}\dfrac{1}{\sqrt{10}}\right)$

21. Prove that $\sin\left(\cos^{-1}\dfrac{7}{25}\right)=\sin\left(2\tan^{-1}\dfrac{3}{4}\right)$.

22. Prove that   **(i)** $\sin(\tan^{-1}x)=\dfrac{x}{\sqrt{1+x^{2}}}$ **(ii)** $\tan^{-1}(x)=\sin^{-1}\left(\dfrac{x}{\sqrt{1+x^{2}}}\right)$.

23. For $0\leqslant x\leqslant 1$, prove that $\sin^{-1}x+\cos^{-1}x=\dfrac{\pi}{2}$.

24. Make sure your calculator is in radian mode.
If $f(x)=\tan^{-1}x$, x in radians, draw the graph of f in the domain $-5\leqslant x\leqslant 5$.

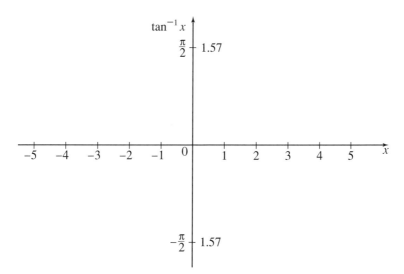

Limits of Trigonometry Functions

Let us consider the value of the expression $\dfrac{\sin \theta}{\theta}$ as θ approaches 0 (θ in radians).

θ (in radians)	$\sin \theta$	$\dfrac{\sin \theta}{\theta}$
1	0.8414709848	0.8414709848
0.5	0.4794255386	0.9588510772
0.1	0.0998334166	0.9983341665
0.01	0.0099998333	0.9999833334
0.001	0.0009999998	0.9999998333

As θ approaches 0, the expression $\dfrac{\sin \theta}{\theta}$ approaches 1.

This is written: $\quad \boxed{\lim\limits_{\theta \to 0} \dfrac{\sin \theta}{\theta} = 1}\quad$ (θ in radians)

The result can be extended to multiple and sub-multiple angles:

$$\lim\limits_{\theta \to 0} \frac{\sin k\theta}{k\theta} = 1 \quad \text{and} \quad \lim\limits_{\theta \to 0} \frac{k\theta}{\sin k\theta} = 1, \quad k \in \mathbf{R}$$

Similarly, where θ is in radians:

$$\lim\limits_{\theta \to 0} \frac{\tan k\theta}{k\theta} = 1 \quad \text{and} \quad \lim\limits_{\theta \to 0} \frac{k\theta}{\tan k\theta} = 1, \quad k \in \mathbf{R}$$

Note: $\lim\limits_{\theta \to 0} \cos \theta = 1.$

Evaluate: **(i)** $\lim_{\theta \to 0} \dfrac{\sin 4\theta + \sin 2\theta}{\theta}$ **(ii)** $\lim_{\theta \to 0} \dfrac{\tan 4\theta}{5\theta}$

Solution:

(i)

$$\dfrac{\sin 4\theta + \sin 2\theta}{\theta}$$

$$= \dfrac{\sin 4\theta}{\theta} + \dfrac{\sin 2\theta}{\theta}$$

$$= 4\left(\dfrac{\sin 4\theta}{4\theta}\right) + 2\left(\dfrac{\sin 2\theta}{2\theta}\right)$$

$$\therefore \lim_{\theta \to 0}\left(\dfrac{\sin 4\theta + \sin 2\theta}{\theta}\right)$$

$$= 4\left(\lim_{\theta \to 0}\left(\dfrac{\sin 4\theta}{4\theta}\right)\right) + 2\left(\lim_{\theta \to 0}\left(\dfrac{\sin 2\theta}{2\theta}\right)\right)$$

$$= 4(1) + 2(1)$$

$$= 4 + 2 = 6$$

(ii)

$$\dfrac{\tan 4\theta}{5\theta}$$

$$= \dfrac{\tan 4\theta}{\theta} \cdot \dfrac{1}{5}$$

$$= \dfrac{\tan 4\theta}{4\theta} \cdot \dfrac{4}{5}$$

$$\therefore \lim_{\theta \to 0} \dfrac{\tan 4\theta}{5\theta}$$

$$= \dfrac{4}{5}\left(\lim_{\theta \to 0} \dfrac{\tan 4\theta}{4\theta}\right)$$

$$= \tfrac{4}{5}(1)$$

$$= \tfrac{4}{5}$$

Sometimes we have to change sums and differences of trigonometric functions to products (using page 9 of the tables).

Evaluate: $\lim_{x \to 0} \dfrac{\cos 5x - \cos 3x}{\cos 4x - \cos 2x}$

Solution:

$$\dfrac{\cos 5x - \cos 3x}{\cos 4x - \cos 2x}$$

$$= \dfrac{-2 \sin\left(\dfrac{5x + 3x}{2}\right)\sin\left(\dfrac{5x - 3x}{2}\right)}{-2 \sin\left(\dfrac{4x + 2x}{2}\right)\sin\left(\dfrac{4x - 2x}{2}\right)}$$

$$= \dfrac{-2 \sin 4x \sin x}{-2 \sin 3x \sin x}$$

$$= \dfrac{\sin 4x}{\sin 3x}$$

$$= \dfrac{\sin 4x}{1} \cdot \dfrac{1}{\sin 3x}$$

$$= \dfrac{\sin 4x}{4x} \cdot \dfrac{3x}{\sin 3x} \cdot \dfrac{4}{3}$$

From page 9 of the tables:

$$\cos A - \cos B = -2 \sin\left(\dfrac{A + B}{2}\right)\sin\left(\dfrac{A - B}{2}\right)$$

$$\therefore \lim_{x \to 0} \dfrac{\cos 5x - \cos 3x}{\cos 4x - \cos 2x}$$

$$= \lim_{x \to 0} \dfrac{\sin 4x}{4x} \cdot \dfrac{3x}{\sin 4x} \cdot \dfrac{4}{3}$$

$$= (1)(1)(\tfrac{4}{3})$$

$$= \tfrac{4}{3}$$

Evaluate each of the following limits:

1. $\lim\limits_{x \to 0} \dfrac{\sin 3x}{x}$

2. $\lim\limits_{x \to 0} \dfrac{\sin 5x}{x}$

3. $\lim\limits_{x \to 0} \dfrac{x}{\sin 2x}$

4. $\lim\limits_{x \to 0} \dfrac{x}{\sin 4x}$

5. $\lim\limits_{x \to 0} \dfrac{\sin 3x}{4x}$

6. $\lim\limits_{x \to 0} \dfrac{\sin 3x}{\sin 2x}$

7. $\lim\limits_{x \to 0} \dfrac{\tan 8x}{x}$

8. $\lim\limits_{x \to 0} \dfrac{\tan 6x}{2x}$

9. $\lim\limits_{x \to 0} \dfrac{\sin^2 x}{2x^2}$

10. $\lim\limits_{x \to 0} \dfrac{\sin^2 x}{3x^2}$

11. $\lim\limits_{x \to 0} \dfrac{\sin x \tan x}{x^2}$

12. $\lim\limits_{x \to 0} \dfrac{\tan^2 2x}{3x^2}$

13. $\lim\limits_{x \to 0} \dfrac{\sin 4x + \sin 2x}{x}$

14. $\lim\limits_{x \to 0} \dfrac{\sin 8x - \sin 2x}{x}$

15. $\lim\limits_{x \to 0} \dfrac{\cos 4x - \cos 2x}{\cos 5x - \cos 3x}$

16. $\lim\limits_{x \to 0} \dfrac{x \sin x}{\sin 3x + \sin x}$

17. $\lim\limits_{x \to 0} \dfrac{\sin 3x \tan 2x}{x^2}$

18. $\lim\limits_{x \to 0} \dfrac{4x}{\sin 4x + \sin 2x}$

19. $\lim\limits_{x \to 0} \dfrac{\sin x^2}{x \tan x}$

20. $\lim\limits_{x \to 0} \dfrac{x \sin 2x}{2 - 2 \cos^2 x}$

21. $\lim\limits_{x \to 0} \dfrac{x \sin x}{1 - \cos x}$

22. Prove that $\cos 2x = 1 - 2 \sin^2 x$.

Hence, show that $\lim\limits_{x \to 0} \dfrac{2x^2}{1 - \cos x} = 4$.

PERIODIC FUNCTIONS

Periodic Functions

A function whose graph repeats itself at regular intervals is called '**periodic**'.
For example, the graph below is a graph of a periodic function, $y = f(x)$.

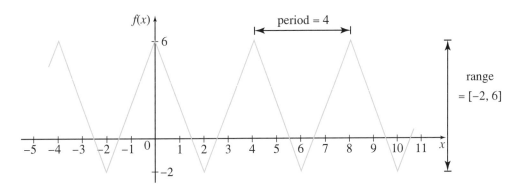

The '**period**' is the horizontal width it takes for a graph to repeat itself.
In this case the period = 4 (graph repeats itself after a distance of 4).
The '**range**' is the interval from the least value of y to the greatest value of y.
In this case the range = $[-2, 6]$ (lower value is written first).

Note:

> A function f is said to be periodic if $f(x + h) = f(x)$ for all values of x.
> If h is the smallest value for which $f(x + h) = f(x)$, then $f(x)$ has period h.

A feature of the graphs of periodic functions is that we can add, or subtract, the period, or integer multiples of the period, to the value of x and the value of the function is unchanged.
For example, using the graph above;

$f(-4) = f(0) = f(4) = f(8) = 6$ $[f(-4) = f(-4 + 4) = f(-4 + 8) = f(-4 + 12)\ldots]$

$f(10) = f(6) = f(2) = f(-2) = -2$ $[f(10) = f(10 - 4) = f(10 - 8) = f(10 - 12)\ldots]$

For the above graph $f(x \pm 4) = f(x)$, as 4 is the period.
On our course we will be given the graph of the periodic function on scaled and labelled axes.
The period will be a positive whole number and the range will be a closed interval $[a, b]$, where a and b are whole numbers, positive or negative.

Part of the graph of the periodic function $y = f(x)$ is shown below.
State the period and range of the function.

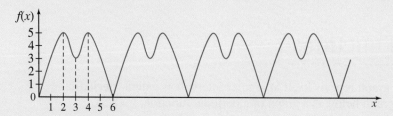

Evaluate $f(2), f(3), f(27)$ and $f(28)$.

Solution:

Basic building block	Basic building block
period = 6	

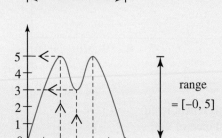

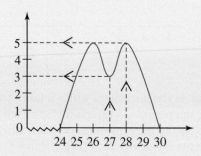

The period = 6

The range = $[0, 5]$

$f(2) = 5$ and $f(8) = 3$

$f(27) = 3$ and $f(28) = 5$

Alternatively, by repeatedly subtracting the period 6,

$f(27) = f(21) = f(15) = f(9) = f(3) = 3$

$f(28) = f(22) = f(16) = f(10) = f(4) = 5$

Exercise 9.1 ▼

1. Shown opposite is part of the graph of the periodic function $y = f(x)$. State its period and range.

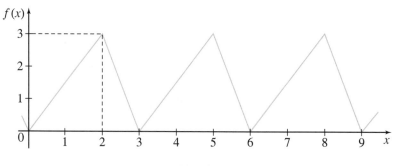

Evaluate:

(i) $f(5)$ **(ii)** $f(6)$ **(iii)** $f(17)$ **(iv)** $f(62)$ **(v)** $f(90)$

2. The graph below shows a portion of the graph of the periodic function $y = f(x)$.

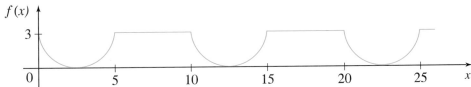

(i) Write down the period and range of $f(x)$.

(ii) Write down the value of **(a)** $f(5)$ **(b)** $f(12.5)$ **(c)** $f(77.5)$ **(d)** $f(-7.5)$.

3. The graph shows a portion of a periodic function $y = f(x)$, $x \in \mathbf{R}$.

(i) Write down the period and the range of $f(x)$.

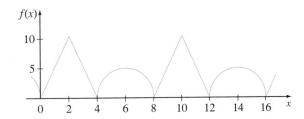

(ii) Complete the following table:

x	2	8	14	20	26	-6	-16	-34
$f(x)$								

4. The diagram shows part of the graph of the periodic function $y = f(x)$ in the domain $0 \leqslant x \leqslant 6k$, $k \in \mathbf{R}$. The period of $f(x)$ is 6 and its range is $[-2, 3]$. Write down the value of k, a and b.

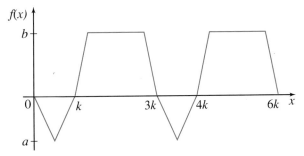

On separate diagrams draw sketches of $f(x)$ in the domain   **(i)** $-3k \leqslant x \leqslant k$ **(ii)** $13k \leqslant x \leqslant 19k$. Complete the following table:

x	1	4	6	7	-2	-10	-12	-16
$f(x)$								

If $f(k) = -2$, write down three values of k, $k \neq 1, 7$.

5. The diagrams below show portions of the periodic functions $f(\theta) = \sin \theta°$ and $g(\theta) = \cos \theta°$.

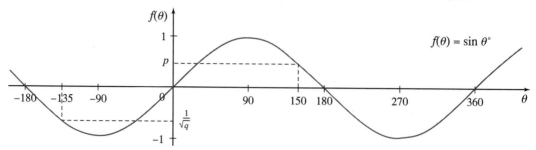

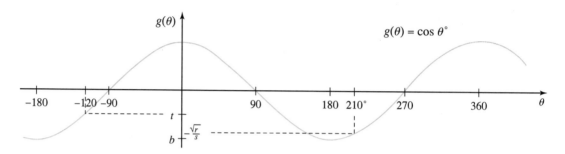

(i) If $\sin(\theta° + h°) = \sin \theta°$, write down the minimum value of h, $h \neq 0$.

(ii) Write down the range of $\cos \theta$.

(iii) Write down the values of p, q, r, s and t.

(iv) Write down the value of:

    (a) $f(720)$ **(b)** $g(300)$ **(c)** $f(-225)$ **(d)** $g(-150)$ **(e)** $f(765)$.

10

LIMITS OF FUNCTIONS

Limits of Functions

The phrase 'x tends to zero', written '$x \to 0$', means that x can be made as small as we please without actually reaching 0.

The phrase 'x tends to 4', written '$x \to 4$', means that x can be made as close to 4 as we please without actually reaching 4.

Definition of a Limit

$$\lim_{x \to a} f(x) = L$$

means that $f(x)$ approaches the number L as x approaches a.

Note: 'lim' is the abbreviation for limit.

Example ▼

Evaluate   (i) $\lim\limits_{x \to 3} \dfrac{x+5}{x-1}$ (ii) $\lim\limits_{x \to 1} \dfrac{3x-4}{x+1}$

Solution:

(i) $\lim\limits_{x \to 3} \dfrac{x+5}{x-1}$

$= \dfrac{3+5}{3-1}$ (put in 3 for x)

$= \dfrac{8}{2} = 4$

(ii) $\lim\limits_{x \to 1} \dfrac{3x-4}{x+1}$

$= \dfrac{3-4}{1+1}$ (put in 1 for x)

$= \dfrac{-1}{2} = -\dfrac{1}{2}$

However, it often happens that when we try to evaluate a function for a particular value we end up with one of the following:

$$\frac{0}{0} \quad \text{or} \quad \frac{\infty}{\infty}$$

These are called '**indeterminate forms**' because we cannot determine the limit directly.

In other words the expressions $\dfrac{0}{0}$ or $\dfrac{\infty}{\infty}$ are undefined.

When this happens, do the following:

> 1. Factorise the top and bottom.
> 2. Divide top and bottom by common factors.
> 3. Try to evaluate the limit again.

Example ▼

Evaluate:

(i) $\displaystyle\lim_{x \to 5} \frac{x^2 - 25}{x - 5}$ (ii) $\displaystyle\lim_{x \to 2} \frac{x^3 - 8}{x^2 - 4}$

Solution:

(i) $\displaystyle\lim_{x \to 5} \frac{x^2 - 25}{x - 5} = \frac{0}{0}$ (indeterminate)

Thus, factorise top and bottom, simplify and try again.

$$\lim_{x \to 5} \frac{x^2 - 25}{x - 5}$$

$$= \lim_{x \to 5} \frac{(x - 5)(x + 5)}{(x - 5)}$$

$$= \lim_{x \to 5} (x + 5) = (5 + 5) = 10$$

(ii) $\displaystyle\lim_{x \to 2} \frac{x^3 - 8}{x^2 - 4} = \frac{0}{0}$ (indeterminate)

Thus, factorise top and bottom, simplify and try again.

$$\lim_{x \to 2} \frac{x^3 - 8}{x^2 - 4}$$

$$= \lim_{x \to 2} \frac{(x - 2)(x^2 + 2x + 4)}{(x - 2)(x + 2)}$$

$$= \lim_{x \to 2} \frac{x^2 + 2x + 4}{x + 2}$$

$$= \frac{4 + 4 + 4}{4} = \frac{12}{4} = 3$$

In some cases we have to evaluate limits that contain surds and are initially indeterminate. In these cases we multiply the top and bottom by the conjugate surd and then divide the top and bottom by the common factor.

Note: Multiply the surd part and its conjugate and simplify. However, do not multiply out the surd and non-surd parts, as this will stop you from finding the common factor.

Evaluate: $\lim_{x \to 3} \dfrac{x-3}{1-\sqrt{4-x}}$

Solution:

$\lim_{x \to 3} \dfrac{x-3}{1-\sqrt{4-x}} = \dfrac{0}{0}$ [indeterminate]

What we do here is multiply top and bottom by $(1+\sqrt{4-x})$, the conjugate surd of $(1-\sqrt{4-x})$, simplify and try again.

Thus, $\lim_{x \to 3} \dfrac{x-3}{1-\sqrt{4-x}} = \lim_{x \to 3} \dfrac{(x-3)}{(1-\sqrt{4-x})} \cdot \dfrac{1+\sqrt{4-x}}{1+\sqrt{4-x}}$

$= \lim_{x \to 3} \dfrac{(x-3)(1+\sqrt{4-x})}{[1-(4-x)]} \longleftarrow$ $\left(\begin{array}{l}\text{Do not multiply out the surd} \\ \text{part and the non-surd part}\end{array}\right)$

$= \lim_{x \to 3} \dfrac{(x-3)(1+\sqrt{4-x})}{(x-3)}$ $\left(\begin{array}{l}\text{divide top and bottom by} \\ \text{the common factor } (x-3)\end{array}\right)$

$= \lim_{x \to 3} (1+\sqrt{4-x})$

$= 1+1 = 2$

The phrase 'x tends to infinity', written '$x \to \infty$', means that x can be made as large as we please. Let us consider the value of the expression $\dfrac{1}{x}$ as $x \to \infty$.

x	$\dfrac{1}{x}$
10	0.1
100	0.01
1000	0.001
1,000,000	0.000001
1,000,000,000	0.000000001

The table indicates that as

$x \to \infty, \quad \dfrac{1}{x} \to 0.$

This is written:

$$\lim_{x \to \infty} \dfrac{1}{x} = 0$$

This limit can be extended: $\qquad \lim_{x \to \infty} \dfrac{c}{x^n} = 0$, for $n > 0$, c a constant

To evaluate the limit, $\lim_{x \to \infty} \dfrac{f(x)}{g(x)}$ **do the following:**

Divide the top and bottom by the dominant term and use the limit above.

The dominant term is the largest term as $x \to$ infinity.
In this section the dominant term is the highest power of x.

129

Example ▼

Evaluate:

(i) $\lim_{x \to \infty} \dfrac{3x^2 - 2}{5x^2 + x}$ (ii) $\lim_{x \to \infty} \dfrac{5}{2 + x}$

Solution:

(i) $\lim_{x \to \infty} \dfrac{3x^2 - 2}{5x^2 + x}$

    $= \lim_{x \to \infty} \dfrac{3 - \dfrac{2}{x^2}}{5 + \dfrac{1}{x}}$

(divide top and bottom by x^2, the dominant term)

    $= \dfrac{3 - 0}{5 + 0} = \dfrac{3}{5}$

(ii) $\lim_{x \to \infty} \dfrac{5}{2 + x}$

    $= \lim_{x \to \infty} \dfrac{\dfrac{5}{x}}{\dfrac{2}{x} + 1}$

(divide top and bottom by x, the dominant term)

    $= \dfrac{0}{0 + 1} = \dfrac{0}{1} = 0$

Exercise 10.1 ▼

Evaluate each of the following limits:

1. $\lim_{x \to 0} (5x + 3)$

2. $\lim_{x \to 3} (2x^2 - 10)$

3. $\lim_{x \to 2} \dfrac{x^2 + 5x + 6}{x + 2}$

4. $\lim_{x \to 3} \dfrac{x^2 - 9}{x + 3}$

5. $\lim_{x \to 2} \dfrac{x^2 + x - 6}{x - 2}$

6. $\lim_{x \to 1} \dfrac{x - 1}{x^2 + x - 2}$

7. $\lim_{x \to 2} \dfrac{x^2 - 4}{x - 2}$

8. $\lim_{x \to 1} \dfrac{x^2 - 1}{x - 1}$

9. $\lim_{x \to 6} \dfrac{x^2 - 36}{x - 6}$

10. $\lim_{x \to 4} \dfrac{x - 4}{x^2 - 16}$

11. $\lim_{x \to 2} \dfrac{x^3 - 8}{x - 2}$

12. $\lim_{x \to 3} \dfrac{x - 3}{x^3 - 27}$

13. $\lim_{x \to 2} \dfrac{x^2 - 2x}{x - 2}$

14. $\lim_{x \to 4} \dfrac{x^3 - 64}{x^2 - 16}$

15. $\lim_{x \to 0} \dfrac{3x^2 + x}{x}$

16. $\lim_{x \to -2} \dfrac{x^2 - 4}{x + 2}$

17. $\lim_{x \to -1} \dfrac{x + 1}{x^2 - 1}$

18. $\lim_{x \to \frac{1}{2}} \dfrac{4x^2 - 1}{2x - 1}$

19. $\lim_{x \to 4} \dfrac{x - 4}{\sqrt{x} - 2}$

20. $\lim_{x \to 9} \dfrac{\sqrt{x} - 3}{x - 9}$

21. $\lim_{x \to 2} \dfrac{\sqrt{x + 7} - 3}{x - 2}$

22. $\lim_{x \to 2} \dfrac{x - 2}{\sqrt{x + 2} - 2}$

23. $\lim_{x \to 4} \dfrac{x - 4}{1 - \sqrt{x - 3}}$

24. $\lim_{x \to 0} \dfrac{1 - \sqrt{1 + x}}{x}$

25. $\lim_{x \to \infty} \dfrac{2x - 1}{x + 1}$

26. $\lim_{x \to \infty} \dfrac{4x + 3}{3x + 5}$

27. $\lim_{x \to \infty} \dfrac{1 + 2x}{3x - 4}$

28. $\lim_{x \to \infty} \dfrac{4x^2 - 3x}{5x^2 - 2}$

29. $\lim_{x \to \infty} \dfrac{3x^2 - 2x + 1}{2x^2 + 5x - 7}$

30. $\lim_{x \to \infty} \dfrac{x^2 + 1}{1 + 2x^3}$

DIFFERENTIAL CALCULUS I
DIFFERENTIATION FROM FIRST PRINCIPLES

Differentiation from First Principles

Differentiation, or differential calculus, is the branch of mathematics measuring rates of change.

Slope of a line

On the right is part of the graph of the line $y = 3x$. There is a relationship between x and y. For every increase in x there is three times this increase in y.

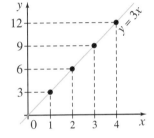

> Rate of change $y = 3$ times rate of change of x

From coordinate geometry the slope of the line $y = 3x$ is 3.

> Slope = 3

$\Rightarrow$ Rate of change = Slope

The key word here is **slope**. The slope of a line will give **the rate of change** of the variable on the vertical axis with respect to the variable on the horizontal. Therefore, to find the rate of change we need only to find the slope.
Note: The y-axis is usually the vertical axis and the x-axis is the horizontal axis.
Therefore, the slope of a line will give the rate of change of y with respect to (the change in) x.

Slope of a curve
Consider the curve below and the tangents that are constructed on it.

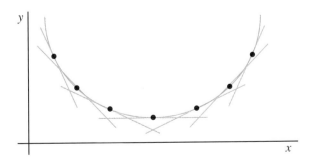

The slope of a curve at a point is equal to the slope of the tangent at that point. As we move along the curve, the slope of each tangent changes. In other words, the rate of change of y with respect to x changes. We need to find a method of finding the slope of the tangent at each point on the curve. The method of finding the slope of a tangent to a curve at any point on the curve is called **differentiation**.

Notation

We will now develop the method for finding the slope of the tangent to the curve $y = f(x)$ at any point $(x, f(x))$ on the curve.

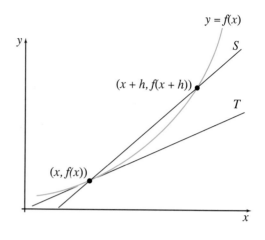

Let the graph shown represent the function $y = f(x)$.
$(x, f(x))$ is a point on this curve and $(x + h, f(x + h))$ is a point further along the curve.
S is a line through these points.
T is a tangent to the curve at the point $(x, f(x))$.

$$\text{Slope of } S = \frac{y_2 - y_1}{x_2 - x_1}$$

$$= \frac{f(x + h) - f(x)}{(x + h) - h}$$

$$= \frac{f(x + h) - f(x)}{h}$$

This would be a good approximation of the slope of the tangent T, at the point $(x, f(x))$, if $(x + h, f(x + h))$ is **very** close to $(x, f(x))$. By letting h get smaller, the point $(x + h, f(x + h))$ moves closer to $(x, f(x))$.

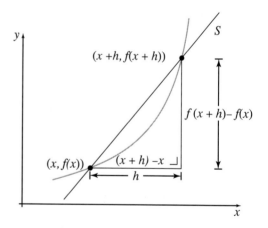

The result is that the slope of S gets closer to the slope of T. In other words, as h approaches 0, the slope of S approaches the slope of T.

Mathematically speaking, we say that the slope of T is equal to the limit of the slope of S as h approaches 0. It is important to realise that h approaches 0, but **never** actually becomes equal to zero.

This is usually written $\displaystyle\lim_{h \to 0} \frac{f(x + h) - f(x)}{h}$.

The process of finding this limiting value is called '**differentiation**'.

For neatness, this limit is written as $\dfrac{dy}{dx}$ (pronounced 'dee y, dee x')

or $f'(x)$, pronounced 'f dash of x' or 'f prime of x'.

$\dfrac{dy}{dx}$ or $f'(x)$ is called the:

'**differential coefficient**' or '**first derivative of y with respect to x**'.

Note: It is important to understand that $\dfrac{dy}{dx}$ does **not** mean $dy \div dx$.

It means the derivative of y with respect to x.

The $\dfrac{d}{dx}$ is an operator. $\dfrac{d}{dx}$ means 'the derivative with respect to x of'.

Thus, $\dfrac{dy}{dx}$ is often written $\dfrac{d}{dx}(y)$.

Definition

> The slope of the tangent to the curve $y = f(x)$ at any point on the curve is given by:
> $$\frac{dy}{dx} = f'(x) = \lim_{h \to 0} \frac{f(x+h) - f(x)}{h}$$

Differentiation from first principles involves four steps:

Find:

> 1. $f(x + h)$
> 2. $f(x + h) - f(x)$
> 3. $\dfrac{f(x+h) - f(x)}{h}$
> 4. $\lim\limits_{h \to 0} \dfrac{f(x+h) - f(x)}{h}$

There are six functions, x^2, x^3, $\sqrt{x}$, $\dfrac{1}{x}$, $\sin x$, $\cos x$, on our course that we can be asked to differentiate from first principles.

Example ▼

Differentiate from first principles with respect to x:

(i) x^2 **(ii)** x^3 **(iii)** $\sqrt{x}$ **(iv)** $\dfrac{1}{x}$ **(v)** $\sin x$ **(vi)** $\cos x$

Solution:

(i)
$$f(x) = x^2$$
$$f(x + h) = (x + h)^2$$
$$f(x + h) - f(x) = (x + h)^2 - x^2$$
$$= x^2 + 2xh + h^2 - x^2$$
$$= 2xh + h^2$$
$$\frac{f(x+h) - f(x)}{h} = 2x + h$$

$$\lim_{h \to 0} \frac{f(x+h) - f(x)}{h} = \lim_{h \to 0} 2x + h$$

$$= 2x$$

Thus, $f'(x) = 2x$

(ii)

$$f(x) = x^3$$

$$f(x+h) = (x+h)^3$$

$$f(x+h) - f(x) = (x+h)^3 - x^3$$

$$= x^3 + 3x^2h + 3xh^2 + h^3 - x^3$$

$$= 3x^2h + 3xh^2 + h^3$$

$$\frac{f(x+h) - f(x)}{h} = 3x^2 + 3xh + h^2$$

$$\lim_{h \to 0} \frac{f(x+h) - f(x)}{h} = \lim_{h \to 0} (3x^2 + 3xh + h^2)$$

$$= 3x^2$$

Thus, $f'(x) = 3x^2$

(iii)

$$f(x) = \sqrt{x}$$

$$f(x+h) = \sqrt{x+h}$$

$$f(x+h) - f(x) = \sqrt{x+h} - \sqrt{x}$$ $\left[\begin{array}{l}\text{multiply top and bottom by } \sqrt{x+h} + \sqrt{x}, \\ \text{the conjugate surd of } \sqrt{x+h} - \sqrt{x}\end{array}\right]$

$$= \frac{\sqrt{x+h} - \sqrt{x}}{1} \cdot \frac{\sqrt{x+h} + \sqrt{x}}{\sqrt{x+h} + \sqrt{x}}$$

$$= \frac{x+h-x}{\sqrt{x+h} + \sqrt{x}}$$

$$= \frac{h}{\sqrt{x+h} + \sqrt{x}}$$

$$\frac{f(x+h) - f(x)}{h} = \frac{1}{\sqrt{x+h} + \sqrt{x}}$$

$$\lim_{h \to 0} \frac{f(x+h) - f(x)}{h} = \lim_{h \to 0} \frac{1}{\sqrt{x+h} + \sqrt{x}}$$

$$= \frac{1}{\sqrt{x} + \sqrt{x}}$$

$$= \frac{1}{2\sqrt{x}}$$

Thus, $f'(x) = \frac{1}{2\sqrt{x}}$

(iv)
$$f(x) = \frac{1}{x}$$

$$f(x+h) = \frac{1}{x+h}$$

$$f(x+h) - f(x) = \frac{1}{x+h} - \frac{1}{x}$$

$$= \frac{x - (x+h)}{x(x+h)}$$

$$= \frac{-h}{x(x+h)}$$

$$\frac{f(x+h) - f(x)}{h} = \frac{-1}{x(x+h)}$$

$$\lim_{h \to 0} \frac{f(x+h) - f(x)}{h} = \lim_{h \to 0} \frac{-1}{x(x+h)}$$

$$= -\frac{1}{x^2}$$

Thus, $f'(x) = -\dfrac{1}{x^2}$

(v)
$$f(x) = \sin x$$

$$f(x+h) = \sin(x+h)$$

$$f(x+h) - f(x) = \sin(x+h) - \sin x$$

$$= 2 \cos\left(\frac{x+h+x}{2}\right)\sin\left(\frac{x+h-x}{2}\right) \qquad \text{[tables, page 9]}$$

$$= 2 \cos\left(\frac{2x+h}{2}\right)\sin\left(\frac{h}{2}\right)$$

$$\frac{f(x+h) - f(x)}{h} = 2 \cos\left(\frac{2x+h}{2}\right) \cdot \frac{\sin\left(\frac{h}{2}\right)}{h}$$

$$= \cos\left(\frac{2x+h}{2}\right) \cdot \frac{\sin\left(\frac{h}{2}\right)}{\frac{h}{2}} \qquad \begin{bmatrix} \text{divide top and} \\ \text{bottom by 2} \end{bmatrix}$$

$$\lim_{h \to 0} \frac{f(x+h) - f(x)}{h} = \lim_{h \to 0} \cos\left(\frac{2x+h}{2}\right) \cdot \frac{\sin\left(\frac{h}{2}\right)}{\frac{h}{2}}$$

$$= (\cos x)(1)$$

$$= \cos x$$

Thus, $f'(x) = \cos x$

(vi)

$$f(x) = \cos x$$

$$f(x + h) = \cos(x + h)$$

$$f(x + h) - f(x) = \cos(x + h) - \cos x$$

$$= -2 \sin\left(\frac{x + h + x}{2}\right)\sin\left(\frac{x + h - x}{2}\right) \quad \text{[tables, page 9]}$$

$$= -2 \sin\left(\frac{2x + h}{2}\right)\sin\left(\frac{h}{2}\right)$$

$$\frac{f(x + h) - f(x)}{h} = -2 \sin\left(\frac{2x + h}{2}\right) \cdot \frac{\sin\left(\frac{h}{2}\right)}{h}$$

$$= -\sin\left(\frac{2x + h}{2}\right) \cdot \frac{\sin\left(\frac{h}{2}\right)}{\dfrac{h}{2}} \qquad \left[\begin{array}{l}\text{divide top and} \\ \text{bottom by 2}\end{array}\right]$$

$$\lim_{h \to 0} \frac{f(x + h) - f(x)}{h} = \lim_{h \to 0} -\sin\left(\frac{2x + h}{2}\right) \cdot \frac{\left(\sin\frac{h}{2}\right)}{\dfrac{h}{2}}$$

$$= (-\sin x)(1)$$

$$= -\sin x$$

$$\text{Thus, } f'(x) = -\sin x$$

DIFFERENTIAL CALCULUS 2
DIFFERENTIATION BY RULE

Differentiation by Rule

Differentiation from first principles can become tedious and difficult. Fortunately, it is not always necessary to use first principles. There are a few rules (which can be derived from first principles) which enable us to write down the derivative of a function quite easily.

Rule 1: General Rule

If:

$$y = x^n \quad \text{then} \quad \frac{dy}{dx} = nx^{n-1}$$

$$y = ax^n \quad \text{then} \quad \frac{dy}{dx} = nax^{n-1}$$

In words:

Multiply by the power and reduce the power by 1.

Example ▼

Differentiate with respect to x:

(i) $y = x^5$ **(ii)** $y = -3x^2$ **(iii)** $y = 5x$ **(iv)** $y = \dfrac{8}{x^2}$

(v) $y = 6\sqrt{x}$ **(vi)** $y = \dfrac{2}{\sqrt{x}}$ **(vii)** $y = \dfrac{6}{x^{1/3}}$ **(viii)** $y = 7$

Solution:

(i) $y = x^5$ $\dfrac{dy}{dx} = 5x^{5-1} = 5x^4$

(ii) $y = -3x^2$ $\dfrac{dy}{dx} = 2 \times -3x^{2-1} = -6x$

(iii) $y = 5x = 5x^1$ $\dfrac{dy}{dx} = 1 \times 5x^{1-1} = 5x^0 = 5 \qquad (x^0 = 1)$

(iv) $y = \dfrac{8}{x^2} = 8x^{-2}$ $\dfrac{dy}{dx} = -2 \times 8x^{-2-1} = -16x^{-3} = -\dfrac{16}{x^3}$

(v) $y = 6\sqrt{x} = 6x^{1/2}$ $\qquad \dfrac{dy}{dx} = \tfrac{1}{2} \times 6x^{1/2-1} = 3x^{-1/2} = \dfrac{3}{x^{1/2}} = \dfrac{3}{\sqrt{x}}$

(vi) $y = \dfrac{2}{\sqrt{x}} = 2x^{-1/2}$ $\qquad \dfrac{dy}{dx} = -\tfrac{1}{2} \times 2x^{-1/2-1} = -1x^{-3/2} = -\dfrac{1}{x^{3/2}}$

(vii) $y = \dfrac{6}{x^{1/3}} = 6x^{-1/3}$ $\qquad \dfrac{dy}{dx} = -\tfrac{1}{3} \times 6x^{-1/3-1} = -2x^{-4/3} = -\dfrac{2}{x^{4/3}}$

(viii) $y = 7 = 7x^0$ $\qquad \dfrac{dy}{dx} = 0 \times 7x^{0-1} = 0$

Part (viii) leads to the rule:

$$\text{The derivative of a constant} = 0.$$

Note: The line $y = 7$ is a horizontal line. Its slope is 0.
Therefore its derivative (also its slope) equals 0.
In other words, the derivative of a constant always equals zero.

Sum or Difference
If the expression to be differentiated contains more than one term, just differentiate, separately, each term in the expression.

Example ▼

Find $f'(x)$ for each of the following:

(i) $f(x) = x + \dfrac{1}{x^2}$

(ii) $f(x) = \dfrac{2}{\sqrt{x}} - \dfrac{1}{x^4} + 5$

Solution:

(i) $f(x) = x + \dfrac{1}{x^2}$

$f(x) = x + x^{-2}$

$f'(x) = 1 - 2x^{-3}$

$f'(x) = 1 - \dfrac{2}{x^3}$

(ii) $f(x) = \dfrac{2}{\sqrt{x}} - \dfrac{1}{x^4} + 5$

$f(x) = 2x^{-1/2} - x^{-4} + 5$

$f'(x) = -x^{-3/2} + 4x^{-5}$

$f'(x) = -\dfrac{1}{x^{3/2}} + \dfrac{4}{x^5}$

Evaluating Derivatives

Often we have to evaluate a derivative for a particular value.

Example ▼

(i) If $s = 3t^2 + 5t - 7$, find the value of $\dfrac{ds}{dt}$ when $t = 2$.

(ii) If $f(x) = \sqrt{x} + 3x$, evaluate $f'(4)$.

Solution:

(i)
$$s = 3t^2 + 5t - 7$$
$$\frac{ds}{dt} = 6t + 5$$
$$\left.\frac{ds}{dt}\right|_{t=2} = 6(2) + 5$$
$$= 12 + 5 = 17$$

(ii)
$$f(x) = \sqrt{x} + 3x$$
$$f(x) = x^{1/2} + 3x$$
$$f'(x) = \tfrac{1}{2}x^{-1/2} + 3$$
$$= \frac{1}{2\sqrt{x}} + 3$$
$$f'(4) = \frac{1}{2\sqrt{4}} + 3$$
$$= \frac{1}{4} + 3 = 3\tfrac{1}{4}$$

$\dfrac{ds}{dt}$ is the derivative of s with respect to t. $\dfrac{dA}{dr}$ is the derivative of A with respect to r.

Second Derivatives

The derivative of $\dfrac{dy}{dx}$, that is $\dfrac{d}{dx}\left(\dfrac{dy}{dx}\right)$, is denoted by $\dfrac{d^2y}{dx^2}$ and is called the

'second derivative of y with respect to x'.

$\dfrac{d^2y}{dx^2}$ is pronounced 'dee two y, dee x squared'.

The derivative of $f'(x)$ is denoted by $f''(x)$ and is called the

'second derivative of $f(x)$ with respect to x'.

(i) If $f(x) = x + \dfrac{1}{x}$, find $f''(x)$ and $f''(2)$.

(ii) If $h = 10 + 30t^2 - 4t^3$, evaluate $\dfrac{d^2 h}{dt^2}$ when $t = 3$.

Solution:

(i)
$$f(x) = x + \frac{1}{x}$$
$$f(x) = x + x^{-1}$$
$$f'(x) = 1 - x^{-2}$$
$$f''(x) = 2x^{-3}$$
$$= \frac{2}{x^3}$$
$$\therefore f''(2) = \frac{2}{2^3} = \frac{2}{8} = \frac{1}{4}$$

(ii)
$$h = 10 + 30t^2 - 4t^3$$
$$\frac{dh}{dt} = 60t - 12t^2$$
$$\frac{d^2 h}{dt^2} = 60 - 24t$$
$$\frac{d^2 h}{dt^2}\bigg|_{t=3} = 60 - 24(3) = -12$$

If $y = x^4$, show that $\dfrac{4y}{3}\left(\dfrac{d^2 y}{dx^2}\right) - \left(\dfrac{dy}{dx}\right)^2 = 0$.

Solution:

$$y = x^4$$
$$\frac{dy}{dx} = 4x^3$$
$$\frac{d^2 y}{dx^2} = 12x^2$$

$$\frac{4y}{3}\left(\frac{d^2 y}{dx^2}\right) - \left(\frac{dy}{dx}\right)^2$$
$$= \frac{4x^4}{3}(12x^2) - (4x^3)^2$$
$$= 16x^6 - 16x^6$$
$$= 0$$

Note: $\left(\dfrac{dy}{dx}\right)^2 \neq \dfrac{d^2 y}{dx^2}$

Differentiate each of the following with respect to x:

1. x^3 **2.** $3x^4$ **3.** $-5x^2$ **4.** $3x$ **5.** $-2x$

6. 5 **7.** -3 **8.** $\dfrac{1}{x^2}$ **9.** $\dfrac{2}{x^3}$ **10.** $-\dfrac{2}{x^5}$

11. $6x^{1/3}$ **12.** $\dfrac{1}{x}$ **13.** $\sqrt{x}$ **14.** $\dfrac{4}{\sqrt{x}}$ **15.** $\dfrac{1}{x^{2/3}}$

16. $x^3 - 5x$ **17.** $1 - x^2$ **18.** $x^2 - \dfrac{5}{x}$ **19.** $2x^2 - \dfrac{3}{x^4}$ **20.** $\dfrac{1}{x^2} + \dfrac{1}{x}$

21. $x^4 - \dfrac{2}{x^2}$ **22.** $6\sqrt{x} - \dfrac{2}{\sqrt{x}}$ **23.** $\dfrac{3}{x} + \dfrac{2}{x^2} + \dfrac{6}{x^{1/3}}$ **24.** $\dfrac{2}{x} - \dfrac{1}{\sqrt{x}} + \dfrac{3}{x^{1/3}}$

Find $\dfrac{d^2 y}{dx^2}$ for each of the following:

25. $y = 4x^3 + 6x^2$ **26.** $y = x^2 - x^4$ **27.** $y = 6x^3 - 12x^2 - 8x + 4$

28. $y = \dfrac{1}{x}$ **29.** $y = x^2 - \dfrac{8}{x}$ **30.** $y = \sqrt{x}$

31. $y = \dfrac{1}{\sqrt{x}} + \sqrt{x}$ **32.** $y = 8\sqrt{x} - \dfrac{1}{x^2}$ **33.** $y = 9x^{1/3} + \dfrac{18}{x^{1/3}}$

34. If $f(x) = 3x^2 - 4x - 7$, evaluate   **(i)** $f'(2)$ **(ii)** $f''(-1)$.

35. If $f(x) = -4\sqrt{x}$, evaluate $f''(9)$.

36. If $A = 3r^2 - 5r$, find the value of $\dfrac{dA}{dr}$ when $r = 3$.

37. If $s = 3t - 2t^2$, find the value of   **(i)** $\dfrac{ds}{dt}$ **(ii)** $\dfrac{d^2 s}{dt^2}$ when $t = 2$.

38. If $V = 3h - h^2 - 3h^3$, find $\dfrac{dV}{dh}$ when $h = 1$.

39. If $A = \pi r^2$, find $\dfrac{dA}{dr}$ when $\dfrac{r}{5} = 1$.

40. If $V = \tfrac{4}{3}\pi r^3$, find $\dfrac{dV}{dr}$ when $2r - 5 = 0$.

41. $f(x) = 3x^2 - 4x$. If $f'(k) = 8$, find the value of k, $k \in \mathbf{R}$.

42. $f(x) = x^3 + 1$. If $f''(a) = 18$, find the value of a, $a \in \mathbf{R}$.

43. If $y = 3x^2 + 2x$, show that $y\dfrac{d^2 y}{dx^2} - 3x\dfrac{dy}{dx} - 6x = 0$.

44. If $y = 4x^3 - 6x^2$, show that $x^2\dfrac{d^2 y}{dx^2} - 2x\dfrac{dy}{dx} - 12x^2 = 0$.

    Find the values of x for which   **(i)** $\dfrac{dy}{dx} = 0$ **(ii)** $\dfrac{d^2 y}{dx^2} = 0$.

45. If $y = \dfrac{1}{x^2}$, show that $y\dfrac{d^2 y}{dx^2} + \left(\dfrac{dy}{dx}\right)^2 - 10y^3 = 0$.

Product, Quotient and Chain Rules

Rule 2: Product Rule

> Suppose u and v are functions of x.
>
> If $\quad y = uv,$
>
> then $\quad \dfrac{dy}{dx} = u\dfrac{dv}{dx} + v\dfrac{du}{dx}.$

In words:

> First by the derivative of the second + second by the derivative of the first.

Example ▼

If $y = (x^2 - 3x + 2)(x^2 - 2)$, find $\dfrac{dy}{dx}$.

Solution:

$$\text{Let} \qquad u = x^2 - 3x + 2 \qquad \text{and} \qquad \text{let } v = x^2 - 2$$

$$\frac{du}{dx} = 2x - 3 \qquad \text{and} \qquad \frac{dv}{dx} = 2x$$

$$\frac{dy}{dx} = u\frac{dv}{dx} + v\frac{du}{dx} \qquad \text{(product rule)}$$

$$= (x^2 - 3x + 2)(2x) + (x^2 - 2)(2x - 3)$$

$$= 2x^3 - 6x^2 + 4x + 2x^3 - 3x^2 - 4x + 6$$

$$= 4x^3 - 9x^2 + 6$$

Rule 3: Quotient Rule

> Suppose u and v are functions of x.
>
> If $\quad y = \dfrac{u}{v}$
>
> then $\quad \dfrac{dy}{dx} = \dfrac{v\dfrac{du}{dx} - u\dfrac{dv}{dx}}{v^2}.$

In words:

> $$\frac{\text{Bottom by the derivative of the top} - \text{Top by the derivative of the bottom}}{(\text{Bottom})^2}$$

If $y = \dfrac{x^2}{x-2}$, find $\dfrac{dy}{dx}$.

Solution:

$$\text{Let } u = x^2 \qquad \text{and} \qquad \text{let} \qquad v = x - 2$$

$$\frac{du}{dx} = 2x \qquad \text{and} \qquad \frac{dv}{dx} = 1$$

$$\frac{dy}{dx} = \frac{v\dfrac{du}{dx} - u\dfrac{dv}{dx}}{v^2} \qquad \text{(quotient rule)}$$

$$= \frac{(x-2)(2x) - (x^2)(1)}{(x-2)^2}$$

$$= \frac{2x^2 - 4x - x^2}{(x-2)^2}$$

$$= \frac{x^2 - 4x}{(x-2)^2}$$

Note: It is usual practice to simplify the top but **not** the bottom.

Function of a function

When we write, for example, $y = (x+5)^3$, we say that y is a function of x.
If we let $u = (x+5)$, then $y = u^3$, where $u = (x+5)$.
We say that y is a function u, and u is a function of x.
The new variable, u, is the **link** between the two expressions.

Rule 4: Chain Rule

Suppose u is a function of x.

If $\quad y = u^n$

then $\quad \dfrac{dy}{dx} = nu^{n-1}\dfrac{du}{dx}.$

The chain rule should be done in **one** step.

Find $\dfrac{dy}{dx}$ for each of the following:

(i) $y = (x^2 - 3x)^4$

(ii) $y = \dfrac{3}{2x+5}$

(iii) $y = \sqrt{4x-3}$

(iv) $y = \left(x^2 + \dfrac{1}{x}\right)^3$

Solution:

(i) $y = (x^2 - 3x)^4$

$\dfrac{dy}{dx} = 4(x^2 - 3x)^3(2x - 3)$

$= (8x - 12)(x^2 - 3x)^3$

(ii) $y = \dfrac{3}{2x+5}$

$y = 3(2x + 5)^{-1}$

$\dfrac{dy}{dx} = -3(2x + 5)^{-2}(2)$

$= \dfrac{-6}{(2x+5)^2}$

(iii) $y = \sqrt{4x-3}$

$y = (4x - 3)^{1/2}$

$\dfrac{dy}{dx} = \tfrac{1}{2}(4x - 3)^{-1/2}(4)$

$= \dfrac{2}{(4x-3)^{1/2}} = \dfrac{2}{\sqrt{4x-3}}$

(iv) $y = \left(x^2 + \dfrac{1}{x}\right)^3$

$y = (x^2 + x^{-1})^3$

$\dfrac{dy}{dx} = 3(x^2 + x^{-1})^2(2x - x^{-2})$

$= 3\left(x^2 + \dfrac{1}{x}\right)^2\left(2x - \dfrac{1}{x^2}\right)$

Often we have to deal with a combination of the product, quotient or chain rules.

Find $\dfrac{dy}{dx}$ if **(i)** $y = x\sqrt{9 - x^2}$ **(ii)** $y = \sqrt{\dfrac{1-x}{1+x}}$

Solution:

(i) $y = x\sqrt{9 - x^2}$

$y = x(9 - x^2)^{1/2}$

$\dfrac{dy}{dx} = (x) \cdot \underbrace{\tfrac{1}{2}(9 - x^2)^{-1/2}(-2x)}_{\text{(chain rule here)}} + (9 - x^2)^{1/2}(1)$ (product rule and chain rule)

$= -x^2(9 - x^2)^{-1/2} + (9 - x^2)^{1/2}$

$= \dfrac{-x^2}{\sqrt{9 - x^2}} + \sqrt{9 - x^2}$

(ii) $y = \sqrt{\dfrac{1-x}{1+x}}$

$$y = \left(\frac{1-x}{1+x}\right)^{1/2}$$

$$\frac{dy}{dx} = \frac{1}{2}\left(\frac{1-x}{1+x}\right)^{-1/2}\left[\frac{(1+x)(-1)-(1-x)(1)}{(1+x)^2}\right] \qquad \left(\begin{array}{c}\text{chain rule followed by}\\ \text{the quotient rule}\end{array}\right)$$

$$= \frac{1}{2}\left(\frac{1+x}{1-x}\right)^{1/2}\left[\frac{-1-x-1+x}{(1+x)^2}\right] \qquad \left(\left(\frac{a}{b}\right)^{-n} = \left(\frac{b}{a}\right)^{n}\right)$$

$$= \frac{(1+x)^{1/2}}{2(1-x)^{1/2}} \cdot \frac{-2}{(1+x)^2}$$

$$= \frac{-1}{(1-x)^{1/2}(1+x)^{3/2}}$$

Exercise 12.2 ▼

In questions 1 to 6, use the product rule to find $\dfrac{dy}{dx}$:

1. $y = (2x+3)(x-4)$ **2.** $y = (x+5)(x^2-3x+2)$ **3.** $y = (3x-4)(x^2-2x+3)$

4. $y = (x+3)(x^2-6x+8)$ **5.** $y = (5x^2-3x)(x^2-5x)$ **6.** $y = (3x^3-2x^2+4)(2x-1)$

In questions 7 to 12, use the quotient rule to find $\dfrac{dy}{dx}$:

7. $y = \dfrac{3x+2}{x+1}$ **8.** $y = \dfrac{2x-1}{x+3}$ **9.** $y = \dfrac{3x-1}{x^2-2}$

10. $y = \dfrac{x^2-1}{x^2+1}$ **11.** $y = \dfrac{1-x}{2x-x^2}$ **12.** $y = \dfrac{x^2-x-6}{x^2+x-6}$

In questions 13–18, use the chain rule to find $\dfrac{dy}{dx}$:

13. $y = (3x+2)^4$ **14.** $y = (x^2+2x)^3$ **15.** $y = (2x^2+1)^5$

16. $y = \sqrt{4x+2}$ **17.** $y = \dfrac{1}{2x-5}$ **18.** $y = \dfrac{1}{\sqrt{2x^2-4x}}$

Find $\dfrac{dy}{dx}$ if:

19. $y = x^2(x+3)^4$ **20.** $y = 3x(x+2)^3$ **21.** $y = 3x^2(2x+3)^2$

22. $y = x^2\sqrt{2x+1}$ **23.** $y = x\sqrt{1+x^2}$ **24.** $y = \sqrt{\dfrac{x+1}{x}}$

25. If $f(x) = \sqrt{\dfrac{x}{x+3}}$, find the value of $f'(1)$.   **26.** If $f(x) = \sqrt{\dfrac{x-1}{x+1}}$, find the value of $f'(\frac{5}{4})$.

Differentiation of Trigonometric Functions

The rules for differentiating also apply to trigonometric functions.
The following are in the tables on page 41, but they are shown only for x.
The chain rule is used throughout, assuming u is a function of x.
Therefore, if you are using the tables, replace x with u and **always** multiply by $\dfrac{du}{dx}$.

Basic rule (page 41 tables)		Chain rule	
$f(x)$	$f'(x)$	$f(u)$	$f'(u) \cdot \dfrac{du}{dx}$
$\cos x$	$-\sin x$	$\cos u$	$-\sin u \cdot \dfrac{du}{dx}$
$\sin x$	$\cos x$	$\sin u$	$\cos u \cdot \dfrac{du}{dx}$
$\tan x$	$\sec^2 x$	$\tan u$	$\sec^2 u \cdot \dfrac{du}{dx}$
$\sec x$	$\sec x \tan x$	$\sec u$	$\sec u \tan u \cdot \dfrac{du}{dx}$
$\operatorname{cosec} x$	$-\operatorname{cosec} x \cot x$	$\operatorname{cosec} u$	$-\operatorname{cosec} u \cot u \cdot \dfrac{du}{dx}$
$\cot x$	$-\operatorname{cosec}^2 x$	$\cot u$	$-\operatorname{cosec}^2 u \cdot \dfrac{du}{dx}$

Example ▼

Find the derivatives of the functions:

(i) $\cos 3x$ **(ii)** $\tan^3 5x$ **(iii)** $x \sin x$ **(iv)** $\sqrt{\cos x}$

Solution:

(i)
$$y = \cos 3x$$
$$\frac{dy}{dx} = (-\sin 3x)(3)$$
$$= -3 \sin 3x$$

(ii)
$$t = \tan^3 5x$$
$$y = (\tan 5x)^3$$
$$\frac{dy}{dx} = 3(\tan 5x)^2(\sec^2 5x)(5)$$
[PTA: (power) (trig. function) (angle)]
$$= 15 \tan^2 5x \sec^2 5x$$

(iii)
$$y = x \sin x$$
(use the product rule)
$$\frac{dy}{dx} = (x)(\cos x) + (\sin x)(1)$$
$$= x \cos x + \sin x$$

(iv)
$$y = \sqrt{\cos x}$$
$$y = (\cos x)^{1/2} \qquad \text{(chain rule)}$$
$$\frac{dy}{dx} = \tfrac{1}{2}(\cos x)^{-1/2}(-\sin x)$$
$$= \frac{-\sin x}{2\sqrt{\cos x}}$$

Example ▼

If $f(x) = \dfrac{x^2}{x + \cos x}$, evaluate $f'\left(\dfrac{\pi}{2}\right)$.

Solution:

$$f(x) = \frac{x^2}{x + \cos x}$$

$$f'(x) = \frac{(x + \cos x)(2x) - x^2(1 - \sin x)}{(x + \cos x)^2} \qquad \text{(quotient rule)}$$

$$f'\left(\frac{\pi}{2}\right) = \frac{\left(\dfrac{\pi}{2} + \cos \dfrac{\pi}{2}\right)(\pi) - \left(\dfrac{\pi}{2}\right)^2\left(1 - \sin \dfrac{\pi}{2}\right)}{\left(\dfrac{\pi}{2} + \cos \dfrac{\pi}{2}\right)^2} \qquad \left(\begin{array}{l}\text{Don't simplify:}\\[4pt] \text{put in } x = \dfrac{\pi}{2}\end{array}\right)$$

$$= \frac{\left(\dfrac{\pi}{2} + 0\right)(\pi) - \left(\dfrac{\pi^2}{4}\right)(1 - 1)}{\left(\dfrac{\pi}{2} + 0\right)^2} \qquad \left(\cos \frac{\pi}{2} = 0,\ \sin \frac{\pi}{2} = 1\right)$$

$$= \frac{\left(\dfrac{\pi}{2}\right)(\pi) - \left(\dfrac{\pi^2}{4}\right)(0)}{\left(\dfrac{\pi}{2}\right)^2} \qquad = \frac{\dfrac{\pi^2}{2}}{\dfrac{\pi^2}{4}} \qquad = \frac{2\pi^2}{\pi^2} \qquad = 2$$

Exercise 12.3 ▼

Find $\dfrac{dy}{dx}$ if:

1. $y = \sin 4x$
2. $y = \cos 3x$
3. $y = \tan 2x$

4. $y = \sec 5x$
5. $y = -\operatorname{cosec} 6x$
6. $y = -2 \cot 4x$

7. $y = \sin(2x - 3)$
8. $y = \tan(3x + 2)$
9. $y = 2 \tan x + \sec x$

10. $y = x^2 \sin x$
11. $y = 3x \tan x$
12. $y = x^2 \cos 2x$

13. $y = \dfrac{\sin x}{x}$
14. $y = \dfrac{1}{1 - \sin x}$
15. $y = \dfrac{1 + \sin x}{\cos x}$

16. $y = \cos^3 x$
17. $y = \sin^2 4x$
18. $y = \tan^4 3x$

19. $y = (1 + \sin^2 x)^3$
20. $y = \sqrt{\sin x}$
21. $y = \sqrt{\cos 2x}$

22. $f(x) = \dfrac{\cos x + \sin x}{\cos x - \sin x}$. Show that $f'(x) = \dfrac{2}{1 - \sin 2x}$.

147

23. If $y = \cos 3x$, show that $\dfrac{d^2y}{dx^2} = -9y$.

24. If $y = 3 \cos x + \sin x$, show that:

    (i) $\cos x \left(\dfrac{dy}{dx} \right) + y \sin x - 1 = 0$
        (ii) $\dfrac{d^2y}{dx^2} - 3 \left(\dfrac{dy}{dx} \right) + 2y - 10 \sin x = 0.$

25. If $f(x) = \sin x \cos x$, evaluate $f'\left(\dfrac{\pi}{4} \right)$.

26. If $y = \cos 2x + 2 \sin x$, evaluate $\dfrac{dy}{dx}$ at $x = \dfrac{\pi}{6}$.

27. $f(x) = \dfrac{\sin x}{1 + \tan x}$. Evaluate $f'(0)$.

Implicit Differentiation

If $y = f(x)$, the variable y is given **explicitly** (clearly) in terms of x.
For example, $y = x^3 - 2x^2 + 5x - 4$ is an explicit function.
Some curves are defined by implicit functions, that is, functions which cannot be expressed in the form $y = f(x)$.
For example, $x^2 + xy + y^3 = 7$ is an **implicit function**.
It cannot be written in the form $y = f(x)$.
It is for this reason that we must have a method for differentiating explicit functions.
An implicit function involving x and y can be differentiated with respect to x as it stands, using the chain rule.

Method for differentiating implicit functions:

> **1.** Differentiate, term by term, on both sides with respect to x.
>
> **2.** Bring all terms with $\dfrac{dy}{dx}$ to the left and bring all other terms to the right.
>
> **3.** Make $\dfrac{dy}{dx}$ the subject of the equation.

It is useful to remember that, by the chain rule,

$$\dfrac{d}{dx}(y^2) = 2y \dfrac{dy}{dx} \qquad \text{and} \qquad \dfrac{d}{dx}(y^3) = 3y^2 \dfrac{dy}{dx}$$

as y is considered as a function of x.

$$\dfrac{d}{dx}(y^n) = ny^{n-1} \left(\dfrac{dy}{dx} \right)$$

Given that $2x^3 + 3xy^2 - y^3 + 6 = 0$, evaluate $\dfrac{dy}{dx}$ at the point $(-1, 1)$.

Solution:

(use product rule here)

$$2x^3 + 3xy^2 - y^3 + 6 = 0$$

$$6x^2 + 3\left[x \cdot 2y\frac{dy}{dx} + y^2(1)\right] - 3y^2\frac{dy}{dx} = 0$$

$$6x^2 + 6xy\frac{dy}{dx} + 3y^2 - 3y^2\frac{dy}{dx} = 0 \qquad \text{(divide each term by } -3)$$

$$6xy\frac{dy}{dx} - 3y^2\frac{dy}{dx} = -6x^2 - 3y^2$$

$$\frac{dy}{dx}(6xy - 3y^2) = -6x^2 - 3y^2$$

$$\frac{dy}{dx} = \frac{-6x^2 - 3y^2}{6xy - 3y^2} = \frac{2x^2 + y^2}{y^2 - 2xy} = \frac{2x^2 + y^2}{y(y - 2x)}$$

$$\left.\frac{dy}{dx}\right|_{\substack{x=-1\\y=1}} = \frac{2(-1)^2 + (1)^2}{1(1 + 2)} = \frac{3}{3} = 1$$

Note: To evaluate $\dfrac{dy}{dx}$ we used both coordinates of the point.

For each of the following curves, express $\dfrac{dy}{dx}$ in terms of x and y:

1. $x^2 + y^2 = 4$ **2.** $x^2 + 2y - y^2 = 5$ **3.** $x^2 - 6y^3 + y = 0$

4. $x^2 + y^2 - 4x - 6y + 9 = 0$ **5.** $x^2 + xy + y^2 = 13$ **6.** $x^2 + 3xy + 2y^2 = 6$

7. $x^2y - 5x = 2$ **8.** $xy^2 + x^2 = 2$ **9.** $x^2y + xy^2 = 2$

Find the value of $\dfrac{dy}{dx}$ at the point specified:

10. $x^2 + y^2 = 25$ at the point $(3, -4)$ **11.** $x^2 + xy + 2y^2 = 28$ at the point $(2, -4)$

12. $x^2 + 4xy - 2y^2 - 8 = 0$ at the point $(0, 2)$ **13.** $x^3 + y^2 + 3x^2y = 21$ at the point $(2, 1)$

14. Find the slope of the tangent to the curve $y^2 - 3xy + 2x^2 = 6$ at the point $(1, -1)$.

15. Find the slope of the tangent to the curve $x \sin y + y^2 = 1 + \dfrac{\pi^2}{4}$ at the point $\left(1, \dfrac{\pi}{2}\right)$.

Note: $\dfrac{d}{dx}(\sin y) = \cos y \dfrac{dy}{dx}$.

Parametric Differentiation

If x and y are each expressed in terms of a third variable, t say (or θ), called the **parameter**, then $x = f(t)$ and $y = g(t)$ give the parametric forms of the equation relating to x and y respectively.

To find $\dfrac{dy}{dx}$ do the following:

> **1.** Find $\dfrac{dx}{dt}$ and $\dfrac{dy}{dt}$, separately.
>
> **2.** Use $\dfrac{dy}{dx} = \dfrac{dy}{dt} \cdot \dfrac{dt}{dx} = \dfrac{\frac{dy}{dt}}{\frac{dx}{dt}}$.

Example ▼

(i) If $x = 4t^3$ and $y = (1 + 3t^2)^2$, express $\dfrac{dy}{dx}$ in terms of t.

Hence, or otherwise, evaluate $\dfrac{dy}{dx}$ when $t = -1$.

(ii) Let $x = a(\cos \theta + \theta \sin \theta)$ and $y = a(\sin \theta - \theta \cos \theta)$; show that $\dfrac{dy}{dx} = \tan \theta$.

$$\left[a \neq 0, -\pi < \theta < \pi \quad \text{and} \quad \theta \neq \pm \frac{\pi}{2} \right]$$

Solution:

$$x = 4t^3 \qquad\qquad\qquad y = (1 + 3t^2)^2$$

(chain rule)

$$\frac{dx}{dt} = 12t^2 \qquad\qquad \frac{dy}{dt} = 2(1 + 3t^2)^1(6t) = 12t(1 + 3t^2)$$

$$\frac{dy}{dx} = \frac{\frac{dy}{dt}}{\frac{dx}{dt}} = \frac{12t(1 + 3t^2)}{12t^2} = \frac{1 + 3t^2}{t}$$

$$\left. \frac{dy}{dx} \right|_{t=-1} = \frac{1 + 3(-1)^2}{-1} = \frac{1 + 3}{-1} = \frac{4}{-1} = -4$$

(ii)

$x = a(\cos\theta + \theta\sin\theta)$

$\dfrac{dx}{d\theta} = a(-\sin\theta + \theta\cdot\cos\theta + \sin\theta\cdot 1)$

$\quad = a(-\sin\theta + \theta\cos\theta + \sin\theta)$

$\quad = a\theta\cos\theta$

$y = a(\sin\theta - \theta\cos\theta)$

$\dfrac{dy}{d\theta} = a[\cos\theta - (\theta\cdot-\sin\theta + \cos\theta\cdot 1)]$

$\quad = a(\cos\theta + \theta\sin\theta - \cos\theta)$

$\quad = a\theta\sin\theta$

$\dfrac{dy}{dx} = \dfrac{\dfrac{dy}{d\theta}}{\dfrac{dx}{d\theta}} = \dfrac{a\theta\sin\theta}{a\theta\cos\theta} = \dfrac{\sin\theta}{\cos\theta} = \tan\theta$

Exercise 12.5 ▼

Find $\dfrac{dy}{dx}$, in terms of t, if:

1. $x = 2t,\qquad y = t^2$

2. $x = 2t + 3,\qquad y = 2t^3$

3. $x = t^2 + 1,\qquad y = t^3$

4. $x = 3t^4,\qquad y = 2t^2 + 5$

5. $x = t(1 - t),\qquad y = t(1 - t^2)$

6. $x = 6t + 5,\qquad y = (2t - 1)^3$

7. $x = \dfrac{1}{t},\qquad y = t^2 + 4t$

8. $x = 2\sqrt{t},\qquad y = 5t + 4$

9. $x = 1 + \dfrac{1}{t},\qquad y = t + \dfrac{1}{t}$

10. $x = \dfrac{t^2}{1 + t^3},\qquad y = \dfrac{t^3}{1 + t^3}$

11. $x = \dfrac{t - 2}{t + 1}$ and $y = \dfrac{t + 2}{t + 1}$. If $\dfrac{dy}{dx} = k$, find the value of k.

12. If $x = \dfrac{2}{t}$ and $y = 3t^2 - 1$, express $\dfrac{dy}{dx}$ in terms of t. Evaluate $\dfrac{dy}{dx}$ at the point $(2, 2)$.

13. If $x = \dfrac{3t - 1}{t}$ and $y = \dfrac{t^2 + 4}{t}$, express $\dfrac{dy}{dx}$ in terms of t.

Find the values of t for which $\dfrac{dy}{dx} = 0$.

14. If $x = 2t + \sin 2t$ and $y = \cos 2t$, show that $\dfrac{dy}{dx} = -\tan t$.

15. If $x = \sec\theta$ and $y = \tan\theta$, show that $\dfrac{dy}{dx} = \operatorname{cosec}\theta$.

16. If $x = k(\theta - \sin\theta)$ and $y = k(1 - \cos\theta)$, $k \in \mathbf{R}$, find $\dfrac{dy}{dx}$.

17. Given $y = \sin\theta\cos\theta - \theta$ and $x = 2\cos\theta$, show that $\quad$ **(i)** $\dfrac{dy}{d\theta} = -2\sin^2\theta$ $\quad$ **(ii)** $\dfrac{dy}{dx} = \sin\theta$.

18. If $x = 3\cos\theta - 4\sin\theta$ and $y = 4\cos\theta + 3\sin\theta$, evaluate $\dfrac{dy}{dx}$ at $\theta = \dfrac{\pi}{2}$.

19. If $x = \sin\theta$ and $y = \sin n\theta$, where $n \in \mathbf{R}$, show that $(1 - x^2)\left(\dfrac{dy}{dx}\right)^2 - n^2(1 - y^2) = 0$.

20. $x = k(1 + \cos\theta)$, $\quad y = 2k\sin^2\theta$, where $0 \leqslant \theta \leqslant \pi$ and k is a positive constant.

   (i) Find $\dfrac{dy}{dx}$ in the form $p\cos\theta$ where $p \in \mathbf{Z}$.

   (ii) Find, in terms of k, the coordinates of the point q where $\theta = \tan^{-1}\dfrac{\sqrt{7}}{3}$.

Differentiation of Inverse Trigonometric Functions

The rules for differentiating also apply to inverse trigonometric functions.
The following are in the tables on page 41, but they are shown only for x.
The chain rule is used throughout, assuming u is a function of x.

Replace a with 1, x with u, and always multiply by $\dfrac{du}{dx}$.

Basic rule (page 41 tables)	
$f(x)$	$f'(x)$
$\sin^{-1}\dfrac{x}{a}$	$\dfrac{1}{\sqrt{a^2 - x^2}}$
$\tan^{-1}\dfrac{x}{a}$	$\dfrac{a}{a^2 + x^2}$

Chain rule	
$f(u)$	$f'(u) \cdot \dfrac{du}{dx}$
$\sin^{-1} u$	$\dfrac{1}{\sqrt{1 - u^2}} \cdot \dfrac{du}{dx}$
$\tan^{-1} u$	$\dfrac{1}{1 + u^2} \cdot \dfrac{du}{dx}$

Note: The derivative of $\cos^{-1} u$ is **not** in the syllabus.

Example ▼

(i) If $y = \tan^{-1}\left(\dfrac{x}{1 + x}\right)$, show that $\dfrac{dy}{dx} = \dfrac{1}{2x^2 + 2x + 1}$, $\quad x \neq -1$.

(ii) Given $y = \sin^{-1}(3x - 1)$, calculate the value of $\dfrac{dy}{dx}$ at $x = \tfrac{1}{3}$.

Solution:

$$y = \tan^{-1}\left(\dfrac{x}{1 + x}\right)$$

(quotient rule)

$$\dfrac{dy}{dx} = \dfrac{1}{1 + \left(\dfrac{x}{1+x}\right)^2} \cdot \left(\dfrac{(1+x)(-1) - (x)(1)}{(1+x)^2}\right)$$

$$\boxed{\begin{array}{l} y = \tan^{-1} u \\ \dfrac{dy}{dx} = \dfrac{1}{1 + u^2} \cdot \dfrac{du}{dx} \end{array}}$$

$$= \frac{1}{1 + \dfrac{x^2}{(1+x)^2}} \cdot \left(\frac{1+x-x}{(1+x)^2}\right)$$

$$= \frac{(1+x)^2}{(1+x)^2 + x^2} \cdot \frac{1}{(1+x)^2} \qquad \left(\begin{array}{l}\text{multiply the top and bottom}\\ \text{of the first fraction by } (1+x)^2\end{array}\right)$$

$$= \frac{1}{(1+x)^2 + x^2}$$

$$= \frac{1}{1 + 2x + x^2 + x^2}$$

$$= \frac{1}{2x^2 + 2x + 1}$$

(ii) $\qquad y = \sin^{-1}(3x - 1)$

$$\frac{dy}{dx} = \frac{1}{\sqrt{1 - (3x-1)^2}} \cdot (3)$$

$$= \frac{3}{\sqrt{1 - (3x-1)^2}}$$

$$\boxed{\begin{array}{c} y = \sin^{-1} u \\[2mm] \dfrac{dy}{dx} = \dfrac{1}{\sqrt{1-u^2}} \cdot \dfrac{du}{dx} \end{array}}$$

$$\left.\frac{dy}{dx}\right|_{x=\frac{1}{3}} = \frac{3}{\sqrt{1-(0)^2}} = \frac{3}{\sqrt{1}} = \frac{3}{1} = 3$$

Exercise 12.6 ▼

Find $\dfrac{dy}{dx}$ for each of the following:

1. $y = \sin^{-1} 2x$

2. $y = \tan^{-1} 3x$

3. $y = \sin^{-1}(x - 1)$

4. $y = \tan^{-1}(2x + 1)$

5. $y = \tan^{-1} x^2$

6. $y = \sin^{-1} 2x^3$

7. $y = (\sin^{-1} 5x)^2$

8. $y = \tan^{-1}\left(\dfrac{x}{3}\right)$

9. $y = \sin^{-1}\left(\dfrac{x}{2}\right)$

10. $y = \sin^{-1}(\cos x)$

11. $y = x \sin^{-1} x$

12. $y = 6x \tan^{-1} 2x$

13. Given $y = \sin^{-1}(4x - 1)$, calculate the value of $\dfrac{dy}{dx}$ at $x = \dfrac{1}{4}$.

14. Given $y = \tan^{-1}\left(\dfrac{1}{x}\right)$, show that $\dfrac{dy}{dx} = -\dfrac{1}{1 + x^2}$.

15. Given $y = \tan^{-1}(\cos x)$, calculate the value of $\dfrac{dy}{dx}$ at $x = \dfrac{\pi}{6}$.

16. If $y = \tan^{-1}\left(\dfrac{x}{a}\right)$, show that $\dfrac{dy}{dx} = \dfrac{a}{a^2 + x^2}$.

17. Explain why $p\sqrt{1 - q} = \sqrt{p^2 - p^2 q}, \qquad p, q \in \mathbf{R}$.

If $y = \sin^{-1}\left(\dfrac{x}{a}\right)$, show that $\dfrac{dy}{dx} = \dfrac{1}{\sqrt{a^2 - x^2}}$.

18. $f(x) = \dfrac{1}{x}\sin^{-1}\left(\dfrac{1}{x}\right)$. Show that $f'(\sqrt{2}) = -\dfrac{1}{2} - \dfrac{\pi}{8}$.

19. If $y = \tan^{-1} x$, show that $\dfrac{d^2 y}{dx^2}(1 + x^2) + 2x\dfrac{dy}{dx} = 0$.

20. If $u = \dfrac{1 + x}{1 - x}$, show that $\dfrac{du}{dx} = \dfrac{2}{(1 - x)^2}$.

Hence, if $y = \tan^{-1}\left(\dfrac{1 + x}{1 - x}\right)$, find $\dfrac{dy}{dx}$.

Verify that $\quad 2x\left(\dfrac{dy}{dx}\right)^2 + \dfrac{d^2 y}{dx^2} = 0$.

21. Explain why $\sqrt{a} = \dfrac{a}{\sqrt{a}}$, $a \in \mathbf{R}$, $a \neq 0$.

Given $y = \sin^{-1} x + x\sqrt{1 - x^2}$, show that $\quad \dfrac{dy}{dx} = 2\sqrt{1 - x^2}$.

Differentiation of Exponential Functions

The rules for differentiating apply also to exponential functions.

Exponent is another word for index. A function such as $y = 2^x$, in which the variable occurs as an index, is called 'an exponential function'.

The function $y = e^x$ is called '**the exponential function**' or '**natural exponential function**'.

e is an irrational constant whose value is 2.71828 correct to six significant figures.

e^x is the only basic function which is its own derivative. That is:

$$\text{If } y = e^x, \qquad \frac{dy}{dx} = e^x.$$

Note: The positive number e behaves just like other positive numbers such as 2 or 5. e^x obeys all the usual laws of indices or exponents.

Using the chain rule:

$$
\begin{array}{c}
\text{Suppose } u \text{ is a function of } x. \\[4pt]
\text{If } \quad y = e^u \\[4pt]
\text{then} \quad \dfrac{dy}{dx} = e^u \cdot \dfrac{du}{dx}.
\end{array}
$$

Example ▼

Find $\dfrac{dy}{dx}$ if   **(i)** $y = e^{x^2-3x}$ **(ii)** $y = \dfrac{2}{e^{3x}}$ **(iii)** $y = e^{\sin 2x}$ **(iv)** $y = \dfrac{x}{e^{2x}}$

Solution:

(i) $y = e^{x^2-3x}$

$\dfrac{dy}{dx} = e^{x^2-3x}(2x-3)$

$\qquad = (2x-3)e^{x^2-3x}$

(ii) $y = \dfrac{2}{e^{3x}} = 2e^{-3x}$

$\dfrac{dy}{dx} = 2e^{-3x}(-3)$

$\qquad = -6e^{-3x} = -\dfrac{6}{e^{3x}}$

(iii) $y = e^{\sin 2x}$

$\dfrac{dy}{dx} = e^{\sin 2x}(\cos 2x)(2)$

$\qquad = (2\cos 2x)e^{\sin 2x}$

(iv) $y = \dfrac{x}{e^{2x}} = xe^{-2x}$

(use the product rule)

$\dfrac{dy}{dx} = xe^{-2x}(-2) + e^{-2x}(1)$

$\qquad = -2xe^{-2x} + e^{-2x}$

$\qquad = e^{-2x}(1-2x) = \dfrac{1-2x}{e^{2x}}$

Note: The quotient rule could also be used in **(ii)** and **(iv)**.

Example ▼

If $y = xe^{-x}$, show that $\dfrac{d^2y}{dx^2} + 2\dfrac{dy}{dx} + y = 0$.

Solution:

$y = xe^{-x}$

$\dfrac{dy}{dx} = x[e^{-x}(-1)] + e^{-x}(1)$ (product rule)

$\qquad = -xe^{-x} + e^{-x}$

$\qquad = e^{-x}(1-x)$

$\dfrac{d^2y}{dx^2} = e^{-x}(-1) + (1-x)[e^{-x}(-1)]$ (product rule, again)

$\qquad = -e^{-x} + (1-x)(-e^{-x})$

$\qquad = -e^{-x} - e^{-x} + xe^{-x}$

$\qquad = xe^{-x} - 2e^{-x}$

$\qquad = e^{-x}(x-2)$

$\dfrac{d^2y}{dx^2} + 2\dfrac{dy}{dx} + y$

$\qquad = e^{-x}(x-2) + 2[e^{-x}(1-x)] + (xe^{-x})$

$\qquad = xe^{-x} - 2e^{-x} + 2e^{-x} - 2xe^{-x} + xe^{-x}$

$\qquad = e^{-x}(x - 2 + 2 - 2x + x) = e^{-x}(0) = 0.$

Find $\dfrac{dy}{dx}$ for each of the following:

1. $y = e^{4x}$

2. $y = 2e^{3x}$

3. $y = e^{x^2}$

4. $y = e^{x^2 - 5x}$

5. $y = e^{4x^2}$

6. $y = e^{-x}$

7. $y = \dfrac{5}{e^{2x}}$

8. $y = \dfrac{2}{e^{x^2}}$

9. $y = e^{\sin x}$

10. $y = e^{\cos 2x}$

11. $y = e^{4 \tan x}$

12. $y = e^{x \sin x}$

13. $y = xe^x$

14. $y = x^2 e^{5x}$

15. $y = e^{2x} \cos x$

16. $y = e^{-x^2} \sin x$

17. $y = \dfrac{x^2}{e^{2x}}$

18. $y = (3 + e^{x^2})^4$

19. $y = \dfrac{1}{3 - e^{2x^2}}$

20. $y = \sqrt{1 - 2e^{4x}}$

21. If $f(x) = \dfrac{1 + e^x}{1 - e^x}$, show that $f'(x) = \dfrac{2e^x}{(1 - e^x)^2}$.

22. If $f(\theta) = e^{1 + \sin \theta}$, evaluate **(i)** $f'(0)$ **(ii)** $f''\left(\dfrac{\pi}{2}\right)$.

23. If $y = e^{2x}$, show that $\dfrac{d^2 y}{dx^2} - 3 \dfrac{dy}{dx} + 2y = 0$.

24. If $y = xe^{-2x}$, show that $\dfrac{d^2 y}{dx^2} + 4 \dfrac{dy}{dx} + 4y = 0$.

25. If $y = e^x \sin x$, show that $\dfrac{d^2 y}{dx^2} - 2 \dfrac{dy}{dx} + 2y = 0$.

26. Given that $y = l^{2x}(1 - 3x)$, show that $\dfrac{d^2 y}{dx^2} - 4 \dfrac{dy}{dx} + 4y = 0$.

27. If $y = e^{kx}$, find the values of $k \in \mathbf{R}$ for which $\dfrac{d^2 y}{dx^2} - 3 \dfrac{dy}{dx} + 2y = 0$.

28. If $y = e^{2t}$ and $x = e^t$, show that $\dfrac{dy}{dx} = 2e^t$.

29. If $y = te^t$ and $x = t^2 e^t$, show that $\dfrac{dy}{dx} = \dfrac{t + 1}{t(t + 2)}$.

30. Given $y = e^\theta \cos \theta$ and $x = e^\theta \sin \theta$, where $-\dfrac{3\pi}{4} < \theta < \dfrac{\pi}{4}$, show that $\left(\dfrac{dy}{d\theta}\right)^2 + \left(\dfrac{dx}{d\theta}\right)^2 = 2e^{2\theta}$.

Evaluate $\dfrac{dy}{dx}$ at $\theta = \dfrac{\pi}{2}$.

31. If $y = e^{-nx} \cos kx$, $n, k \in \mathbf{R}$, show that $\dfrac{d^2 y}{dx^2} + 2n \dfrac{dy}{dx} + (n^2 + k^2)y = 0$.

Differentiation of Natural Logarithmic Functions

Logarithms to the base e are called '**natural logarithms**'.
The notation ln x is used as an abbreviation of $\log_e x$.
The function $y = \ln x$ is the inverse function of $y = e^x$
(exponents and logs are inverse functions of each other).

Note: $\log_e x$ or ln x is defined only for $x > 0$.

Natural logarithms obey the same laws as logarithms to any other base.

Laws of Logs:

$\ln ab = \ln a + \ln b$	$\ln \dfrac{a}{b} = \ln a - \ln b$	$\ln a^n = n \ln a$

Using the laws of logs before differentiating can simplify the work.

The following is worth remembering when evaluating the derivatives of natural logarithmic functions:

$$\ln e^k = k, \qquad \text{for any } k \in \mathbf{R}.$$

For example,

$$\ln 1 = \ln e^0 = 0, \qquad\qquad \ln e = \ln e^1 = 1, \qquad\qquad \ln e^2 = 2, \qquad\qquad \ln\sqrt{e} = \ln e^{1/2} = \tfrac{1}{2}.$$

The rules for differentiating also apply to natural logarithmic functions.

> Suppose u is a function of x.
>
> If $\quad y = \ln u$
>
> then $\quad \dfrac{dy}{dx} = \dfrac{1}{u} \cdot \dfrac{du}{dx}.$

Example ▼

Find $\dfrac{dy}{dx}$ if   **(i)** $y = \ln(x^2 + 1)$ **(ii)** $y = \ln(\sin x)$ **(iii)** $y = \ln\sqrt{x^2 - 3}$ **(iv)** $y = x \ln x$.

Solution:

(i) $y = \ln(x^2 + 1)$

$$\frac{dy}{dx} = \frac{1}{x^2 + 1} \cdot 2x$$

$$= \frac{2x}{x^2 + 1}$$

(ii) $y = \ln(\sin x)$

$$\frac{dy}{dx} = \frac{1}{\sin x} \cdot \cos x$$

$$= \frac{\cos x}{\sin x} = \cot x$$

(iii) $y = \ln\sqrt{x^2 - 3}$

$$y = \ln(x^2 - 3)^{1/2} = \tfrac{1}{2} \ln(x^2 - 3)$$

(using $\ln a^n = n \ln a$)

$$\frac{dy}{dx} = \frac{1}{2} \cdot \frac{1}{x^2 - 3} \cdot 2x$$

$$= \frac{x}{x^2 - 3}$$

(iv) $y = x \ln x$

$$\frac{dy}{dx} = x\left(\frac{1}{x}\right) + \ln(x)(1)$$

(using the product rule)

$$= 1 + \ln x$$

Find $\dfrac{dy}{dx}$ for each of the following:

1. $y = \ln 5x$

2. $y = \ln(2x + 3)$

3. $y = \ln(x^2 + 3)$

4. $y = \ln(\cos x)$

5. $y = \ln\left(\dfrac{1}{x}\right)$

6. $y = \ln(e^x + 2)$

7. $y = \ln(\sin 2x)$

8. $y = \ln(\tan 3x)$

9. $y = \ln(e^{2x})$

10. $y = x \ln x^2$

11. $y = x^3 \ln(x + 1)$

12. $y = x^2 \ln 4x$

Use the rules of logarithms, or otherwise, to find $\dfrac{dy}{dx}$ for each of the following:

13. $y = \ln\left(\dfrac{2x}{x+1}\right)$

14. $y = \ln(2x + 3)^2$

15. $y = \ln\left(\dfrac{1}{e^x}\right)$

16. $y = \ln\sqrt{1 + x^2}$

17. $y = \ln\sqrt{\sin x}$

18. $y = \ln\sqrt{\dfrac{x}{1+x}}$

19. If $f(x) = \ln(e^x \cos x)$, show that $f'(x) = 1 - \tan x$.

20. If $y = \ln(\sec x + \tan x)$, show that $\dfrac{dy}{dx} = \sec x$.

21. If $f(x) = x^2 \ln x$, evaluate   **(i)** $f'(e)$ **(ii)** $f'(1)$.

22. Given $f(x) = \ln\left(\dfrac{1 + \cos x}{1 - \cos x}\right)$, show that $f'(x) = -2 \operatorname{cosec} x$.

23. If $f(x) = \ln(\ln x)$, evaluate $f'(e)$.

24. If $f(x) = \ln\left(\dfrac{e^x}{1 + e^x}\right)$ evaluate $f'(0)$.

25. If $y = \dfrac{\ln x}{x}$, show that $\dfrac{dy}{dx} = \dfrac{1 - \ln x}{x^2}$.

Evaluate $\dfrac{d^2 y}{dx^2}$ at $x = e$.

26. Given $f(x) = e^x \ln x$, $x > 0$, evaluate $f''(1)$.

27. Given $y = \ln(t + 1)$ and $x = 1 + \ln t$, express $\dfrac{dy}{dx}$ in terms of t.

28. If $y = e^{t+1}$ and $x = e^t$, find the value of $\ln\left(\dfrac{dy}{dx}\right)$.

29. If $y = \ln t$ and $x = \frac{1}{2}\left(t + \dfrac{1}{t}\right)$, show that $\dfrac{dy}{dx} = \dfrac{2t}{t^2 - 1}$.

30. If $x = \ln\left(\dfrac{e^t}{1 + e^t}\right)$ and $y = \ln\left(\dfrac{1 + e^t}{e^t}\right)$, $t \in \mathbf{R}$, evaluate $\dfrac{dy}{dx}$.

31. Given $y = x \ln(x^2)$, show that $x\left(\dfrac{dy}{dx}\right) - 2x = y$.

32. Using $\ln \dfrac{a}{b} = \ln a - \ln b$, or otherwise, show that if $y = \ln\left(\dfrac{1+x}{1-x}\right)$,

    (i) $(1-x^2)\dfrac{dy}{dx} = 2$ **(ii)** $\left(\dfrac{2x}{1-x^2}\right)\dfrac{dy}{dx} - \dfrac{d^2y}{dx^2} = 0.$

33. Factorise $a^x + a^{2x}$.   If $y = \ln(1 + e^x)$, show that $\dfrac{d^2y}{dx^2} + \left(\dfrac{dy}{dx}\right)^2 = \dfrac{dy}{dx}.$

34. If $y = \ln e^{-x}\sqrt{\dfrac{1+2x}{1-2x}}$, show that $\dfrac{dy}{dx} = \dfrac{1+4x^2}{1-4x^2}.$

    Find the value of $\dfrac{dy}{dx}$ at $x = -1$.

    (Hint: $\ln\dfrac{ab}{c} = \ln a + \ln b - \ln c$)

Logarithmic Differentiation

Functions of the form 2^x, x^x or $3^{\sin x}$ are differentiated using '**logarithmic differentiation**'.

The method involves three steps:

> 1. Take natural logs of both sides and use the fact that $\ln a^x = x \ln a$.
> 2. Differentiate both sides with respect to x, using implicit differentiation.
> 3. Multiply both sides by y to get $\dfrac{dy}{dx}$ on its own.

Example ▼

Differentiate   **(i)** 2^x **(ii)** x^x with respect to x.

Solution:

(i) Let $y = 2^x$

        $\ln y = \ln 2^x$

        $\ln y = x \ln 2$

        $\dfrac{1}{y}\dfrac{dy}{dx} = \ln 2$

        $\dfrac{dy}{dx} = y \ln 2$

            $= 2^x \ln 2$

(ii) Let $y = x^x$

        $\ln y = \ln x^x$

        $\ln y = x \ln x$

        $\dfrac{1}{y}\dfrac{dy}{dx} = x\left(\dfrac{1}{x}\right) + \ln x(1)$

        (using the product rule)

        $\dfrac{1}{y}\dfrac{dy}{dx} = 1 + \ln x$

        $\dfrac{dy}{dx} = y(1 + \ln x)$

            $= x^x(1 + \ln x)$

Use logarithmic differentiation to find the derivative of each of the following:

1. 3^x

2. 5^x

3. 3^{2x}

4. 4^{3x+1}

5. $2^{\sin x}$

6. $2^{\ln x}$

7. $(\sin x)^x$

8. $2^x x^2$

9. If $f(x) = x4^x$, evaluate $f'(1)$.

10. If $y = a^x$, $a > 0$, $a \in \mathbf{R}$, show that $\dfrac{dy}{dx} = a^x \ln a$.

11. If $x^y = e^x$, show that $\dfrac{dy}{dx} = \dfrac{x-y}{x \ln x}$ or $\dfrac{\ln x - 1}{(\ln x)^2}$.

DIFFERENTIAL CALCULUS 3
APPLICATIONS OF DIFFERENTIATION

Finding the Equation of a Tangent to a Curve at a Point on the Curve

$\dfrac{dy}{dx}$ = the slope of a tangent to a curve at any point on the curve

To find the equation of a tangent to a curve at a given point, (x_1, y_1), on the curve, do the following:

Step 1: Find $\dfrac{dy}{dx}$.

Step 2: Evaluate $\dfrac{dy}{dx}\Big|_{x=x_1}$ [this gives m, the slope of the tangent]

$\left(\text{If the equation of the curve is given implicitly, use } \dfrac{dy}{dx}\Big|_{\substack{x=x_1 \\ y=y_1}}\right)$

Step 3: Use m (from step 2) and the given point (x_1, y_1) in the equation: $(y - y_1) = m(x - x_1)$.

Note: Sometimes only the value of x is given. When this happens, substitute the value of x into the original function to find y for step 3.

Example ▼

(i) Find the equation of the tangent to the curve $x^2 + xy + y^2 = 3$ at the point $(1, 1)$.
(ii) Find the equation of the tangent to the curve defined by:
$x = t - 2\cos t$ and $y = 2\sin t - 2\cos t$ at the point where $t = 0$.

Solution:

(i)
$$x^2 + xy + y^2 = 3 \quad \text{(implicit differentiation required)}$$
$$2x + x\frac{dy}{dx} + y(1) + 2y\frac{dy}{dx} = 0 \quad \text{(use the product rule on } xy\text{)}$$
$$x\frac{dy}{dx} + 2y\frac{dy}{dx} = -2x - y$$
$$\frac{dy}{dx}(x + 2y) = -2x - y$$
$$\frac{dy}{dx} = \frac{-2x - y}{x + 2y}$$
$$\frac{dy}{dx}\Big|_{\substack{x=1 \\ y=1}} = \frac{-2(1) - (1)}{1 + 2(1)} = \frac{-3}{3} = -1$$

At the point $(1, 1)$ the slope $= -1$.
Equation of the tangent at the point $(1, 1)$:
$$(y - 1) = -1(x - 1)$$
$$y - 1 = -x + 1$$
$$x + y - 2 = 0$$

(ii) $x = t - 2 \cos t$ $y = 2 \sin t - 2 \cos t$

(parametric differentiation required)

$x = t - 2 \cos t$

$\dfrac{dx}{dt} = 1 - 2(-\sin t)$

$\quad = 1 + 2 \sin t$

$y = 2 \sin t - \cos t$

$\dfrac{dy}{dt} = 2 \cos t - 2(-\sin t)$

$\quad = 2 \cos t + 2 \sin t$

$\dfrac{dy}{dx} = \dfrac{\dfrac{dy}{dt}}{\dfrac{dx}{dt}} = \dfrac{2 \cos t + 2 \sin t}{1 + 2 \sin t}$

$\left.\dfrac{dy}{dx}\right|_{t=0} = \dfrac{2 \cos(0) + \sin(0)}{1 + 2 \sin(0)}$

$\quad = \dfrac{2(1) + 2(0)}{1 + 2(0)}$

$\quad = \dfrac{2}{1}$

$\quad = 2$

$t = 0$

$x = t - 2 \cos t$	$y = 2 \sin t - 2 \cos t$
$= 0 - 2(1)$	$= 2(0) - 2(1)$
$= -2$	$= -2$

Thus, the point $(-2, -2)$ is on the curve at $t = 0$.
Equation of the tangent at $t = 0$:

$(y + 2) = 2(x + 2)$

$y + 2 = 2x + 4$

$2x - y + 2 = 0$

Sometimes we are given the value of $\dfrac{dy}{dx}$ and asked to find unknown coefficients.

Example ▼

The slope of the tangent to the curve $y = ax^3 + bx + 4$ is 21 at the point $(2, 14)$ on the curve.
Find the value of a and the value of b.

Solution:

$y = ax^3 + bx + 4$

$\dfrac{dy}{dx} = 3ax^2 + b = 21$ (when $x = 2$)

$3a(2)^2 + b = 21$ (put in $x = 2$)

$12a + b = 21$ ①

Given: $(2, 14)$ is on the curve

Thus, $14 = a(2)^3 + b(2) + 4$

$14 = 8a + 2b + 4$

$8a + 2b = 10$ ②

Solving the simultaneous equations ① and ② gives $a = 2$ and $b = -3$.

Find the equation of the tangent to the curve at the indicated point:

1. $y = 3 + 2x - x^2$ at $(2, 3)$

2. $y = x^3 - 2x^2 - 4x + 1$ at $(-1, 2)$

3. $y = (2x + 3)^3$ at $(-1, 1)$

4. $y = \dfrac{6x - 3}{4x + 2}$ at $(1, \frac{1}{2})$

5. $x^2 + y^2 - 10y = 0$ at $(4, 2)$

6. $y^3 - xy - 6x^3 = 0$ at $(1, 2)$

7. $x = 3t^2, \qquad y = 6t$ at $t = 1$

8. $y = \ln x$ at $x = 1$

9. $y = 2 \cos x + \sin x$ at $(0, 2)$

10. $y = \tan^{-1} x$ at $x = 0$

11. Find the equation of the tangent to the curve $y = x + e^{2x}$ at the point where $x = 0$.

12. Find the equation of the tangent to the curve $x = e^t + t, \qquad y = e^{3t} - 2t$, at the point where $t = 0$.

13. Find the equation of the tangent to the curve $x = 2 + \ln t, \qquad y = t^3$, at the point $(2, 1)$.

14. Find the equation of the tangent to the curve $x = (1 + t)^2, \qquad y = (1 - t)^2$, at the point where $y = x$.

15. Find the equations of the two tangents to the curve $y^2 + 3xy + 4x^2 = 14$ at the points where $x = 1$.

16. Find the equation of the tangent to the curve $x = 4 \cos \theta + 3 \sin \theta + 2, \qquad y = 3 \cos \theta - 4 \sin \theta - 1$, at the point where $\theta = \dfrac{\pi}{2}$.

17. Find the coordinates of the points on the curve $y = \dfrac{x}{1 + x}$ at which the tangents to the curve are parallel to the line $x - y + 8 = 0$. Find the equations of the two tangents at these points.

18. The slope of the tangent to the curve $y = x^4 - 1$ at the point p is 32. Find the coordinates of p.

19. The slope of the tangent to the curve $y = ax^2 + bx + 6$ at the point $(2, 4)$ is 3. Find the value of a and the value of b.

20. The slope of the tangent to the curve $y = px^2 + 1$ at the point $(1, q)$ is 6. Find the value of p and the value of q.

21. The curve $y = \dfrac{p + qx}{x(x + 2)}, \qquad p, q \in \mathbf{R}, x \neq 0, x \neq -2$, has zero slope at the point $(1, -2)$. Find the value of p and the value of q.

22. A curve is given by the equation $x^2 + 4xy = 2y^2 - 8$. Find the coordinates of the points on the curve at which $\dfrac{dy}{dx} = 1$.

Increasing and Decreasing

$\dfrac{dy}{dx}$, being the slope of a tangent to a curve at any point on the curve, can be used to determine if, and where, a curve is increasing or decreasing.

Note: Graphs are read from left to right.

Where a curve is increasing, the tangent to the curve will have a positive slope. Therefore, where a curve is increasing, $\dfrac{dy}{dx}$ will be positive.

Where a curve is decreasing, the tangent to the curve will have a negative slope. Therefore, where a curve is decreasing, $\dfrac{dy}{dx}$ will be negative.

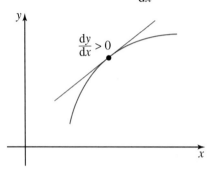

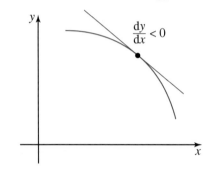

Example ▼

If $y = \dfrac{2x}{1-x}$, show that $\dfrac{dy}{dx} > 0$ for all $x \neq 1$.

Solution:

$$y = \frac{2x}{1-x}$$

$$\frac{dy}{dx} = \frac{(1-x)(2) - (2x)(-1)}{(1-x)^2} \qquad \text{(quotient rule)}$$

$$= \frac{2 - 2x + 2x}{(1-x)^2}$$

$$= \frac{2}{(1-x)^2}$$

$$\therefore \frac{dy}{dx} = \frac{2}{(1-x)^2}$$

$(1-x)^2 > 0$ for all $x \neq 1$, $\qquad 2 > 0 \qquad$ (top and bottom both positive)

$$\therefore \frac{2}{(1-x)^2} > 0 \text{ for all } x \neq 1$$

$$\therefore \frac{dy}{dx} > 0 \text{ for all } x \neq 1.$$

Note: (any real number)^2 will always be a positive number unless the number is zero

$\therefore (1-x)^2$ must always be positive, unless $x = 1$, which gives $0^2 = 0$.

1. Let $f(x) = x^2 - 2x - 8$. Find the values of x for which $f(x)$ is **(i)** decreasing **(ii)** increasing.

2. Let $f(x) = x^3 + 4x + 2$. Show that $\dfrac{dy}{dx} > 0$ for all $x \in \mathbf{R}$.

3. Let $y = \dfrac{x+2}{x-1}$. Show that $\dfrac{dy}{dx} < 0$ for all $x \in \mathbf{R}$, $x \neq 1$.

4. Let $y = 10 - 3x + 3x^2 - x^3$. Show that $\dfrac{dy}{dx} < 0$ for all $x \in \mathbf{R}$.

5. Let $f(x) = x^3 - 3x^2 - 9x + 2$. Find the values of x for which $f'(x) < 0$.

6. Let $f(x) = \dfrac{x^2+3}{x+1}$. Find the values of x for which $f'(x) > 0$.

7. Let $f(x) = x - \sin x$. Show that $f'(x) > 0$ for $0 < x < \dfrac{\pi}{2}$.

8. An artificial ski-slope is described by the function $h = 2 - 8s - 4s^2 - \frac{2}{3}s^3$, where s is the horizontal distance and h is the height of the slope. Show that the slope is all downhill.

9. Let $f(x) = x \ln x$, $\quad x > 0$. Find the values of x for which $f'(x) > 0$.

10. $f(x) = \dfrac{\sin x + \cos x}{\sin x - \cos x}$. Show that $f(x)$ is decreasing for all $x \in \mathbf{R}$, $\tan x \neq 1$.

11. Prove that the curve $y = \dfrac{px+q}{rx+s}$, $\quad x \neq -\dfrac{s}{r}$, is increasing for all x, as long as $ps - qr > 0$.

Local Maximum Point, Local Minimum Point and Point of Inflection

Local maximum point

To the left of p	At p	To the right of p
$\dfrac{dy}{dx} > 0$	$\dfrac{dy}{dx} = 0$	$\dfrac{dy}{dx} < 0$

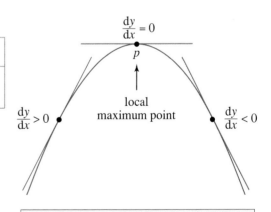

As the curve passes through the point p,

$\dfrac{dy}{dx}$ changes from positive to negative,

i.e. $\dfrac{dy}{dx}$ is decreasing.

Thus, the rate of change of $\dfrac{dy}{dx}$ is negative,

i.e. $\dfrac{d^2y}{dx^2} < 0$ for a maximum point.

For a local maximum point:
$$\dfrac{dy}{dx} = 0 \quad \text{and} \quad \dfrac{d^2y}{dx^2} < 0$$

Local minimum point

To the left of q	At q	To the right of q
$\dfrac{dy}{dx} < 0$	$\dfrac{dy}{dx} = 0$	$\dfrac{dy}{dx} > 0$

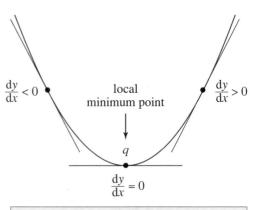

As the curve passes through the point q,

$\dfrac{dy}{dx}$ changes from negative to positive,

i.e. $\dfrac{dy}{dx}$ is increasing. Thus, the rate of

change of $\dfrac{dy}{dx}$ is positive,

i.e. $\dfrac{d^2y}{dx^2} > 0$ for a minimum point.

> For a local minimum point:
> $$\frac{dy}{dx} = 0 \quad \text{and} \quad \frac{d^2y}{dx^2} > 0$$

Note: Local maximum points or local minimum points are also called '**turning points**'. They are called 'local maximum points' or 'local minimum points' as the terms 'maximum' and 'minimum' values apply only in the vicinity of (close to) the turning points, and not to the values of y in general.

Point of Inflection

This is a point at which the curvature of a curve changes. In other words, at a point of inflection, a curve stops bending in one direction and starts bending the other way. At a point of inflection, the tangent to the curve cuts the curve at that point.

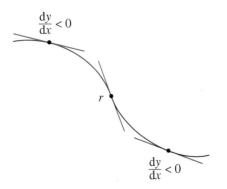

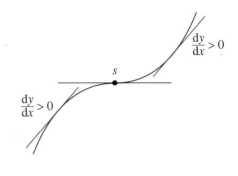

The points r and s are points of inflection.
Note: The point s is called a '**horizontal point of inflection**' or '**saddle point**'.

The slope of the tangent, $\dfrac{dy}{dx}$, does **not** change sign as a curve passes through a point of inflection.

> For a point of inflection:
> $$\frac{d^2y}{dx^2} = 0 \quad \text{and} \quad \frac{d^3y}{dx^3} \neq 0$$

Note: If $\dfrac{d^3y}{dx^3} = 0$, it will be necessary to consider the sign of $\dfrac{d^2y}{dx^2}$ on either side of the point of inflection. $\dfrac{d^2y}{dx^2}$ **changes** sign before and after a point of inflection.

Alternatively, $\dfrac{dy}{dx}$ does **not** change sign on either side of a point of inflection.

Summary of conditions for a function $y = f(x)$:

1.	Increasing	$\dfrac{dy}{dx} > 0$
2.	Decreasing	$\dfrac{dy}{dx} < 0$
3.	Maximum point	$\dfrac{dy}{dx} = 0$ and $\dfrac{d^2y}{dx^2} < 0$
4.	Minimum point	$\dfrac{dy}{dx} = 0$ and $\dfrac{d^2y}{dx^2} > 0$
5.	Point of inflection	$\dfrac{d^2y}{dx^2} = 0$ and $\dfrac{d^3y}{dx^3} \neq 0$

Note: Points on a curve where $\dfrac{dy}{dx} = 0$ are called '**stationary points**'. At a stationary point, the tangent to the curve is horizontal. Local maximum turning points, local minimum turning points and horizontal points of inflection (saddle points) are stationary points.

Example ▼

Find the coordinates of the local maximum point, the local minimum point and the point of inflection of the curve $y = x^3 - 3x^2 + 5$.
Draw a rough graph of the curve $y = x^3 - 3x^2 + 5$.

Solution:

$$y = x^3 - 3x^2 + 5$$
$$\frac{dy}{dx} = 3x^2 - 6x$$
$$\frac{d^2y}{dx^2} = 6x - 6$$

For a maximum or a minimum:
$$\frac{dy}{dx} = 0$$
$$\therefore \quad 3x^2 - 6x = 0$$
$$x^2 - 2x = 0$$
$$x(x - 2) = 0$$
$$x = 0 \quad \text{or} \quad x = 2$$

$\dfrac{d^2y}{dx^2}\bigg|_{x=0} = 6(0) - 6 = -6 < 0$

$\therefore$ local maximum at $x = 0$

$x = 0;\quad y = (0)^3 - 3(0)^2 + 5 = 5$

$\therefore$ local maximum point is $(0, 5)$

$\dfrac{d^2y}{dx^2}\bigg|_{x=2} = 6(2) - 6 = 6 > 0$

$\therefore$ local minimum at $x = 2$

$x = 2;\quad y = (2)^3 - 3(2)^2 + 5 = 1$

$\therefore$ local minimum point is $(2, 1)$

For a point of inflection:
$$\frac{d^2y}{dx^2} = 0$$
$$\therefore \quad 6x - 6 = 0$$
$$6x = 6$$
$$x = 1$$
$$x = 1; \quad y = (1)^3 - 3(1)^2 + 5 = 3$$
$$\therefore \quad \text{point of inflection is } (1, 3)$$
$$\text{Check: } \frac{d^3y}{dx^3} = 6 \ne 0.$$

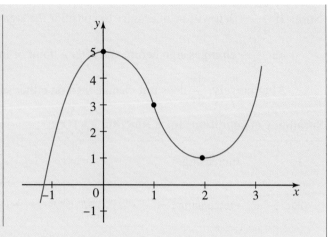

Example ▼

Let $f(x) = xe^{-ax}$, $x \in \mathbf{R}$, a constant and $a > 0$.

Show that $f(x)$ has a local maximum and express the coordinates of this local maximum point in terms of a.

Find, in terms of a, the coordinates of the point at which the second derivative of $f(x)$ is zero.

Solution:

For a maximuim: **1.** $f'(x) = 0$ and   **2.** $f''(x) < 0$.

$$f(x) = xe^{-ax}$$
$$f'(x) = x(e^{-ax})(-a) + e^{-ax}(1)$$
$$= -axe^{-ax} + e^{-ax}$$
$$= e^{-ax}(1 - ax)$$

$$f'(x) = 0$$
$$e^{-ax}(1 - ax) = 0$$
$$\therefore \quad 1 - ax = 0$$
$$ax = 1$$
$$x = \frac{1}{a}$$

Note: $e^{-ax} \ne 0$ for any value of x.

$$f''(x) = e^{-ax}(-a) + (1 - ax)(e^{-ax})(-a)$$
$$= -ae^{-ax} - ae^{-ax} + a^2xe^{-ax}$$
$$= ae^{-ax}(-1 - 1 + ax)$$
$$= ae^{-ax}(ax - 2)$$

$$f''\left(\frac{1}{a}\right) = ae^{-a(1/a)}\left[a\left(\frac{1}{a}\right) - 2\right]$$
$$= ae^{-1}(1 - 2)$$
$$= -ae^{-1}$$
$$= -\frac{a}{e} < 0 \quad (\text{as } a > 0)$$

$$\therefore \quad \text{local maximum occurs at } x = \frac{1}{a}$$

$$f(x) = xe^{-ax}$$
$$f\left(\frac{1}{a}\right) = \frac{1}{a}e^{-a(1/a)} = \frac{1}{a}e^{-1} = \frac{1}{a} \cdot \frac{1}{e} = \frac{1}{ae}$$

Thus, the coordinates of the local maximum point are $\left(\frac{1}{a}, \frac{1}{ae}\right)$.

$$f''(x) = 0$$
$$ae^{-ax}(ax - 2) = 0$$
$$ax - 2 = 0$$
$$ax = 2$$
$$x = \frac{2}{a}$$

Note: $ae^{-ax} \neq 0$ for any value of x.

$$f(x) = xe^{-ax}$$
$$f\left(\frac{2}{a}\right) = \frac{2}{a}e^{-a(2/a)}$$
$$= \frac{2}{a}e^{-2}$$
$$= \frac{2}{a} \cdot \frac{1}{e^2}$$
$$= \frac{2}{ae^2}$$

Thus, the coordinates of the point at which $f''(x) = 0$ are $\left(\dfrac{2}{a}, \dfrac{2}{ae^2}\right)$.

Exercise 13.3 ▼

Find the coordinates of the turning point of each of the following functions and determine if each turning point is a local maximum or local minimum:

1. $y = x^2 - 2x + 5$

2. $y = 3x^2 + 6x - 5$

3. $y = 1 - 12x - 2x^2$

Find the coordinates of the local maximum point, the local minimum point and the point of inflection of each of the following functions. Draw a rough graph of the function in each case:

4. $y = x^3 - 6x^2 + 9x - 5$

5. $y = 12x - x^3$

6. $y = x^3 - 9x^2 + 15x + 10$

7. $y = 2 - 3x^2 - x^3$

8. Let $f(x) = x + \dfrac{1}{x}$, $x \neq 0$. Find the coordinates of the local maximum and the local minimum of $f(x)$.

Verify that $f(x)$ has no points of inflection.

9. If $f(x) = x^4 - 4x^3$, find the coordinates of any points of inflection.

10. $f(x) = x^4 - 2x^2$. Verify that $f(x)$ has one local maximum and two local minimum points, and calculate the coordinates of these points.
Find the coordinates of the two points of inflection of $f(x)$.

11. Let $f(x) = \dfrac{4x - 3}{x^2 + 1}$.

Calculate the coordinates of the local maximum point and the local minimum point of $f(x)$.

Find the coordinates of any turning points of each of the following and determine whether they are local maximum points or local minimum points:

12. $y = x \ln x - 2x$, $x > 0$

13. $y = \dfrac{\ln x}{x}$, $x > 0$

14. $y = e^{x^2}$

15. $y = xe^x$

16. $y = x^2 e^{-x}$

17. $y = (1 - \ln x)^2$, $x > 0$.

18. Let $f(x) = xe^{-x}$. Find   **(i)** $f'(x)$ and   **(ii)** $f''(x)$.
Find the coordinates of the turning point and determine if it is a maximum or a minimum.
Find the coordinates of the point of inflection.

19. Let $x + y = 13$, where $x, y > 0$.
If $A = 2x + 3y + xy$, write A as a quadratic in x.
Calculate the maximum value of A.

20. Let $x + y = 12$, where $x, y > 0$.
If $A = x^2 + y^2$, calculate the minimum value of A.

21. Given that the curve $y = ax^2 + 12x + 1$ has a turning point at $x = 2$, calculate the value of a.
Is the point a maximum or a minimum?

22. The curve $y = px^2 + qx + r$ has a maximum turning point at $(2, 18)$.
If $(0, 10)$ is a point on the curve, find the value of p, q and r.

23. The curve $y = e^x(px^2 + q)$ has a local minimum point at $(1, -4e)$.
Find the value of p and the value of q.

24. Given that $y = e^{2x} \cos 2x$, find $\dfrac{dy}{dx}$ and $\dfrac{d^2y}{dx^2}$.

Verify that $e^{2x} \cos 2x$ has a maximum value at $x = \dfrac{\pi}{8}$ and write down this maximum value.

25. $y = e^{2x} - 2e^x$ has one turning point. Find its coordinates.
Determine if it is a local maximum or a local minimum point.

26. Let $f(x) = e^{2x} - ae^x$, $x \in \mathbf{R}$ and a constant, $a > 0$.
Show that $f(x)$ has a local minimum at a point $(b, f(b))$, specifying the value of b in terms of a.

27. Let $f(x) = ax^3 + bx^2 + cx + d$, $a \neq 0$. Verify $\dfrac{d^3y}{dx^3} \neq 0$.

If $b^2 = 3ac$, show that $f(x)$ has only one turning point.

28. Let $f(x) = 2x^3 - kx^2 + \dfrac{10k^3}{27}$, $x \in \mathbf{R}$ and $k > 0$.

Find the coordinates of the local minimum and the local maximum points, in terms of k.

Asymptotes

An '**asymptote**' is a straight line that a curve approaches but never meets.

On our course we will meet two types of asymptote:

1. Vertical asymptote   **2. Horizontal asymptote**

A **rational function** is a function of the form $f(x) = \dfrac{g(x)}{h(x)}$.

The rational functions on our course are ones of the form:

1. $f(x) = \dfrac{a}{x + b}$ **2.** $f(x) = \dfrac{x}{x + b}$

Properties of these rational functions:

> **1.** They have no turning points or points of inflection.
> **2.** They are always increasing or decreasing.
> **3.** Vertical asymptote. Bottom − 0, i.e. $x + b = 0$ or $x = -b$.
> **4.** Horizontal asymptote: $y = \lim\limits_{x \to \infty} f(x)$.

Example ▼

Let $f(x) = \dfrac{x}{x-3}$, $x \neq 3$ and $x \in \mathbf{R}$.

(i) Show that $f(x)$ has no turning points and that it is decreasing for all $x \neq 3$, in its domain.
(ii) Show that the curve $f(x)$ has no points of inflection.
(iii) Find the equations of the asymptotes of the curve $f(x)$.
(iv) Draw a sketch of the curve $f(x)$.
(v) Find how x_1 and x_2 are related if the tangents at $(x_1, f(x_1))$ and $(x_2, f(x_2))$ are parallel and $x_1 \neq x_2$.

Solution:

$$f(x) = \frac{x}{x-3}$$

(i) $f'(x) = \dfrac{(x-3)(1) - (x)(1)}{(x-3)^2}$ (quotient rule)

$$= \frac{x - 3 - x}{(x-3)^2}$$

$$= \frac{-3}{(x-3)^2}$$

$\dfrac{-3}{(x-3)^2} < 0$ for all $x \neq 3$

(as top is always negative and bottom is always positive).
Thus, the curve has no stationary points and is decreasing for all $x \neq 3$.

(ii) $f'(x) = \dfrac{-3}{(x-3)^2} = -3(x-2)^{-2}$

$f''(x) = (-2)(-3)(x-3)^{-3}(1)$ (chain rule)

$$= 6(x-3)^{-3}$$

$$= \frac{6}{(x-3)^3}$$

$f''(x) = 0$ (for a point of inflection)

$\Rightarrow \quad \dfrac{6}{(x-3)^3} = 0$

$\Rightarrow \quad\quad 6 = 0$ (not true)

Thus, $f''(x) \neq 0$

∴ No points of inflexion.

(iii) $f(x) = \dfrac{x}{x-3}$

Vertical asymptote:

Bottom $= 0$

$x - 3 = 0$

$x = 3$

Horizontal asymptote:

$$y = \lim_{x \to \infty} f(x)$$

$$y = \lim_{x \to \infty} \frac{x}{x-3}$$

$$y = \lim_{x \to \infty} \frac{1}{1 - \dfrac{3}{x}}$$

$$y = \frac{1}{1-0}$$

$$y = 1$$

(iv) For the graph, $y = f(x)$.

When $x = 0$, $y = 0$,

thus, the point $(0, 0)$ is on the curve.

Sketch:

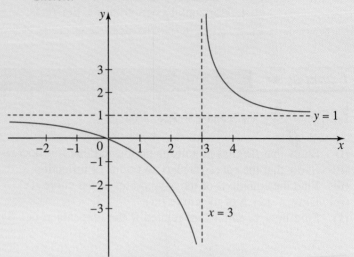

The asymptotes are shown by the broken lines.

(v)

$$\frac{dy}{dx} = \frac{-3}{(x-3)^2}$$

$$\frac{dy}{dx}\bigg|_{x=x_1} = \frac{-3}{(x_1-3)^2}$$

$$\frac{dy}{dx}\bigg|_{x=x_2} = \frac{-3}{(x_2-3)^2}$$

Parallel tangents

$$\frac{-3}{(x_1-3)^2} = \frac{-3}{(x_2-3)^2}$$

$$(x_1-3)^2 = (x_2-3)^2$$

$$(x_1-3) = \pm(x_2-3)$$

$$x_1 - 3 = x_2 - 3 \quad \text{or} \quad x_1 - 3 = -x_2 + 3$$

$$x_1 = x_2 \quad \text{or} \quad x_1 + x_2 = 6$$

Thus, $x_1 + x_2 = 6 \quad [\text{as } x_1 \neq x_2]$

Exercise 13.4 ▼

In each case, find the equations of the asymptotes of the graph of $f(x)$:

1. $f(x) = \dfrac{x}{x+2}$

2. $f(x) = \dfrac{4}{x-5}$

3. $f(x) = \dfrac{3}{x}$

4. $f(x) = \dfrac{x}{x-3}$

5. $f(x) = \dfrac{x}{x+1}$, where $x \in \mathbf{R}, x \neq -1$.

(i) Find the horizontal and vertical asymptotes of $y = f(x)$.

(ii) Show that $y = f(x)$ has no stationary points, and that it is increasing for all $x \neq -1$.

(iii) Draw a rough sketch of the curve $y = f(x)$.

6. $f(x) = \dfrac{2}{x-3}$, where $x \in \mathbf{R}, x \neq 3$.

   (i)   Show that $f(x)$ has no turning points and that it is decreasing for all $x \neq 3$, in its domain.

   (ii)   Show that the curve $f(x)$ has no points of inflection.

   (iii)   Find the equations of the asymptotes of the curve $f(x)$.

   (iv)   Draw a sketch of the curve $f(x)$.

   (v)   Find how x_1 and x_2 are related if the tangents at $(x_1, f(x_1))$ and $(x_2, f(x_2))$ are parallel and $x_1 \neq x_2$.

7. $f(x) = \dfrac{4}{x+2}$, where $x \in \mathbf{R}, x \neq -2$.

   (i)   Find the equations of the asymptotes of $f(x)$.

   (ii)   Draw a sketch of the curve of $f(x)$.

   (iii)   Show that the curve of $f(x)$ is always decreasing and has no points of inflection.

   (iv) $x + y = 2$ is a tangent to the curve at the point $(0, 2)$. Find the point of tangency of the other tangent parallel to $x + y + 2$.

8. $f(x) = \dfrac{2}{x-2}$, where $x \in \mathbf{R}, x \neq 2$.

   (i)   Find the equations of the asymptotes of the graph of $f(x)$.

   (ii)   Prove that the graph of $f(x)$ has no turning points or points of inflection.

   (iii)   If the tangents to the curve at $x = x_1$ and $x = x_2$ are parallel and if $x_1 \neq x_2$, show that $x_1 + x_2 - 4 = 0$.

9. $f(x) = \dfrac{x}{x+4}$, $x \in \mathbf{R}$ and $x \neq -4$.

   (i)   Find the equations of the asymptotes of the graph of $f(x)$.

   (ii)   Prove that the graph of $f(x)$ has no turning points or points of inflection.

   (iii)   Find the range of values of x for which $f'(x) \leqslant 1$, where $f'(x)$ is the derivative of $f(x)$.

Rates of Change I

Displacement (position), Velocity and Acceleration

The derivative $\dfrac{dy}{dx}$ is called the '**rate of change of y with respect to x**'.

It shows how changes in y are related to changes in x.

If $\dfrac{dy}{dx} = 5$, then y is increasing 5 times as fast as x increases.

If $\dfrac{dy}{dx} = -3$, then y decreases 3 times as fast as x increases.

In mechanics, for example, letters other than x and y are used.

If s denotes the displacement (position) of a particle from a fixed point, at time t, then:

> **1.** Velocity $= v = \dfrac{ds}{dt}$,
>
> the rate of change of position with respect to time.
>
> **2.** Acceleration $= a = \dfrac{dv}{dt} = \dfrac{d^2s}{dt^2}$,
>
> the rate of change of velocity with respect to time.

A particle moves along a straight line such that, after t seconds, the distance moved, s metres, is given by $s = t^3 - 9t^2 + 15t - 3$. Find:

(i) the velocity and acceleration of the particle, in terms of t
(ii) the values of t when its velocity is zero
(iii) the acceleration after $3\frac{1}{2}$ seconds
(iv) the time at which the acceleration is 6 m/s², and the velocity at this time.

Solution:

(i)
$$s = t^3 - 9t^2 + 15t - 3$$
$$v = \frac{ds}{dt} = 3t^2 - 18t + 15 \qquad \text{(velocity at any time } t\text{)}$$
$$a = \frac{d^2s}{dt^2} = 6t - 18 \qquad \text{(acceleration at any time } t\text{)}$$

(ii)   Velocity = 0

$$\therefore \quad \frac{ds}{dt} = 0$$
$$3t^2 - 18t + 15 = 0$$
$$t^2 - 6t + 5 = 0$$
$$(t - 1)(t - 5) = 0$$
$$t = 1 \quad \text{or} \quad t = 5$$

Thus, the particle is stopped after 1 second and again after 5 seconds.

(iii)
$$\frac{d^2s}{dt^2} = 6t - 18$$
$$\therefore \quad \frac{d^2s}{dt^2}\bigg|_{t=3\frac{1}{2}} = 6(3\tfrac{1}{2}) - 18$$
$$= 21 - 18$$
$$= 3 \text{ m/s}^2$$

Thus, after $3\frac{1}{2}$ seconds the acceleration is 3 m/s².

(iv) acceleration = 6 m/s²

$$\therefore \quad \frac{d^2s}{dt^2} = 6$$
$$\therefore \quad 6t - 18 = 6$$
$$6t = 24$$
$$t = 4$$

After 4 seconds the acceleration is 6 m/s².

Velocity after 4 seconds
$$\frac{ds}{dt}\bigg|_{t=4} = 3(4)^2 - 18(4) + 15$$
$$= 48 - 72 + 15$$
$$= -9 \text{ m/s}$$

After 4 seconds the velocity is –9 m/s. The negative value means after 4 seconds it is going in the opposite direction to when it started.

Exercise 13.5 ▼

1. If $s = t^3 - 2t^2$, evaluate $\dfrac{ds}{dt}$ at $t = 3$.

2. If $\theta = 3t^2 - \frac{1}{3}t^3$, evaluate $\dfrac{d\theta}{dt}$ at $t = 2$.

3. If $V = \frac{4}{3}\pi r^3$, evaluate $\dfrac{dV}{dr}$ at $r = 5$.

4. A particle is moving in a straight line. Its distance, s metres, from a fixed point o after t seconds is given by $s = t^3 - 9t^2 + 15t + 2$.
Calculate:
(i) its velocity at any time t.   **(ii)** its velocity after 6 seconds.
(iii) the distances of the particle from o when it is instantly at rest.
(iv) its acceleration after 4 seconds.

5. A car, starting at $t = 0$ seconds, travels a distance of s metres in t seconds where $s = 30t - \frac{9}{4}t^2$.
(i) Find the speed of the car after 2 seconds.
(ii) After how many seconds is the speed of the car equal to zero?
(iii) Find the distance travelled by the car up to the time its speed is zero.

6. The air resistance R to a body moving with speed v metres per second is given by $R = \dfrac{v^2}{100}$.
(i) Find the rate of change of the air resistance with respect to the speed.
(ii) Calculate this rate of change when $v = 16$ m/s.

7. A parachutist jumps out of an aeroplane. The distance, h metres, through which she falls after t seconds is given by $h = 10\,t - \dfrac{5t}{t+1}$. Find:
(i) the distance she falls in the first second.
(ii) her velocity after two seconds.

8. A particle moves in a straight line so that its distance s metres from a fixed point o at time t is given by $s = 1.5t^3 - 10.5t^2 - 4t + 10$.
(i) If its velocity after k seconds is 3.5 m/s, find the value of k.
(ii) If its acceleration after q seconds is 6 m/s^2, find the value of q.

9. The position, x metres, of a particle moving on the x-axis is given by $x = \cos 4t$ where t is in seconds. Find the velocity and the acceleration of the particle at $t = \dfrac{\pi}{4}$ seconds.

10. The distance, s metres, travelled by a car in t seconds after the brakes are applied is given by $s = 10t - t^2$. Show that its acceleration is constant. Find:
(i) the speed of the car when the brakes are applied.
(ii) the distance the car travels before it stops.

11. The distance, s metres, of an object from a fixed point in t seconds is given by $s = \dfrac{t+1}{t+3}$.
What is the speed of the object, in terms of t, at t seconds?
After how many seconds will the speed of the object be less than 0.02 m/s?

12. The equation $\theta = 3\pi + 20t - 2t^2$ gives the angle θ, in radians, through which a wheel turns in t seconds. Find:
(i) the rate of change of θ with respect to time t.
(ii) the time the wheel takes to come to rest.
(iii) the angle turned through in the last second of motion.

Rates of Change 2

Related rates of change

By convention, unless specified otherwise, the phrase 'rate of change' refers to the rate at which a variable is changing 'with respect to time'. For example, if we are told the rate of change of h is 10, this means 'the rate of change of h with respect to time is 10'. In other words, we are given $\dfrac{dh}{dt} = 10$.

Related rates of change, using differentials, can be related using the chain rule.

For example:

$$\frac{dy}{dt} = \frac{dy}{dx} \times \frac{dx}{dt}$$

$$\frac{dV}{dr} = \frac{dV}{dt} \times \frac{dt}{dr}$$

In many rate of change problems we will deal with 3 things:

1. What we want to find.　　2. What we are given.
3. What we need to complete the fraction (look for a link connecting the variables).

$$\text{Find} = (\text{Given}) \times \left(\begin{array}{c} \text{What we need to} \\ \text{complete the fraction} \end{array} \right)$$

Note: cm/s means centimetres per second, etc.

Example ▼

The radius of a circle increases at 4 cm/s. What is the rate of increase of the area when the radius is 5 cm?

Solution:

The radius increases at 4 cm/s.

Thus, we are given $\dfrac{dr}{dt} = 4$ and asked to find $\dfrac{dA}{dt}$ when $r = 5$

Find = Given × Need

$$\frac{dA}{dt} = \frac{dr}{dt} \times \frac{dA}{dr}$$
$$= 4 \times 2\pi r$$
$$= 8\pi r$$

$$\left. \frac{dA}{dt} \right|_{r=5} = 8\pi(5) = 40\pi \text{ cm}^2/\text{s}$$

Link connecting A and r

$$A = \pi r^2$$
$$\frac{dA}{dr} = 2\pi r$$

Air is pumped into a spherical balloon at the rate of 300 cm^3/s. When the radius of the balloon is 15 cm, calculate

(i) the rate at which its radius is increasing.

(ii) the rate at which its surface area is increasing.

Solution:

(i) Air is pumped in at a rate of 300 cm^3/s.

Thus, we are given $\dfrac{dV}{dt} = 300$ and asked to find $\dfrac{dr}{dt}$.

Find = Given × Need

$$\frac{dr}{dt} = \frac{dV}{dt} \times \frac{dr}{dV}$$

$$= 300 \times \frac{1}{4\pi r^2}$$

$$= \frac{300}{4\pi r^2} = \frac{75}{\pi r^2}$$

$$\left.\frac{dr}{dt}\right|_{r=15} = \frac{75}{\pi(15)^2} = \frac{75}{225\pi} = \frac{1}{3\pi} \text{ cm/s}$$

Link connecting V and r

$$V = \tfrac{4}{3}\pi r^3$$

$$\frac{dV}{dr} = 3 \times \tfrac{4}{3}\pi r^2$$

$$\frac{dV}{dr} = 4\pi r^2$$

$$\frac{dr}{dV} = \frac{1}{4\pi r^2}$$

(ii) Let the surface area = S.

Find = Given × Need

$$\frac{dS}{dt} = \frac{dr}{dt} \times \frac{dS}{dr}$$

$$= \frac{1}{3\pi} \times 8\pi r$$

$$= \frac{8r}{3}$$

$$\left.\frac{dS}{dt}\right|_{r=15} = \frac{8(15)}{3} = 40 \text{ cm}^2/\text{s}$$

We are given $\dfrac{dr}{dt} = \dfrac{1}{3\pi}$ and asked to find $\dfrac{dS}{dt}$ when $r = 15$.

Link connecting S and r

$$S = 4\pi r^2$$

$$\frac{dS}{dr} = 8\pi r$$

Complete each of the following derivatives using the chain rule:

1. $\dfrac{dy}{dx} = \dfrac{dy}{du} \times \underline{\hspace{1cm}}$

2. $\dfrac{dV}{dt} = \dfrac{dr}{dt} \times \underline{\hspace{1cm}}$

3. $\dfrac{dS}{dr} = \dfrac{dS}{dt} \times \underline{\hspace{1cm}}$

4. $\dfrac{dA}{dt} = \dfrac{dr}{dt} \times \underline{\hspace{1cm}}$

5. $\dfrac{dh}{dt} = \dfrac{dV}{dt} \times \underline{\hspace{1cm}}$

6. $\dfrac{dA}{dr} = \dfrac{dA}{dt} \times \underline{\hspace{1cm}}$

7. If $\dfrac{dx}{dt} = 5$ and $y = 2x^2 - 3x + 4$, find $\dfrac{dy}{dt}$ in terms of x.

8. If $y = (x^2 - 3x)^3$, find $\dfrac{dy}{dt}$ when $x = 2$, given $\dfrac{dx}{dt} = \dfrac{1}{2}$.

9. If $y = \left(\dfrac{x-1}{x}\right)^2$, find $\dfrac{dx}{dt}$ when $x = 2$, given $\dfrac{dy}{dt} = 4$.

10. The path of a projectile is given by $y = 2x - \dfrac{x^2}{20}$, $\quad x \geqslant 0$.

If $\dfrac{dx}{dt} = 4$, for all t, find $\dfrac{dy}{dt}$ when $x = 5$.

11. The radius of a circle is increasing at a rate of $\dfrac{1}{\pi}$ cm/s. Find the rate of increase of the circumference.

12. The area of a square, of side x cm, is increasing at the rate of 8 cm^2/s. Find an expression, in terms of x, for the rate of increase of the length of a side. Find this rate of increase when $x = 16$ cm.

13. If $\dfrac{dV}{dt} = \dfrac{\pi}{2}$ and $V = \dfrac{4}{3}\pi r^3$, evaluate $\dfrac{dr}{dt}$ at $r = 2$.

14. A spherical snowball melts at the rate of 20 cm^3/h.
What is the rate of change of the radius when:
(i) the radius is r?　　**(ii)** the radius is 2 cm?
What is the rate of change of the surface area when the radius is 5 cm?

15. A metallic cube, of side length x cm, is being heated in a furnace. The side lengths are expanding at the rate of 0.2 cm/s. Find the rates at which the cube's surface area and the cube's volume are changing when $x = 5$ cm.

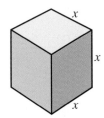

16. If a hemispherical bowl of radius 6 cm contains water to a depth of h cm, the volume of the water is $\frac{1}{3}\pi h^2(18 - h)$. Water is poured into the bowl at a rate of 4 cm^3/s. Find the rate at which the water level is rising when the depth is 2 cm.

17. A vessel is shaped such that when the depth of water is h cm, the volume is given by $v = \sqrt{5 + h^2}$. If the height of the water is increasing at 18 cm/s, calculate the rate at which v is increasing when $h = 2$ cm.

Solving Cubic Equations Using the Newton–Raphson Method

Locating roots by a 'change of sign'

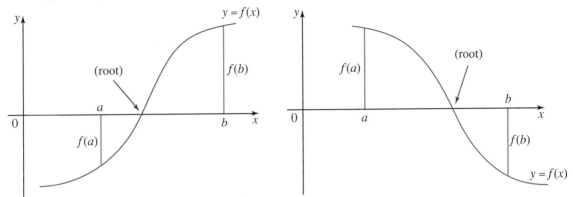

Suppose $f(x)$ is a continuous function between $x = a$ and $x = b$. If $f(a)$ and $f(b)$ have different signs, then somewhere between a and b there must be a root (solution) of the equation $f(x) = 0$.

By looking for a change of sign in the value of $f(x)$ between nearby values of x, the approximate location of the roots of the equation $f(x) = 0$ can be found.

If a cubic equation has real coefficients, then there must be either '**one real root**' or '**three real roots**'. The number of real roots of a cubic equation can be found by determining the turning points $\left(\dfrac{dy}{dx} = 0\right)$ of the curve of the cubic function.

Method for determining the number of real roots of the equation $ax^3 + bx^2 + cx + d = 0$:

1. Let $y = ax^3 + bx^2 + cx + d$.
2. Find $\dfrac{dy}{dx}$ and then solve the equation $\dfrac{dy}{dx} = 0$ to find any turning points.
3. We consider three possible outcomes:

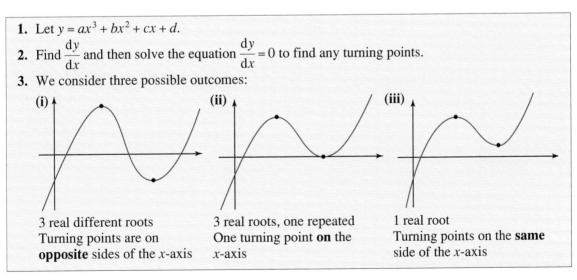

| (i) 3 real different roots Turning points are on **opposite** sides of the x-axis | (ii) 3 real roots, one repeated One turning point **on** the x-axis | (iii) 1 real root Turning points on the **same** side of the x-axis |

Note: It is possible for a cubic equation to have a real triple root. This happens when the graph of the cubic function has a horizontal point of inflection (saddle point) on the x-axis. The graph has no turning points. The equation $(x - k)^3 = 0$ has a triple root, $x = k$. If the graph of $f(x)$ has no turning points, then $f(x) = 0$ has only one real root.

(i) Show that the equation $x^3 + 2x - 5 = 0$ has only one real root.

(ii) Show that the equation $x^3 - 3x + 1 = 0$ has three real roots.

Solution:

(i)   Let $f(x) = x^3 + 2x - 5$

$$f'(x) = 3x^2 + 2$$

Since $3x^2 + 2 > 0$ for all $x \in \mathbf{R}$, the graph of $f(x)$ is always increasing (no turning points). Therefore, the graph of $f(x)$ cuts the x-axis at most once.

$\therefore \ x^3 + 2x - 5 = 0$ has only one real root.

Alternative method,

       $f'(x) = 0$ for a maximum or minimum turning point.

$$\therefore \ 3x^2 + 2 = 0$$
$$3x^2 = -2$$
$$x^2 = -\tfrac{2}{3}$$
$$x = \pm\sqrt{-\tfrac{2}{3}} \text{ non-real roots}$$

Thus, $f'(x) \neq 0$ for all $x \in \mathbf{R}$.

Therefore, $f(x)$ has no turning points.

Therefore, the graph of $f(x)$ cuts the x-axis at most once.

$\therefore \ x^3 + 2x - 5 = 0$ has only one real root.

(ii)   Let $f(x) = x^3 - 3x + 1$

$$f'(x) = 3x^2 - 3$$
$$f''(x) = 6x$$
$$f'(x) = 0 \quad \text{(max/min)}$$
$$\therefore \ 3x^2 - 3 = 0$$
$$x^2 - 1 = 0$$
$$x^2 = 1$$
$$x = \pm 1$$

$f''(1) = 6(1) = 6 > 0 \ \ \therefore$ minimum turning point.

$f''(-1) = 6(-1) = -6 < 0 \ \ \therefore$ maximum turning point.

$x = 1, \quad f(1) = (1)^3 - 3(1) + 1 = -1$

Thus a minimum turning point at $(1, -1)$.

$x = -1, \quad f(-1) = (-1)^3 - 3(-1) + 1 = 3$

Thus a maximum turning point at $(-1, 3)$.

As both turning points are on **opposite** sides of the x-axis, the graph of $f(x)$ cuts the x-axis three times.

$\therefore \ x^3 - 3x + 1 = 0$ has three real roots.

The Newton–Raphson Method

> If x_n is an approximate solution of the equation $f(x) = 0$,
> then x_{n+1} is a better approximation, where:
> $$x_{n+1} = x_n - \frac{f(x_n)}{f'(x_n)}$$

When a first approximation, x_1, to a root of the equation $f(x) = 0$, is found, the Newton–Raphson method uses the approximation to work out a second, more accurate, approximation, x_2. The method then uses x_2 to find an even more accurate approximation, x_3, and so on. It is an iterative (repetitive) procedure and is continued until the required degree of accuracy is achieved.

Example ▼

Show that the equation $1 - 3x - x^3 = 0$ has a root between 0 and 1.

Starting with $x_1 = 0$ as a first approximation of a real root of the equation $1 - 3x - x^3 = 0$, use two iterations of the Newton–Raphson method to find x_2 and x_3, the second and third approximations. Give your answers as fractions.

Solution:

Let $f(x) = 1 - 3x - x^3$

$f(0) = 1 - 3(0) - (0)^3 = 1 > 0$

$f(1) = 1 - 3(1) - (1)^3 = -3 < 0$

Since $f(x)$ changes sign between 0 and 1, the graph of the function $y = f(x)$ must cut the x-axis between 0 and 1.

$\therefore\ 1 - 3x - x^3 = 0$ has a root between 0 and 1.

$$f(x) = 1 - 3x - x^3 \quad\Rightarrow\quad f'(x) = -3 - 3x^2$$

$$x_{n+1} = x_n - \frac{f(x_n)}{f'(x_n)} \quad \text{(Newton–Raphson)}$$

$x_1 = 0 \quad$ (given)

$$x_2 = x_1 - \frac{f(x_1)}{f'(x_1)} = 0 - \frac{f(0)}{f'(0)} = 0 - \frac{1 - 3(0) - (0)^3}{-3 - 3(0)^2} = 0 - \frac{1}{-3} = \frac{1}{3}$$

$$x_3 = x_2 - \frac{f(x_2)}{f'(x_2)}$$

$$= \frac{1}{3} - \frac{f(\frac{1}{3})}{f'(\frac{1}{3})} = \frac{1}{3} - \frac{1 - 3(\frac{1}{3}) - (\frac{1}{3})^3}{-3 - 3(\frac{1}{3})^2} = \frac{1}{3} - \frac{1 - 1 - \frac{1}{27}}{-3 - \frac{1}{3}} = \frac{1}{3} - \frac{-\frac{1}{27}}{-\frac{10}{3}} = \frac{1}{3} - \frac{1}{90} = \frac{29}{90}$$

Let $f(x) = x^3 - kx^2 + 9,$ $k \in \mathbf{R}$ and $k > 0.$

Taking $x_1 = 2$ as the first approximation of one of the roots of $f(x) = 0$, the Newton–Raphson method gives the second approximation as $\dfrac{13}{8}$.

Find the value of k.

Solution:

$$f(x) = x^3 - kx^2 + 9 \Rightarrow f'(x) = 3x^2 - 2kx$$

$$x_2 = x_1 - \frac{f(x_1)}{f'(x_1)} \qquad \text{(Newton–Raphson method)}$$

$$\frac{13}{8} = 2 - \frac{f(2)}{f'(2)} \qquad \text{(put in } x_1 = 2 \text{ and } x_2 = \tfrac{13}{8})$$

$$\frac{13}{8} = 2 - \frac{(2)^3 - k(2)^2 + 9}{3(2)^2 - 2k(2)}$$

$$\frac{13}{8} = 2 - \frac{8 - 4k + 9}{12 - 4k}$$

$$\frac{13}{8} = 2 - \frac{17 - 4k}{12 - 4k}$$

$$\frac{17 - 4k}{12 - 4k} = 2 - \frac{13}{8}$$

$$\frac{17 - 4k}{12 - 4k} = \frac{3}{8}$$

$$136 - 32k = 36 - 12k \qquad \text{(multiply both sides by } 8(12 - 4k))$$

$$-20k = -100$$

$$20k = 100$$

$$k = 5$$

1. Show that the equation $x^3 + x - 5 = 0$ has a root between 1 and 2. Taking $x_1 = 1$, as a first approximation, use the Newton–Raphson method to find x_2, the second approximation.

2. Show that the equation $x^3 + 5x - 3 = 0$ has only one real root and that this root is between 0 and 1. Taking $x_1 = 0.6$ as the first approximation of the real root of the equation, find, using the Newton–Raphson method, x_2, the second approximation, correct to two decimal places.

3. Show that the equation $x^3 - 12x + 6 = 0$ has three real roots.
   Show that one of these roots lies between 0 and 1. Taking $x_1 = \frac{1}{2}$ as a first approximation of the root, apply the Newton–Raphson method once to obtain x_2, the second approximation, giving your answer as a fraction.

4. Given that $f(x) = x^3 - 3x^2 - 1$, show that the equation $f(x) = 0$ has only one real root and that this real root lies in the interval $3 < x < 4$.

Use two iterations of the Newton–Raphson method applied to $f(x) = 0$, with $x_1 = 3$, to find an approximation to the real root, giving your answer correct to three decimal places.

In each of the following, take x_1 as the first approximation of a real root of the given equation. Then, using one iteration of the Newton–Raphson method, find x_2, the second approximation. Write each answer as a fraction.

5. $x^3 - 5 = 0$, $x_1 = 2$

6. $x^3 - 5x = 0$, $x_1 = 2$

7. $x^3 - 3x^2 - 1 = 0$, $x_1 = 3$

8. $x^3 - 5x^2 - x + 6 = 0$, $x_1 = 1$

In each of the following, take x_1 as the first approximation of a real root of the given equation. Then, using two iterations of the Newton–Raphson method, find x_2 and x_3, the second and third approximations. Write your answers as fractions.

9. $x^3 - 4 = 0$, $x_1 = 1$

10. $x^3 + 3x - 1 = 0$, $x_1 = 0$

11. $x^3 - 7x + 5 = 0$, $x_1 = 1$

12. $x^3 - 3x^2 + 3x - 3 = 0$, $x_1 = 2$

13. Let $f(x) = a - x^3$, $a \in \mathbf{R}$ and $a > 0$.
Taking $x_1 = 1$ as the first approximation to the real root of $f(x) = 0$, the Newton–Raphson method gives the second approximation as $x_2 = \frac{4}{3}$. Find the value of a.
Using this value of a, find x_3, the third approximation. Give your answer as a fraction.

14. Let $f(x) = x^3 - kx + 4$, $k \in \mathbf{R}$ and $k > 0$.
Taking $x_1 = 2$ as the first approximation to a real root of $f(x) = 0$, the Newton–Raphson method gives the second approximation as $x_2 = 3$. Find the value of k.
Using this value of k, find x_3, the third approximation. Give your answer as a fraction.

15. The equation $x^3 + ax - 1 = 0$ is known to have a root close to $x = \frac{1}{2}$. When $x = \frac{1}{2}$ is used as the first approximation in the Newton–Raphson method, the second approximation is $\frac{5}{11}$. Find the value of a.

16. **(a)** Write $x + \dfrac{x^2 + 3x}{x + 1}$ as one fraction.

(b) Show that the Newton–Raphson method for approximating a root of the equation $x^3 + x - 6 = 0$, is given by $x_{n+1} = \dfrac{2x_n^3 + 6}{3x_n^2 + 1}$.

Taking 1.5 as a first approximation, apply the Newton–Raphson method once to obtain a better approximation, giving your answer correct to two decimal places.

17. Let $f(x) = x^3 - 3x^2 + k$, $k \in \mathbf{R}$.
(i) Find the coordinates of the maximum, minimum and point of inflexion in terms of k.
(ii) Find the values of k for which the equation $f(x) = 0$ has three real roots.
(iii) If $k = 2$, use the Newton–Raphson method, with first approximation $x_1 = 3$, to find x_2, the second approximation. Write your answer in the form $\dfrac{p}{q}$, $p, q \in \mathbf{N}$.

INTEGRATION

The Indefinite Integral

> Integration is the **reverse** process of differentiation.

The process of finding a function from its derivative is called '**integration**'.
For example, we know that if $f(x) = x^2$, then $f'(x) = 2x$.
Now suppose that we are given $f'(x) = 2x$ and asked to find $f(x)$. In other words, we start with the derivative and work '*backwards*' to the original function.
However, if $f(x) = x^2 + 10$, $f'(x) = 2x$ and if $f(x) = x^2 - 3$, $f'(x) = 2x$.
In fact, if $f(x) = x^2 + c$, then $f'(x) = 2x$, where c is a constant.
In other words, we do not know whether the original function contained a constant term or not.

Notation:

$$\int f'(x)\, dx = f(x) + c$$

The symbol for integration is $\int$, an elongated s.

dx indicates that the integration is with respect to the variable x.
c is called the 'constant of integration'.

Note: $\int 2x\, dx$ is read as 'the integral of $2x\, dx$' or 'the integral of $2x$ with respect to x'.

Basic rule:

$$\int x^n\, dx = \frac{x^{n+1}}{n+1} + c \qquad (n \neq -1)$$

In words: Increase the power by 1 and divide by the new power.

If a is a constant, $\int ax^n\, dx = a\int x^n\, dx = a\,\frac{x^{n+1}}{n+1} + c,\ (n \neq -1)$.

A constant factor of the integrand can be taken outside the symbol of integration.

$$\int (f(x) \pm g(x))\, dx = \int f(x)\, dx \pm \int g(x)\, dx.$$

To integrate a sum or difference, add or subtract the individual integrals.

Note: Before integrating, **all** terms must be written in the form x^n or ax^n, where a is a constant.

There is no 'product', 'quotient' or 'chain' rule in integration.

It is possible to check your answer in integration by differentiating your answer and seeing whether you get back to the original integral.

Example ▼

Find: **(i)** $\int 3x^2\,dx$ **(ii)** $\int \dfrac{1}{x^3}\,dx$ **(iii)** $\int \dfrac{1}{\sqrt{x}}\,dx$

Solution:

(i) $\int 3x^2\,dx$

$= \dfrac{3x^3}{3} + c$

$= x^3 + c$

(ii) $\int \dfrac{1}{x^3}\,dx$

$= \int x^{-3}\,dx$

$= \dfrac{x^{-2}}{-2} + c$

$= -\dfrac{1}{2x^2} + c$

(iii) $\int \dfrac{1}{\sqrt{x}}\,dx$

$= \int x^{-1/2}\,dx$

$= \dfrac{x^{1/2}}{\frac{1}{2}} + c$

$= 2x^{1/2} + c$ or $2\sqrt{x} + c$

Sometimes it is necessary to manipulate the integrand to write each part in the form ax^n.

Example ▼

Find: **(i)** $\int \left(x + \dfrac{1}{x}\right)^2 dx$ **(ii)** $\int \dfrac{3+x}{\sqrt{x}}\,dx$

Solution

(i) $\int \left(x + \dfrac{1}{x}\right)^2 dx$

$= \int \left(x^2 + 2 + \dfrac{1}{x^2}\right) dx$

$= \int (x^2 + 2 + x^{-2})\,dx$

$= \dfrac{x^3}{3} + 2x + \dfrac{x^{-1}}{-1} + c$

$= \tfrac{1}{3}x^3 + 2x - \dfrac{1}{x} + c$

(ii) $\int \left(\dfrac{3+x}{\sqrt{x}}\right) dx$

$= \int \left(\dfrac{3}{x^{1/2}} + \dfrac{x^1}{x^{1/2}}\right) dx$ $\left(\dfrac{a+b}{c} = \dfrac{a}{c} + \dfrac{b}{c}\right)$

$= \int (3x^{-1/2} + x^{1/2})\,dx$

$= \dfrac{3x^{1/2}}{\frac{1}{2}} + \dfrac{x^{3/2}}{\frac{3}{2}} + c$

$= 6x^{1/2} + \tfrac{2}{3}x^{3/2} + c$

Sometimes if we are given some extra information, we may be asked to find the constant of integration or an expression for $f(x)$.

Example ▼

(i) Find the constant of integration, given that $\int (3x^2 + 1)\, dx = 6$ when $x = 2$.

(ii) Find the function $y = f(x)$, given that $f'(x) = 5 - 2x$ and that the graph of $y = f(x)$ passes through the point $(1, 7)$.

Solution:

(i) $\int (3x^2 + 1)\, dx$

$= \dfrac{3x^3}{3} + x + c$

$= x^3 + x + c$

Given: this is $= 6$ when $x = 2$.

$\therefore \quad (2)^3 + (2) + c = 6$

$8 + 2 + c = 6$

$10 + c = 6$

$c = -4$

Thus, the constant of integration is -4.

(ii) **Given:** $f'(x) = 5 - 2x$

$\int f'(x)dx = \int (5 - 2x)\, dx$

(integrate both sides with respect to x)

$f(x) = 5x - x^2 + c$

Given: $f(1) = 7$ (or $y = 7$ when $x = 1$)

$\therefore \quad 5(1) - (1)^2 + c = 7$

$5 - 1 + c = 7$

$4 + c = 7$

$c = 3$

Thus, $f(x) = 3 + 5x - x^2$

Exercise 14.1 ▼

Find:

1. $\int x^3\, dx$

2. $\int x^2\, dx$

3. $\int 5x^4\, dx$

4. $\int -x\, dx$

5. $\int -2x^2\, dx$

6. $\int 5\, dx$

7. $\int -2\, dx$

8. $\int \dfrac{1}{x^2}\, dx$

9. $\int \sqrt{x}\, dx$

10. $\int \dfrac{2}{\sqrt{x}}\, dx$

11. $\int (3x^2 + 8x)\, dx$

12. $\int (x^2 + 2x)\, dx$

13. $\int (2x^2 - 5x)\, dx$

14. $\int \left(x^2 - \dfrac{1}{x^2}\right)\, dx$

15. $\int \left(4x^3 - \dfrac{2}{x^3}\right)\, dx$

16. $\int \left(\sqrt{x} + \dfrac{1}{\sqrt{x}}\right)\, dx$

17. $\int x(2 + x)\, dx$

18. $\int x^2(x + 5)\, dx$

19. $\int \sqrt{x}(x + 1)\, dx$

20. $\int \left(\dfrac{x^2 + 3}{x^2}\right)\, dx$

21. $\int \left(\dfrac{x + 1}{x^3}\right)\, dx$

22. $\int \left(\dfrac{3x^2 - 5}{\sqrt{x}}\right)\, dx$

23. $\int \left(\dfrac{x^4 - 2x^3 + x^2}{x}\right)\, dx$

24. $\int \left(x - \dfrac{1}{x}\right)^2\, dx$

25. $\int \left(x^2 + \dfrac{1}{x}\right)^2\, dx$

26. If $f'(x) = 3x^2 - 2x$, and $f(2) = 9$, find $f(x)$.

27. If $f'(x) = 3x^2 - \sqrt{x}$ and $f(0) = 4$, find $f(x)$.

28. If $f'(t) = 4t^3 - 6t$ and $f(-2) = 8$, find $f(t)$.

29. A curve contains the point $(\frac{1}{2}, 3)$ and its slope at any point (x, y) on the curve is given by $f'(x) = 16x^3 + 2x + 1$. Find $f(x)$.

30. A curve contains the point $(1, 7)$ and its slope at any point (x, y) on the curve is given by $\dfrac{dy}{dx} = 3x^2 + 4$. Find the equation of the curve.

The Definite Integral

$$\int_a^b f'(x)\, dx = \left[f(x)\right]_a^b = f(b) - f(a)$$

We call $\displaystyle\int_a^b f'(x)\, dx$ a **definite integral**, as it gives a definite answer.

The dx indicates that the limits a and b are x limits.
The constant a is called the **lower limit** of the integral.
The constant b is called **upper limit** of the integral.
The is no constant of integration when we evaluate definite integrals, as they cancel each other out.

$$\int_a^b f'(x)\, dx = -\int_b^a f'(x)\, dx$$

If the limits are swopped, the sign of the definite integral is changed.
Definite integrals can be used to find the area beneath a curve and volumes of rotation.

Example ▼

Evaluate: **(i)** $\displaystyle\int_1^3 (x^2 + 2x)\,dx$ **(ii)** $\displaystyle\int_1^4 \left(\sqrt{x} - \frac{3}{x}\right)^2 dx$

Solution:

(i)
$$\int_1^3 (x^2 + 2x)\,dx$$
$$= \left[\frac{x^3}{3} + x^2\right]_1^3$$
$$= \left[\frac{(3)^3}{3} + (3)^2\right] - \left[\frac{(1)^3}{3} + (1)^2\right]$$
$$= [\tfrac{27}{3} + 9] - [\tfrac{1}{3} + 1]$$
$$= 18 - \tfrac{4}{3}$$
$$= 16\tfrac{2}{3}$$

(ii)
$$\int_1^4 \left(\sqrt{x} - \frac{3}{x}\right)^2 dx = \int_1^4 \left(x - \frac{6}{\sqrt{x}} + \frac{9}{x^2}\right) dx$$
$$= \int_1^4 (x - 6x^{-1/2} + 9x^{-2})\,dx$$
$$= \left[\frac{x^2}{2} - \frac{6x^{1/2}}{\frac{1}{2}} + \frac{9x^{-1}}{-1}\right]_1^4$$
$$= \left[\frac{x^2}{2} - 12\sqrt{x} - \frac{9}{x}\right]_1^4$$
$$= \left[\frac{4^2}{2} - 12\sqrt{4} - \frac{9}{4}\right] - \left[\frac{1^2}{2} - 12\sqrt{1} - \frac{9}{1}\right]$$
$$= [8 - 24 - 2\tfrac{1}{4}] - [\tfrac{1}{2} - 12 - 9]$$
$$= -18\tfrac{1}{4} + 20\tfrac{1}{2} = 2\tfrac{1}{4}$$

Exercise 14.2 ▼

Evaluate each of the following definite integrals:

1. $\displaystyle\int_1^2 3x^2\,dx$ **2.** $\displaystyle\int_0^2 4x^3\,dx$ **3.** $\displaystyle\int_1^2 x^3\,dx$ **4.** $\displaystyle\int_1^4 \sqrt{x}\,dx$

5. $\displaystyle\int_0^4 (4x - x^2)\,dx$ **6.** $\displaystyle\int_1^3 x(2 - 3x)\,dx$ **7.** $\displaystyle\int_{-2}^2 x(x + 4)\,dx$ **8.** $\displaystyle\int_2^3 \frac{1}{x^2}\,dx$

9. $\displaystyle\int_{-1}^1 \frac{1}{x^3}\,dx$ **10.** $\displaystyle\int_2^4 \left(\frac{1}{x^2} + 3\right) dx$ **11.** $\displaystyle\int_4^9 \left(1 - \frac{3}{\sqrt{x}}\right) dx$ **12.** $\displaystyle\int_1^4 \left(3 - \frac{1}{\sqrt{x}}\right) dx$

13. $\displaystyle\int_1^2 \left(x + \frac{1}{x}\right)^2 dx$ **14.** $\displaystyle\int_1^{16} \left(\frac{\sqrt{x} - 4}{\sqrt{x}}\right) dx$ **15.** $\displaystyle\int_1^2 \frac{x^2 + x}{x^4}\,dx$ **16.** $\displaystyle\int_1^4 \frac{3x - 2\sqrt{x}}{x}\,dx$

17. Express $\dfrac{4x^2 - 9}{4x - 6}$ in the form $\dfrac{1}{a}(ax + b)$ and, hence, evaluate $\displaystyle\int_0^2 \frac{4x^2 - 9}{4x - 6}\,dx$.

18. Express $\dfrac{x^3 - 8}{x - 2}$ in the form $x^2 + px + q$ and, hence, evaluate $\displaystyle\int_0^1 \frac{x^3 - 8}{x - 2}\,dx$.

In each of the following find the value of $k > 0$:

19. $\displaystyle\int_0^k x^2 \, \mathrm{d}x = 9$

20. $\displaystyle\int_1^k (2x + 3) \, \mathrm{d}x = 6$

21. $\displaystyle\int_0^9 \frac{k}{\sqrt{x}} \, \mathrm{d}x = 30$

22. Verify that $\displaystyle\int_{4-k}^{4+k} (x - 4) \, \mathrm{d}x = 0$

Integration by Substitution

Some integrals may be found more easily by using substitution. When evaluating an indefinite integral by substitution the answer **must be transformed back to a function of the original variable**.

Example ▼

Find: **(i)** $\displaystyle\int 2x(x^2 + 1)^4 \, \mathrm{d}x$ **(ii)** $\displaystyle\int x\sqrt{1 - x^2} \, \mathrm{d}x$

Solution:

(i) $\displaystyle\int 2x(x^2 + 1)^4 \, \mathrm{d}x$

Substitution

$$\text{let} \quad u = x^2 + 1$$
$$\mathrm{d}u = 2x \, \mathrm{d}x$$

$$\int 2x(x^2 + 1)^4 \, \mathrm{d}u$$

$$= \int u^4 \, \mathrm{d}u$$

$$= \frac{u^5}{5} + c$$

$$= \frac{(x^2 + 1)^5}{5} + c$$

(ii) $\displaystyle\int x\sqrt{1 - x^2} \, \mathrm{d}x$

Substitution

$$\text{let} \quad u = 1 - x^2$$
$$\mathrm{d}u = -2x \, \mathrm{d}x$$
$$-\tfrac{1}{2} \, \mathrm{d}u = x \, \mathrm{d}x$$

$$\int x\sqrt{1 - x^2} \, \mathrm{d}x$$

$$= -\tfrac{1}{2} \int u^{1/2} \, \mathrm{d}u$$

$$= -\tfrac{1}{2} \cdot \frac{u^{3/2}}{\frac{3}{2}} + c$$

$$= -\tfrac{1}{2} \cdot \tfrac{2}{3} u^{3/2} + c$$

$$= -\tfrac{1}{3} u^{3/2} + c$$

$$= -\tfrac{1}{3} (1 - x^2)^{3/2} + c$$

Sometimes we have to rearrange as well as substitute.

Evaluate: $\displaystyle\int_1^3 \frac{x}{\sqrt{x-1}}\,dx$

Solution:

$$\int \frac{x}{\sqrt{x-1}}\,dx$$

$$= \int \left(\frac{u+1}{u^{1/2}}\right)du = \int (u^{1/2} + u^{-1/2})\,du$$

Substitution

let $u = x - 1$
$du = dx$
We must also do some
rearranging
$u = x - 1$
$u + 1 = x$

$$= \frac{u^{3/2}}{\frac{3}{2}} + \frac{u^{1/2}}{\frac{1}{2}}$$

$$= \tfrac{2}{3}u^{3/2} + 2u^{1/2}$$

$$= \left[\tfrac{2}{3}(x-1)^{3/2} + 2(x-1)^{1/2}\right]$$

$$\therefore \int_1^3 \frac{x}{\sqrt{x-1}}\,dx \qquad (2^{3/2} = 2^1 \cdot 2^{1/2} = 2\sqrt{2})$$

$$= \left[\tfrac{2}{3}(x-1)^{3/2} + 2(x-1)^{1/2}\right]_1^3$$

$$= \left[\tfrac{2}{3}(2)^{3/2} + 2(2)^{1/2}\right] - \left[\tfrac{2}{3}(1-1)^{3/2} + 2(1-1)^{1/2}\right] = \tfrac{2}{3}(2\sqrt{2}) + 2\sqrt{2} = 2\sqrt{2}(\tfrac{2}{3} + 1) = 2\sqrt{2} \cdot \tfrac{5}{3} = \frac{10\sqrt{2}}{3}$$

However, rather than remain with the limits for x, which necessitates expressing the integral in terms of x, we may change the limits to those of u.

Change of limits

$$\therefore \int_1^3 \frac{x}{\sqrt{x-1}}\,dx$$

$$= \int_0^2 \frac{u+1}{u^{1/2}}\,du$$

$u = x - 1$	
$x = 3$	$x = 1$
$u = 3 - 1$	$u = 1 - 1$
$u = 2$	$u = 0$

$$= \left[\tfrac{2}{3}u^{3/2} + 2u^{1/2}\right]_0^2$$

$$= \left[\tfrac{2}{3}(2)^{3/2} + 2(2)^{1/2}\right] - \left[\tfrac{2}{3}(0)^{3/2} + 2(0)^{1/2}\right] = \tfrac{2}{3}(2\sqrt{2}) + 2(\sqrt{2}) = 2\sqrt{2}(\tfrac{2}{3} + 1) = 2\sqrt{2} \cdot \tfrac{5}{3} = \frac{10\sqrt{2}}{3}$$

To change the limits to those of u, or not, is a matter of personal choice. However, it often turns that the substitution is easier when the limits are changed to those of u.

Choosing the substitution is a skill most students take a long time to master. However, do not be afraid to try a substitution. If you use a wrong one, you will soon find out. So go back to the start and try a different substitution.

Find the following integrals, in each case using the suggested substitution:

1. $\int (x+1)^4\, dx$ $(u = x + 1)$ 2. $\int 2x(x^2 - 4)^3\, dx$ $(u = x^2 - 4)$

3. $\int 4x(2x^2 - 3)^3\, dx$ $(u = 2x^2 - 3)$ 4. $\int 3x^2(x^3 + 1)^5\, dx$ $(u = x^3 + 1)$

5. $\int \sqrt{4x + 3}\, dx$ $(u = 4x + 3)$ 6. $\int 2x\sqrt{x^2 + 5}\, dx$ $(u = x^2 + 5)$

7. $\int x\sqrt{x^2 - 3}\, dx$ $(u = x^2 - 3)$ 8. $\int \dfrac{3x^2 + 2}{(x^3 + 2x)^6}\, dx$ $(u = x^3 + 2x)$

9. $\int x^2\sqrt{x^3 - 2}\, dx$ $(u = x^3 - 2)$ 10. $\int \dfrac{x}{\sqrt{x - 3}}\, dx$ $(u = x - 3)$

Find each of the following:

11. $\int x(x^2 + 1)^5\, dx$ 12. $\int \dfrac{x}{\sqrt{x^2 + 3}}\, dx$ 13. $\int \dfrac{4x}{(1 + x^2)^3}\, dx$

14. $\int x(x + 3)^5\, dx$ 15. $\int x(x - 2)^4\, dx$ 16. $\int \dfrac{x}{\sqrt{x + 4}}\, dx$

Evaluate each of the following:

17. $\displaystyle\int_1^2 2x(x^2 + 1)^3\, dx$ 18. $\displaystyle\int_1^2 x^2(x^3 + 1)^3\, dx$ 19. $\displaystyle\int_0^1 \dfrac{x^2}{(x^3 + 1)^4}\, dx$

20. $\displaystyle\int_0^1 x(1 + x^2)^5\, dx$ 21. $\displaystyle\int_3^{\sqrt{14}} x\sqrt{x^2 - 5}\, dx$ 22. $\displaystyle\int_1^{\sqrt{6}} \dfrac{2x}{\sqrt{x^2 + 3}}\, dx$

23. Verify that   (i) $\displaystyle\int_3^4 x\sqrt{25 - x^2}\, dx = \frac{37}{3}$ (ii) $\displaystyle\int_0^{\sqrt{3}} \dfrac{x}{\sqrt{x^2 + 1}}\, dx = 1$

Integrating Trigonometric Functions

$$\int \cos(nx + k)\, dx = \frac{\sin(nx + k)}{n} + c$$

$$\int \sin(nx + k)\, dx = -\frac{\cos(nx + k)}{n} + c$$

These integrals can be written down directly without substitution.

Note: When integrating the angle **must** be in radians.

Find: **(i)** $\int \cos 3x \, dx$ **(ii)** $\int \sin(5x + 2) \, dx$ **(iii)** $\int \left[\cos 2\theta + \sin\left(4\theta - \frac{\pi}{2}\right) \right] d\theta$

Solution:

(i) $\int \cos 3x \, dx = \dfrac{\sin 3x}{3} + c$

(ii) $\int \sin(5x + 2) \, dx = -\dfrac{\cos(5x + 2)}{5} + c$

(iii) $\int \left[\cos 2\theta + \sin\left(4\theta - \dfrac{\pi}{2}\right) \right] d\theta = \dfrac{\sin 2\theta}{2} - \dfrac{\cos\left(4\theta - \dfrac{\pi}{2}\right)}{4} + c$

Products $\int \sin mx \cdot \cos nx$

Always write the bigger angle first and then use the formulae on page 9 of the tables to change the product into a sum or difference.

Evaluate: $\displaystyle\int_0^{\pi/6} \cos 2\theta \sin 4\theta \, d\theta$

Solution:

$$\int_0^{\pi/6} \cos 2\theta \sin 4\theta \, d\theta$$

$$= \int_0^{\pi/6} \sin 4\theta \cos 2\theta \, d\theta \quad \text{[put bigger angle first]}$$

$$= \int_0^{\pi/6} \tfrac{1}{2}\left[\sin(4\theta + 2\theta) + \sin(4\theta - 2\theta)\right] d\theta$$

(from page 9, $\sin A \cos B = \tfrac{1}{2}[\sin(A + B) + \sin(A - B)]$)

$$= \frac{1}{2} \int_0^{\pi/6} (\sin 6\theta + \sin 2\theta) \, d\theta$$

$$= \frac{1}{2}\left[-\frac{\cos 6\theta}{6} - \frac{\cos 2\theta}{2} \right]_0^{\pi/6}$$

$$= -\frac{1}{2}\left[\frac{\cos 6\theta}{6} + \frac{\cos 2\theta}{2} \right]_0^{\pi/6}$$

$$= -\frac{1}{2}\left[\left(\frac{\cos \pi}{6} + \frac{\cos \frac{\pi}{3}}{2} \right) - \left(\frac{\cos 0}{6} + \frac{\cos 0}{2} \right) \right]$$

$$= -\tfrac{1}{2}\left[\left(-\tfrac{1}{6} + \tfrac{1}{4}\right) - \left(\tfrac{1}{6} + \tfrac{1}{2}\right) \right]$$

$$= -\tfrac{1}{2}\left(-\tfrac{7}{12}\right) = \tfrac{7}{24}$$

Even powers of cos x and sin x

To integrate even powers of cos x and sin x, rewrite the integrand using the double angle identities on page 9 of the tables. Find:

$$\cos^2 A = \tfrac{1}{2}(1 + \cos 2A) \qquad \text{and} \qquad \sin^2 A = \tfrac{1}{2}(1 - \cos 2A)$$

Example ▼

Evaluate: **(i)** $\displaystyle\int_0^{\pi/4} \sin^2 x\, dx$ **(ii)** $\displaystyle\int_{\pi/8}^{\pi/4} 2\cos^2 4\theta\, d\theta$

Solution:

(i) $\displaystyle\int_0^{\pi/4} \sin^2 x\, dx$

$= \displaystyle\int_0^{\pi/4} \tfrac{1}{2}(1 - \cos 2x)\, dx$

$= \dfrac{1}{2}\displaystyle\int_0^{\pi/4} (1 - \cos 2x)\, dx$

$= \dfrac{1}{2}\left[x - \dfrac{\sin 2x}{2} \right]_0^{\pi/4}$

$= \dfrac{1}{2}\left(\left[\dfrac{\pi}{4} - \dfrac{\sin \frac{\pi}{2}}{2} \right] - \left[0 - \dfrac{\sin 0}{2} \right] \right)$

$= \dfrac{1}{2}\left(\left[\dfrac{\pi}{4} - \dfrac{1}{2} \right] - [0 - 0] \right)$

$= \dfrac{1}{2}\left[\dfrac{\pi}{4} - \dfrac{1}{2} \right] = \dfrac{\pi}{8} - \dfrac{1}{4}$

(ii) $\displaystyle\int_{\pi/8}^{\pi/4} 2\cos^2 4\theta\, d\theta$

$= \displaystyle\int_{\pi/8}^{\pi/4} 2 \cdot \tfrac{1}{2}(1 + \cos 8\theta)\, d\theta$

$= \displaystyle\int_{\pi/8}^{\pi/4} (1 - \cos 8\theta)\, d\theta$

$= \left[\theta + \dfrac{\sin 8\theta}{8} \right]_{\pi/8}^{\pi/4}$

$= \left[\dfrac{\pi}{4} + \dfrac{\sin 2\pi}{8} \right] - \left[\dfrac{\pi}{8} + \dfrac{\sin \pi}{8} \right]$

$= \left[\dfrac{\pi}{4} + 0 \right] - \left[\dfrac{\pi}{8} + 0 \right]$

$= \dfrac{\pi}{4} - \dfrac{\pi}{8} = \dfrac{\pi}{8}$

Exercise 14.4 ▼

1. $\displaystyle\int \cos 2x\, dx$ **2.** $\displaystyle\int \sin 4x\, dx$ **3.** $3\displaystyle\int \cos 3x\, dx$

4. $\displaystyle\int \sin(2x + 3)\, dx$ **5.** $\displaystyle\int \cos(5x + 4)\, dx$ **6.** $\displaystyle\int \sin\left(8x - \dfrac{\pi}{4}\right) dx$

7. $\displaystyle\int (\cos 4\theta - \sin 2\theta)\, d\theta$ **8.** $8\displaystyle\int (\cos 2\theta - \sin 8\theta)\, d\theta$ **9.** $\displaystyle\int 2\sin 4x \cos 2x\, dx$

10. $\displaystyle\int 2\cos 6x \sin x\, dx$ **11.** $\displaystyle\int \sin 3x \sin 5x\, dx$ **12.** $\displaystyle\int \cos 2x \cos 3x\, dx$

13. $\displaystyle\int \cos^2 x\, dx$ **14.** $\displaystyle\int 2\sin^2 2\theta\, d\theta$ **15.** $\displaystyle\int 4\sin^2 3x\, dx$

16. $\displaystyle\int \cos^2 5\theta\, d\theta$

Evaluate each of the following:

17. $\displaystyle\int_0^{\pi/4} \cos\theta\, d\theta$

18. $\displaystyle\int_0^{\pi/2} \cos 2x\, dx$

19. $\displaystyle 3\int_0^{\pi/4} \sin 4x\, dx$

20. $\displaystyle\int_0^{\pi/2} \cos 3x \cos 2x\, dx$

21. $\displaystyle\int_0^{\pi/6} \cos 2x \sin 4x\, dx$

22. $\displaystyle\int_0^{\pi/4} \cos^2 x\, dx$

23. $\displaystyle\int_0^{\pi/6} \cos^2 3x\, dx$

24. $\displaystyle 2\int_{\pi/8}^{\pi/4} 2\sin^2 4\theta\, d\theta$

For integrals of the form $\displaystyle\int \cos^2 x \sin x\, dx,\ \int \sin^2 x \cos x\, dx$ or $\displaystyle\int \cos^4 x \sin x\, dx$:

the substitution required is let u = (trigonometric function with the even power).

25. Evaluate: **(i)** $\displaystyle\int_0^{\pi/2} \cos^2 x \sin x\, dx$ **(ii)** $\displaystyle\int_0^{\pi/2} \cos\theta(2 + 3\sin^2\theta)\, d\theta$

26. Find $\displaystyle\int \sin^2 x \cos x\, dx$. Hence, or otherwise, evaluate $\displaystyle\int_0^{\pi/2} \cos^3 x\, dx$.

(**Hint:** Let $\cos^3 x = \cos^2 x \cos x = (1 - \sin^2 x)\cos x$.)

Integration of Exponential Functions

$$\int e^{ax}\, dx = \frac{e^{ax}}{a} + c \qquad \text{or} \qquad \int e^{ax+b}\, dx = \frac{e^{ax+b}}{a} + c$$

These integrals can be written down directly without substitution.
However, if the power of e is not ax or $ax + b$, we use the method of substitution.

The substitution is: let u = (power of e)

Example ▼

(i) Find $\displaystyle\int e^{4x-3}\, dx$ **(ii) Evaluate** $\displaystyle\int_0^1 4xe^{x^2}\, dx$

Solution:

(i) $\displaystyle\int e^{4x-3}\, dx = \frac{e^{4x-3}}{4} + c$

(ii) $\displaystyle\int_0^1 4xe^{x^2}\, dx$

Substitution

$\displaystyle\int 4xe^{x^2}\, dx = 2\int e^u\, du$

$\qquad = 2e^u$

$\qquad = 2e^{x^2}$

$u = x^2$	(power of e)
$du = 2x\, dx$	
$2\, du = 4x\, dx$	

$\therefore\ \displaystyle\int_0^1 4xe^{x^2}\, dx = 2\big[e^{x^2}\big]_0^1 = 2\big[e^1 - e^0\big] = 2(e - 1)$

Evaluate: $\displaystyle\int_0^1 (x+2)e^{x(x+4)}\,dx$.

Solution:

$$\int (x+2)e^{x(x+4)}\,dx$$

$$= \int (x+2)e^{x^2+4x}\,dx$$

$$= \tfrac{1}{2}\int e^u\,du$$

$$= \tfrac{1}{2}e^u = \tfrac{1}{2}e^{x^2+4x}$$

$$\therefore \int_0^1 (x+2)e^{x^2+4x}\,dx = \tfrac{1}{2}\Big[e^{x^2+4x}\Big]_0^1 = \tfrac{1}{2}(e^5 - e^0) = \tfrac{1}{2}(e^5 - 1)$$

Substitution

$$u = x^2 + 4x$$
$$du = (2x+4)\,dx$$
$$\tfrac{1}{2}\,du = (x+2)\,dx$$

Exercise 14.5 ▼

Find:

1. $\displaystyle\int e^{3x}\,dx$ **2.** $\displaystyle\int e^{2x+3}\,dx$ **3.** $\displaystyle\int e^{-4x}\,dx$ **4.** $\displaystyle\int e^{1-3x}\,dx$

5. $\displaystyle\int \frac{1}{e^{2x}}\,dx$ **6.** $\displaystyle 2\int e^{x/2}\,dx$ **7.** $\displaystyle\int (e^{2x} + e^x)\,dx$ **8.** $\displaystyle\int\left(e^{3x} - \frac{1}{e^{3x}}\right)dx$

9. $\displaystyle\int 3x^2 e^{x^3}\,dx$ **10.** $\displaystyle\int (2x+3)e^{x^2+3x}\,dx$ **11.** $\displaystyle\int (1 + \cos x)e^{x+\sin x}\,dx$

Evaluate each of the following:

12. $\displaystyle\int_0^1 e^{2x}\,dx$ **13.** $\displaystyle\int_{-1}^1 e^{3x-1}\,dx$ **14.** $\displaystyle\int_0^2 e^{4x-1}\,dx$

15. $\displaystyle\int_0^1 2x e^{x^2+1}\,dx$ **16.** $\displaystyle\int_0^2 \frac{e^{2x}-2}{e^x}\,dx$ **17.** $\displaystyle\int_2^3 (x-1)e^{x(x-2)}\,dx$

18. Evaluate $\displaystyle\int_0^{\pi/2} \cos x\, e^{\sin x}\,dx$. (Hint: let $u = \sin x$)

19. Evaluate $\displaystyle\int_0^1 \frac{e^x}{1+e^x}\,dx$. (Hint: let $u = 1 + e^x$)

20. Evaluate $\displaystyle\int_0^{\ln 2} \frac{e^x}{e^x + 3}\,dx$.

21. Evaluate $\displaystyle\int_0^1 \frac{e^{\sqrt{x}}}{\sqrt{x}}\,dx$. $\left(\text{Hint: } \dfrac{e^{\sqrt{x}}}{\sqrt{x}} = \dfrac{1}{\sqrt{x}}\,e^{\sqrt{x}}\right)$

Integrals leading to a Logarithmic Function

$$\int \frac{1}{x}\,dx = \ln x + c \quad \text{or} \quad \int \frac{1}{ax+b}\,dx = \frac{\ln(ax+b)}{a} + c$$

These integrals can be written down directly without substitution.
However, in many cases we have to use the method of substitution and often, after the substitution, there is also some rearranging to do.

The substitution is: let $u = $ (the bottom).

Notes:
$$\int \frac{5}{x}\,dx = \int 5\frac{1}{x}\,dx = 5\int \frac{1}{x}\,dx = 5\ln x + c$$

$$\int \frac{dx}{x} = \int \frac{1}{x}\,dx = \ln x + c$$

$$\int \frac{f'(x)}{f(x)} = \ln f(x) + c$$

If the top is the derivative of the bottom, then the answer is $\ln$ (bottom) $+ c$,

i.e. $\int \dfrac{\text{derivative of the bottom}}{\text{bottom}} = \ln$ (bottom) $+ c$

This can also be written down directly without substitution.

Example ▼

Find: (i) $\displaystyle\int \frac{3}{5x+2}\,dx$ (ii) $\displaystyle\int \frac{2x}{x^2+3}\,dx$

Solution:

(i) $\displaystyle\int \frac{3}{5x+2}\,dx = 3\int \frac{1}{5x+2}\,dx$

Substitution

$$u = 5x + 2 \text{ (bottom)}$$
$$du = 5\,dx$$
$$\tfrac{1}{5}\,du = dx$$

$\therefore\ 3\displaystyle\int \frac{1}{5x+2}\,dx = 3 \cdot \frac{1}{5}\int \frac{1}{u}\,du$
$$= \tfrac{3}{5}\ln u + c$$
$$= \tfrac{3}{5}\ln (5x+2) + c$$

(ii) $\displaystyle\int \frac{2x}{x^2+3}\,dx$

Substitution

$$u = x^2 + 3 \text{ (bottom)}$$
$$du = 2x\,dx$$

$\therefore\ \displaystyle\int \frac{2x}{x^2+3}\,dx$
$$= \int \frac{1}{u}\,du$$
$$= \ln u + c$$
$$= \ln (x^2 + 3) + c$$

Evaluate: $\displaystyle\int_0^2 \frac{x}{x+2}\,dx.$

Solution:

Substitution

$$\int \frac{x}{x+2}\,dx = \int \frac{u-2}{u}\,du$$

$$= \int \left(1 - \frac{2}{u}\right)du$$

$$= \int \left(1 - 2\frac{1}{u}\right)du$$

$$= u - 2\ln u$$

$$= (x+2) - 2\ln(x+2)$$

$$\therefore \int_0^2 \frac{x}{x+2}\,dx = \Big[(x+2) - 2\ln(x+2)\Big]_0^2$$

$$= (4 - 2\ln 4) - (2 - 2\ln 2)$$

$$= 4 - 2\ln 4 - 2 + 2\ln 2$$

$$= 2 - 2(\ln 4 - \ln 2)$$

$$= 2 - 2\ln\left(\tfrac{4}{2}\right) = 2 - 2\ln 2$$

$u = x + 2$
$du = dx$
We must also do some rearranging
$u = x + 2$
$u - 2 = x$

Find:

1. $\displaystyle\int \frac{1}{x+2}\,dx$ **2.** $\displaystyle\int \frac{3}{x-5}\,dx$ **3.** $\displaystyle\int \frac{1}{2x}\,dx$ **4.** $\displaystyle\int \frac{4}{4x+5}\,dx$

5. $\displaystyle\int \frac{2x}{x^2+1}\,dx$ **6.** $\displaystyle\int \frac{8}{4x+3}\,dx$ **7.** $\displaystyle\int \frac{2}{1-2x}\,dx$ **8.** $\displaystyle\int \frac{x}{1+x^2}\,dx$

Evaluate each of the following:

9. $\displaystyle\int_1^2 \frac{1}{x}\,dx$ **10.** $\displaystyle\int_0^4 \frac{5}{x+1}\,dx$ **11.** $\displaystyle\int_1^2 \frac{3x^2}{x^3+1}\,dx$ **12.** $\displaystyle\int_3^4 \frac{2x-6}{x^2-6x+10}\,dx$

13. $\displaystyle\int_1^2 \frac{x^2+1}{x}\,dx = \frac{a}{b} + \ln b,$ $a, b \in \mathbf{N}.$ Evaluate $\sqrt{a^2 + 3b + 1}.$

14. Evaluate: **(i)** $\displaystyle\int_0^6 \frac{x}{x+2}\,dx$ **(ii)** $\displaystyle\int_3^4 \frac{x}{x-2}\,dx$ **(iii)** $\displaystyle\int_1^3 \frac{x}{x+1}\,dx$

15. Evaluate: **(i)** $\ln\sqrt{e}$ **(ii)** $\displaystyle\int_{\sqrt{e}}^e \frac{1}{x}\,dx$

Integrals of the Form $\displaystyle\int \frac{dx}{\sqrt{a^2 - x^2}}$ and $\displaystyle\int \frac{dx}{a^2 + x^2}$

$$\int \frac{dx}{\sqrt{a^2 - x^2}} = \sin^{-1}\frac{x}{a} + c$$

and

$$\int \frac{dx}{a^2 + x^2} = \frac{1}{a}\tan^{-1}\frac{x}{a} + c$$

These integrals are on page 41 of the tables and can be written down directly as long as the coefficient of x^2 is 1.

Example ▼

Find: (i) $\displaystyle\int \frac{dx}{\sqrt{16 - x^2}}$ (ii) $\displaystyle\int \frac{dx}{9 + x^2}$

Solution:

(i)
$$\int \frac{dx}{\sqrt{16 - x^2}}$$
$$= \int \frac{dx}{\sqrt{4^2 - x^2}}$$
$$= \sin^{-1}\frac{x}{4} + c$$

(ii)
$$\int \frac{dx}{9 + x^2}$$
$$= \int \frac{dx}{3^2 + x^2}$$
$$= \tfrac{1}{3}\tan^{-1}\frac{x}{3} + c$$

When the coefficient of x^2 is not 1 we use a substitution. If we use u as the new variable, we arrange our substitution so that the coefficient of u^2 is 1.

Example ▼

Evaluate: (i) $\displaystyle\int_0^{1/4} \frac{dx}{\sqrt{1 - 4x^2}}$ (ii) $\displaystyle\int_0^{2/3} \frac{dx}{4 + 9x^2}$

Solution:

(i) $\displaystyle\int \frac{dx}{\sqrt{1-4x^2}} = \int \frac{dx}{\sqrt{1^2-(2x)^2}}$

$\qquad$ Substitution

$$\begin{aligned} u &= 2x \\ du &= 2\,dx \\ \tfrac{1}{2}\,du &= dx \end{aligned}$$

$\qquad = \dfrac{1}{2}\displaystyle\int \dfrac{du}{\sqrt{1^2-u^2}}$

$\qquad = \tfrac{1}{2}\sin^{-1}u = \tfrac{1}{2}\sin^{-1}2x$

$\therefore \displaystyle\int_0^{1/4} \frac{dx}{\sqrt{1-4x^2}} = \tfrac{1}{2}\Big[\sin^{-1}2x\Big]_0^{1/4}$

$\qquad = \tfrac{1}{2}\Big[\sin^{-1}\tfrac{1}{2} - \sin^{-1}0\Big]$

$\qquad = \dfrac{1}{2}\left[\dfrac{\pi}{6}-0\right] = \dfrac{\pi}{12}$

(ii) $\displaystyle\int \frac{dx}{4+9x^2} = \int \frac{dx}{2^2+(3x)^2}$

$\qquad$ Substitution

$$\begin{aligned} u &= 3x \\ du &= 3\,dx \\ \tfrac{1}{3}\,du &= dx \end{aligned}$$

$\qquad = \dfrac{1}{3}\displaystyle\int \dfrac{du}{2^2+u^2}$

$\qquad = \tfrac{1}{3}\cdot\tfrac{1}{2}\tan^{-1}\dfrac{u}{2} = \tfrac{1}{6}\tan^{-1}\dfrac{3x}{2}$

$\therefore \displaystyle\int_0^{2/3} \frac{dx}{4+9x^2} = \tfrac{1}{6}\Big[\tan^{-1}\tfrac{3x}{2}\Big]_0^{2/3}$

$\qquad = \tfrac{1}{6}\Big[\tan^{-1}1 - \tan^{-1}0\Big]$

$\qquad = \dfrac{1}{6}\left[\dfrac{\pi}{4}-0\right] = \dfrac{\pi}{24}$

Exercise 14.7 ▼

Find:

1. $\displaystyle\int \frac{dx}{\sqrt{4-x^2}}$ $\qquad$ **2.** $\displaystyle\int \frac{dx}{\sqrt{9-x^2}}$ $\qquad$ **3.** $\displaystyle\int \frac{dx}{\sqrt{25-x^2}}$

4. $\displaystyle\int \frac{dx}{16+x^2}$ $\qquad$ **5.** $\displaystyle\int \frac{3\,dx}{9+x^2}$ $\qquad$ **6.** $\displaystyle\int \frac{10\,dx}{25+x^2}$

In questions 7–12, use the suggested substitution:

7. $\displaystyle\int \frac{dx}{9+4x^2}, \qquad u = 2x$ $\qquad$ **8.** $\displaystyle\int \frac{dx}{16+9x^2}, \qquad u = 3x$ $\qquad$ **9.** $\displaystyle\int \frac{dx}{\sqrt{4-25x^2}}, \qquad u = 5x$

10. $\displaystyle\int \frac{dx}{1+16x^2}, \qquad u = 4x$ $\qquad$ **11.** $\displaystyle\int \frac{2\,dx}{1+4x^2}, \qquad u = 2x$ $\qquad$ **12.** $\displaystyle\int \frac{4\,dx}{\sqrt{9-16x^2}}, \qquad u = 4x$

Evaluate each of the following:

13. $\displaystyle\int_0^2 \frac{dx}{4+x^2}$ $\qquad$ **14.** $\displaystyle\int_0^3 \frac{dx}{9+x^2}$ $\qquad$ **15.** $\displaystyle\int_0^1 \frac{dx}{\sqrt{4-x^2}}$

16. $\displaystyle\int_2^4 \frac{dx}{\sqrt{16-x^2}}$ $\qquad$ **17.** $\displaystyle\int_{1/\sqrt{3}}^1 \frac{dx}{1+x^2}$ $\qquad$ **18.** $\displaystyle\int_{1/2}^{\sqrt{3}/2} \frac{dx}{\sqrt{1-x^2}}$

19. $\displaystyle\int_0^{1/3} \frac{3\,dx}{\sqrt{1-9x^2}}$ $\qquad$ **20.** $\displaystyle\int_0^{2/3} \frac{dx}{4+9x^2}$ $\qquad$ **21.** $\displaystyle\int_0^{2/5} \frac{dx}{\sqrt{4-25x^2}}$

22. If $\displaystyle\int_0^k \frac{dx}{x^2+25} = \frac{\pi}{20}$, find the value of k, $\qquad k \in \mathbf{R}$.

23. If $\displaystyle\int_{3/2}^{a} \frac{dx}{\sqrt{9-x^2}} = \frac{\pi}{3}$, find the value of a, $a \in \mathbf{R}$.

24. If $\displaystyle\int_{0}^{p} \frac{dx}{16+9x^2} = \frac{\pi}{48}$, find the value of p, $p \in \mathbf{R}$.

More difficult variations on the above standard integrals involve completing the square.

Example ▼

(i) Express $x^2 - 4x + 29$ in the form $(x-p)^2 + q^2$ and, hence, evaluate $\displaystyle\int_{2}^{7} \frac{dx}{x^2 - 4x + 29}$.

(ii) Express $3 - 2x^2 - x^2$ in the form $a^2 - (x+b)^2$ and, hence, evaluate $\displaystyle\int_{-1}^{0} \frac{dx}{\sqrt{3-2x-x^2}}$.

Solution:

(i)
$$x^2 - 4x + 29$$
$$= x^2 - 4x + 4 + 25$$
$$= (x-2)^2 + 5^2$$
$$\int \frac{dx}{x^2 - 4x + 29} = \int \frac{dx}{(x-2)^2 + 5^2}$$

Substitution

$$u = x - 2$$
$$du = dx$$

$$= \int \frac{du}{5^2 + u^2} = \frac{1}{5}\tan^{-1}\frac{u}{5} = \frac{1}{5}\tan^{-1}\left(\frac{x-2}{5}\right)$$

$$\therefore \int_{2}^{7} \frac{dx}{x^2 - 4x + 29} = \frac{1}{5}\left[\tan^{-1}\left(\frac{x-2}{5}\right)\right]_{2}^{7}$$

$$= \tfrac{1}{5}\left[\tan^{-1} 1 - \tan^{-1} 0\right]$$

$$= \frac{1}{5}\left[\frac{\pi}{4} - 0\right] = \frac{\pi}{20}$$

(ii) $3 - 2x - x^2$ (add 1 and subtract 1)
$$= 3 - (x^2 + 2x)$$
$$= 3 + 1 - (x^2 + 2x + 1)$$
$$= 4 - (x+1)^2 = 2^2 - (x+1)^2$$

$$\int \frac{dx}{\sqrt{3-2x-x^2}} = \int \frac{dx}{\sqrt{2^2 - (x+1)^2}}$$

Substitution

$$u = x + 1$$
$$du = dx$$

$$= \int \frac{dx}{\sqrt{2^2 - u^2}} = \sin^{-1}\frac{u}{2} = \sin^{-1}\left(\frac{x+1}{2}\right)$$

$$\therefore \int_{-1}^{0} \frac{dx}{\sqrt{3-2x-x^2}} = \left[\sin^{-1}\left(\frac{x+1}{2}\right)\right]_{-1}^{0}$$

$$= \sin^{-1}\tfrac{1}{2} - \sin^{-1} 0$$

$$= \frac{\pi}{6} - 0 = \frac{\pi}{6}$$

Exercise 14.8 ▼

Express each of the following in the form $(x+p)^2 + q^2$:

1. $x^2 + 4x + 13$ **2.** $x^2 + 8x + 25$ **3.** $x^2 - 6x + 10$ **4.** $x^2 - 2x + 17$

Express each of the following in the form $a^2 - (x+b)^2$:

5. $8 - 2x - x^2$ **6.** $7 - 6x - x^2$ **7.** $11 - 10x - x^2$ **8.** $8x - x^2$

Evaluate each of the following:

9. $\displaystyle\int_{-1}^{3} \frac{dx}{16 + (x+1)^2}$

10. $\displaystyle\int_{-1}^{2} \frac{dx}{x^2 + 2x + 10}$

11. $\displaystyle\int_{1}^{4} \frac{dx}{\sqrt{9 - (x-1)^2}}$

12. $\displaystyle\int_{0}^{1} \frac{dx}{\sqrt{3 - 2x - x^2}}$

13. $\displaystyle\int_{-1}^{0} \frac{4\,dx}{x^2 + 2x + 2}$

14. $\displaystyle\int_{-2}^{1} \frac{2\,dx}{\sqrt{5 - 4x - x^2}}$

15. Find the values of p and q such that $x^2 - 4x + 13 = (x - p)^2 + q^2$.

Hence, evaluate $\displaystyle\int_{2}^{3} \frac{dx}{x^2 - 4x + 13}$, giving your answer in the form $k \tan^{-1} k$.

16. Write $(1 - x)(7 + x)$ in the form $a^2 - (x + b)^2$ and, hence, evaluate $\displaystyle\int_{-5}^{1} \frac{3\,dx}{\sqrt{(1 - x)(7 + x)}}$.

17. Find the real number k given that $\displaystyle\int_{k}^{3} \frac{dx}{x^2 - 2x + 5} = \frac{\pi}{8}$.

Integrals of the Form $\displaystyle\int \sqrt{a^2 - x^2}\, dx$

Integrals of the form $\displaystyle\int \sqrt{a^2 - x^2}\, dx$ can be calculated by the substitution:

$$x = a \sin \theta$$

This substitution removes the square root and turns the integral into a trigonometrical substitution.

Note: It is simpler to change the limits to the corresponding limits for θ.
Integrals of this form are not in the tables.

Example ▼

Evaluate: $\displaystyle\int_{0}^{4} \sqrt{16 - x^2}\, dx$.

Solution:

$\displaystyle\int \sqrt{16 - x^2}\, dx = \int \sqrt{4^2 - x^2}\, dx$

$16 - x^2 = 16 - 16 \sin^2 \theta = 16(1 - \sin^2 \theta) = 16 \cos^2 \theta$

$\therefore \quad \sqrt{16 - x^2} = \sqrt{16 \cos^2 \theta} = 4 \cos \theta$

$\therefore \quad \displaystyle\int_{0}^{4} \sqrt{16 - x^2}\, dx$

$= \displaystyle\int_{0}^{\pi/2} 4 \cos \theta \,.\, 4 \cos \theta \, d\theta$

$= 16 \displaystyle\int_{0}^{\pi/2} \cos^2 \theta \, d\theta = 16 \int_{0}^{\pi/2} \tfrac{1}{2}(1 + \cos 2\theta) \, d\theta = 8 \int_{0}^{\pi/2} (1 + \cos 2\theta) \, d\theta$

$= 8\left[\theta + \tfrac{1}{2} \sin 2\theta\right]_{0}^{\pi/2}$

$= 8\left[\left(\dfrac{\pi}{2} + 0\right) - (0 - 0)\right] = 8\left(\dfrac{\pi}{2}\right) = 4\pi$

Substitution

$x = 4 \sin \theta$
$dx = 4 \cos \theta \, d\theta$

Limits

$x = 4$	$x = 0$
$4 \sin \theta = 4$	$4 \sin \theta = 0$
$\sin \theta = 1$	$\sin \theta = 0$
$\theta = \dfrac{\pi}{2}$	$\theta = 0$

Evaluate each of the following, in each case using the suggested substitution:

1. $\displaystyle\int_0^2 \sqrt{4-x^2}\,dx$, $x = 2\sin\theta$

2. $\displaystyle\int_0^3 \sqrt{9-x^2}\,dx$, $x = 3\sin\theta$

3. $\displaystyle\int_0^5 \sqrt{25-x^2}\,dx$, $x = 5\sin\theta$

4. $\displaystyle\int_0^{1/\sqrt{2}} \sqrt{1-x^2}\,dx$, $x = \sin\theta$

5. $\displaystyle\int_0^{1/2} \sqrt{1-4x^2}\,dx$, $2x = \sin\theta$

6. $\displaystyle\int_0^{2/3} \sqrt{4-9x^2}\,dx$, $3x = 2\sin\theta$

7. $\displaystyle\int_0^{3/4} \sqrt{9-16x^2}\,dx$, $4x = 3\sin\theta$

8. $\displaystyle\int_0^{\sqrt{2}} \sqrt{4-x^2}\,dx$, $x = 2\sin\theta$

9. $\displaystyle\int_0^3 \sqrt{36-x^2}\,dx$, $x = 6\sin\theta$

10. $\displaystyle\int_0^{2\sqrt{3}} \sqrt{16-x^2}\,dx$, $x = 4\sin\theta$

11. Verify that $\displaystyle\int_0^{3/2} \sqrt{3-x^2}\,dx = \frac{\pi}{2} + \frac{3\sqrt{3}}{8}$. (Hint: Let $x = \sqrt{3}\sin\theta$).

Area Under a Curve

Area between a curve and the x-axis:

The area, A, of the region bounded by the curve $y = f(x)$, the x-axis and the lines $x = a$ and $x = b$ is given by:

$$A = \int_a^b y\,dx \qquad \text{or} \qquad A = \int_a^b f(x)\,dx$$

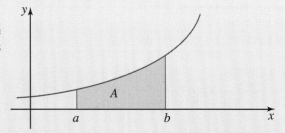

This is positive if the area is above the x-axis.
This is negative if the area is below the x-axis.

If the curve cuts the x-axis between the limits, then:

(i)   find the areas above and below the x-axis separately;

(ii) add these two values together.

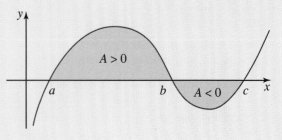

Area between a curve and the y-axis:

The area, A, bounded by the curve $y = f(x)$, the y-axis and the lines $y = a$ and $y = b$ is given by:

$$A = \int_a^b x\,dy$$

In this case, x must be expressed as a function of y before we can integrate.

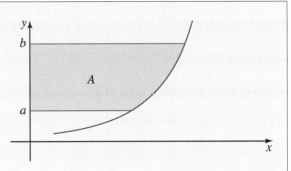

This is positive if the area is to the right of the y-axis.
This is negative if the area is to the left of the y-axis.

If the curve cuts the y-axis between the limits, then:

(i) find the areas to the right and the left of the y-axis separately;
(ii) add these two values together.

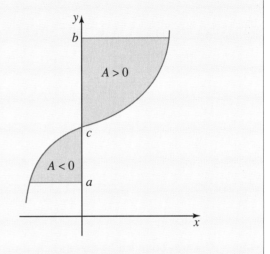

If not given, it is good practice to draw a sketch of the function and check to see if the curve cuts the x-axis, or y-axis, between the given limits. If the curve is completely above, or below, the x-axis between the limits, we can evaluate the integral between the limits given. If the curve is completely to the right, or left, of the y-axis between the limits, we can evaluate the integral between the limits given.

Example ▼

$C : y = 3x - x^2$ and $L : y = x$ represent a curve and a line respectively. Find the coordinates of the points where the curve and line intersect and draw a rough sketch of C and L.
Find the area bounded by the curve C, the line L and the x-axis.

Solution:

$$\text{curve} = \text{line}$$
$$3x - x^2 = x$$
$$-x^2 + 2x = 0$$
$$x^2 - 2x = 0$$
$$x(x - 2) = 0$$
$$x = 0 \quad \text{or} \quad x = 2$$

As $y = x$,
when $x = 0$, $y = 0$ and when $x = 2$, $y = 2$.
Thus, the curve and line intersect at $(0, 0)$ and $(2, 2)$.
We also need to find where the curve cuts the x-axis.

On the x-axis: $y = 0$

$$\therefore \quad 3x - x^2 = 0$$
$$x^2 - 3x = 0$$
$$x(x - 3) = 0$$
$$x = 0 \quad \text{or} \quad x = 3$$

Thus the curve cuts the x-axis at $x = 0$ and $x = 3$.

$$\text{Shaded area} = \int_0^2 (\text{line})\, dx + \int_2^3 (\text{curve})\, dx$$

$$= \int_0^2 x\, dx + \int_2^3 (3x - x^2)\, dx$$

$$= \left[\frac{x^2}{2} \right]_0^2 + \left[\frac{3x^2}{2} - \frac{x^3}{3} \right]_2^3$$

$$= \left[\left(\tfrac{4}{2}\right) - (0) \right] + \left[\left(\tfrac{27}{2} - \tfrac{27}{3}\right) - \left(\tfrac{12}{2} - \tfrac{8}{3}\right) \right]$$

$$= 2 + \tfrac{7}{6} = \tfrac{19}{6}$$

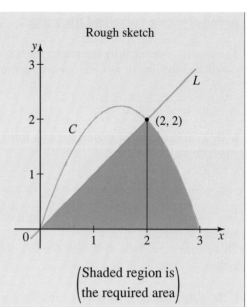

Rough sketch

$\left(\begin{array}{l}\text{Shaded region is}\\\text{the required area}\end{array}\right)$

Note: The area bounded by the line and the x-axis between $x = 0$ and $x = 2$ could also have been calculated by calculating the area of a triangle.

$$\int_0^2 (\text{line})\, dx = \int_0^2 x\, dx = \quad\boxed{}\quad = \tfrac{1}{2}(2)(2) = 2.$$

Example ▼

Find the area bounded by the curve $y = x^2 - 2x - 8$, the x-axis and the lines $x = 1$ to $x = 5$.

Solution:

First make a sketch of the curve $y = x^2 - 2x - 8$.
It cuts the x-axis at $y = 0$.
Thus, $x^2 - 2x - 8 = 0$
$$(x - 4)(x + 2) = 0$$
$$x = 4 \quad \text{or} \quad x = -2$$

The graph is shown on the right. The sketch shows that the required area is in two parts. One part lies below the x-axis, A_1, and is negative, the other part lies above the x-axis, A_2, and is positive. Thus, we calculate the two areas separately.

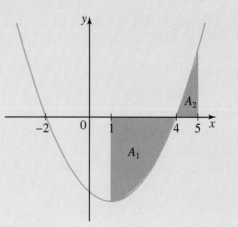

204

$$A_1 = \int_1^4 (x^2 - 2x - 8)\, dx$$

$$= \left[\frac{x^3}{3} - x^2 - 8x \right]_1^4$$

$$= \left[\frac{64}{3} - 16 - 32 \right] - \left[\frac{1}{3} - 1 - 8 \right]$$

$$= -\frac{80}{3} + \frac{26}{3} = -18 = 18$$

(as area must be positive)

$$A_2 = \int_4^5 (x^2 - 2x - 8)\, dx$$

$$= \left[\frac{x^3}{3} - x^2 - 8x \right]_4^5$$

$$= \left[\frac{125}{3} - 25 - 40 \right] - \left[\frac{64}{3} - 16 - 32 \right]$$

$$= -\frac{70}{3} + \frac{80}{3} = \frac{10}{3}$$

Thus, Area $= A_1 + A_2 = 18 + \frac{10}{3} = \frac{64}{3}$

Area between two curves:

1. We need to find where the curves intersect.
2. Subtract the areas under the curves between the points of intersection.

This can be done by the evaluation of one integral using the x coordinates of the point of intersection as the limits.

Example ▼

The diagram shows part of the curve

$C : y = 3 + 6x - x^2$ and the line $L : y = 15 - 2x$

(i) Find the x coordinates of p and q.
(ii) Calculate the area bounded by C and L.

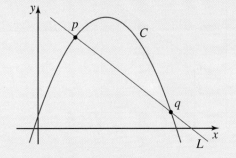

Solution:

(i) We need to find the x coordinates where the curve and line intersect.

$$C : y = 3 + 6x - x^2 \qquad L : y = 15 - 2x$$

Thus,

$$3 + 6x - x^2 = 15 - 2x$$
$$-x^2 + 8x - 12 = 0$$
$$x^2 - 8x + 12 = 0$$
$$(x - 2)(x - 6) = 0$$
$$x = 2 \quad \text{or} \quad x = 6$$

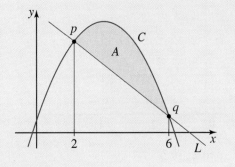

(ii) The shaded region represents the area bounded by the curve, C, and the line, L, i.e. the area under the curve *less* the area under the line, between the limits $x = 2$ and $x = 6$.

$$\text{Shaded area} = A = \int_2^6 (3 + 6x - x^2)\, dx - \int_2^6 (15 - 2x)\, dx$$

$$= \int_2^6 (3 + 6x - x^2 - 15 + 2x)\, dx$$

$$= \int_2^6 (8x - x^2 - 12)\, dx$$

$$= \left[4x^2 - \frac{x^3}{3} - 12x \right]_2^6$$

$$= (144 - 72 - 72) - (16 - \tfrac{8}{3} - 24)$$

$$= 10\tfrac{2}{3}$$

Exercise 14.10 ▼

Calculate the area of the shaded region in each of the following diagrams:

1.

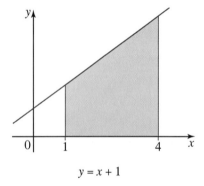

$y = x + 1$

2.

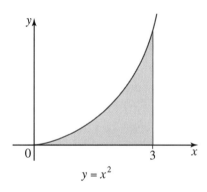

$y = x^2$

3.

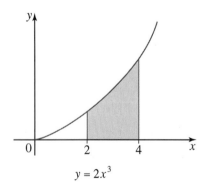

$y = 2x^3$

4.

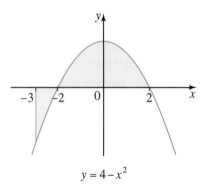

$y = 4 - x^2$

5.

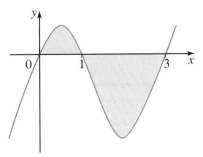

$$y = x^3 - 4x^2 + 3x$$

6.

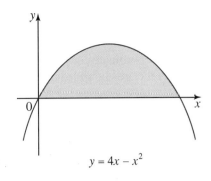

$$y = 4x - x^2$$

7.

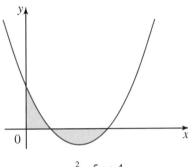

$$y = x^2 - 5x + 4$$

8.

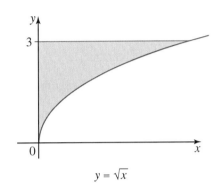

$$y = \sqrt{x}$$

9.

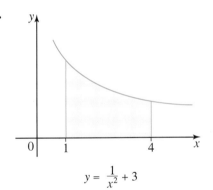

$$y = \frac{1}{x^2} + 3$$

10.

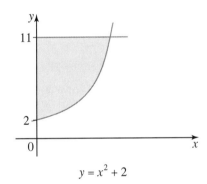

$$y = x^2 + 2$$

11.

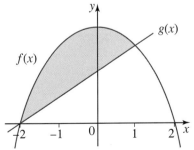

$$f(x) = 4 - x^2 \text{ and } g(x) = x + 2$$

12.

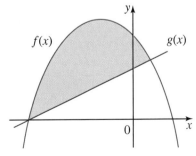

$$f(x) = 6 - x - x^2 \text{ and } g(x) = x + 3$$

13. The diagram shows part of the curve

$C : y = 5x - x^2$ and the line $L : y = 8 - x$

   (i) Find the x coordinates of p and q.
   (ii) Calculate the area bounded by C and L.

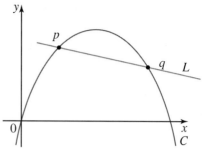

14. $f(x) = x^2 + 3$ and $g(x) = 3x + 1$. $f(x)$ and $g(x)$ meet at the points a and b.
   (i) Find the coordinates of a and b.
   (ii) Sketch $f(x)$ and $g(x)$ on the same axes and scales.
   (iii) Find the area of the bounded region enclosed by $f(x)$ and $g(x)$.

15. Find the area of the bounded region enclosed by the curve $y = 4x - x^2$ and the lines $x = 0$ and $x = 5$.

16. Find the area of the bounded region enclosed by the curve $y = 5x - 2x^2$ and the line $y = x$.

17. Find the area of the bounded region enclosed by the curve $y = x^2 - 3x + 3$ and the line $y = 2x - 1$.

18. Find the area enclosed by the curve $y = x^2 + 1$ and the line $y = 5$.

19. Find the area enclosed by the curve $y = x^2$ and the y-axis from $y = 1$ to $y = 4$.

20. The diagram shows part of the graph of the function $f(x) = \dfrac{x^2 - 1}{x}$.

Calculate the area of the shaded region.

Write your answer in the form $a - \ln b$.

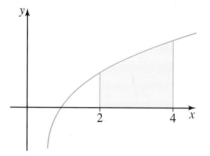

21. The diagram shows part of the graph of the curve $f(x) = \dfrac{12}{x^2}$. If the region bounded by $f(x)$, the x-axis and lines $x = 2$ and $x = k$, $k > 2$, is 4, find the value of k.

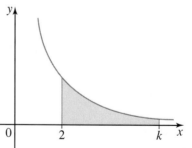

22. The diagram shows part of the graph of the function $f(x) = 4x - x^2$. If the areas of the two shaded regions are equal, find the value of p, $p > 0$.

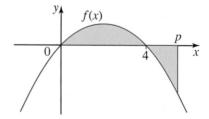

208

23. The diagram shows a sketch of the functions:

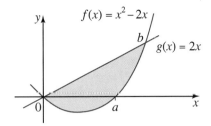

$f(x) = x^2 - 2x$ and $g(x) = 2x$.
$f(x)$ cuts the x-axis at the points o and a.
$f(x)$ and $g(x)$ meet at the point b.
(i) Find the coordinates of a and b.
(ii) Find the area of the shaded region.

24. (i) If $y = x^3$, express x as a function of y.

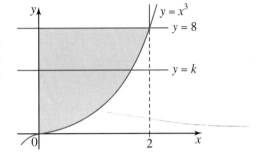

(ii) The region bounded by the y-axis, the curve $y = x^3$ and the line $y = 8$ is divided into two regions of equal area by the line $y = k$.
Show that $k^4 = 512$

25. (i) Evaluate $\displaystyle\int_0^6 \sqrt{36 - x^2}\, dx$ (let $x = 6\sin\theta$)

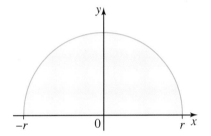

(ii) $x^2 + y^2 = r^2$ is the equation of a circle, centre the origin and radius r.
Express y in terms of r and x.

(iii) The diagram shows the graph of the function $y = \sqrt{r^2 - x^2}$.
Using integration methods, prove that the area of circle of radius r is πr^2.

Volumes of Revolution

If an area is rotated about the x- or y-axis, the three-dimensional object formed is called a '**solid of revolution**' and its volume is a '**volume of revolution**'.

Rotation about the x-axis:

The volume, V_x, generated by rotating, once, the area bounded by the curve $y = f(x)$, the x-axis and the lines $x = a$ and $x = b$ is given by:

$$V_x = \pi \int_a^b y^2\, dx$$

A triangle would generate a cone.

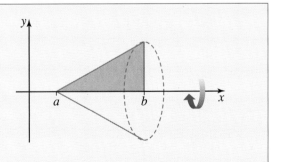

Rotation about the *y*-axis:

The volume, V_y, generated by rotating, once, the area bounded by the curve $y = f(x)$, the *y*-axis and the lines $y = a$ and $y = b$ is given by:

$$V_y = \pi \int_a^b x^2 \, dy$$

A semi-circle would generate a sphere.
In this case, *x* must be expressed as a function of *y* first.

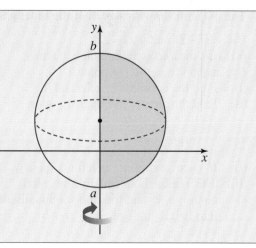

On our course, the solids of revolution are confined to cones, or parts of cones, and spheres, or parts of spheres.

Example ▼

Find the volume of the solid generated by rotating about the *y*-axis the area bounded by the *y*-axis, the line $2x - y + 2 = 0$ and the lines $y = 4$ and $y = 7$.

Solution:

The diagram on the right represents the situation.
The line $2x - y + 2 = 0$ cuts the *x*-axis
at $(-1, 0)$ and the *y*-axis at $(2, 0)$.

$$V_y = \pi \int_a^b x^2 \, dy$$

$$= \pi \int_4^7 \tfrac{1}{4}(y^2 - 4y + 4) \, dy$$

$$= \frac{\pi}{4} \int_4^7 (y^2 - 4y + 4) \, dy$$

$$= \frac{\pi}{4} \left[\frac{y^3}{3} - 2y^2 + 4y \right]_4^7$$

$$= \frac{\pi}{4} \left[(\tfrac{343}{3} - 98 + 28) - (\tfrac{64}{3} - 32 + 16) \right]$$

$$= \frac{\pi}{4} \left[\tfrac{133}{3} - \tfrac{16}{3} \right]$$

$$= \frac{\pi}{4} \left[39 \right]$$

$$= \tfrac{39}{4} \pi$$

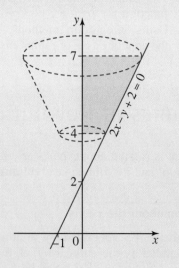

Generates a frustrum

$$2x - y + 2 = 0$$
$$2x = y - 2$$
$$x = \tfrac{1}{2}(y - 2)$$
$$x^2 = \tfrac{1}{4}(y - 2)^2$$
$$x^2 = \tfrac{1}{4}(y^2 - 4y + 4)$$

Using integration methods, prove that the volume of a sphere of radius r is $\frac{4}{3}\pi r^3$.

Solution:

$$V_x = \pi \int_a^b y^2 \, dx$$

$$= \pi \int_{-r}^r (r^2 - x^2) \, dx$$

$$= \pi \left[r^2 x - \frac{x^3}{3} \right]_{-r}^r$$

$$= \pi \left[\left(r^3 - \frac{r^3}{3} \right) - \left(-r^3 + \frac{r^3}{3} \right) \right]$$

$$= \pi \left(r^3 - \frac{r^3}{3} + r^3 - \frac{r^3}{3} \right)$$

$$= \pi \left(\frac{4}{3} r \right)$$

$$= \frac{4}{3} \pi r^3$$

Note: r is a constant.

Consider the circle $x^2 + y^2 = r^2$.
We rotate the top half (semi-circle) of the circle about the x-axis. This generates a sphere.

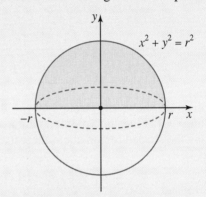

The circle cuts the x-axis at $-r$ and r.
Thus, the limits of integration are $-r$ and r.

$$x^2 + y^2 = r^2$$
$$y^2 = (r^2 - x^2)$$

Exercise 14.11 ▼

1. The diagram shows the line $y = 2x$.
   Find the volume of the cone generated by rotating about the x-axis the area bounded by the line $y = 2x$ and the lines $x = 0$ and $x = 4$.

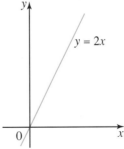

2. Sketch the line $x + y - 2 = 0$.
   Find the volume of the solid generated by rotating about the y-axis the area bounded by the y-axis, the line $x + y - 2 = 0$ and the lines $x = 0$ and $x = 2$.

3. Find the volume of the solid generated by rotating about the y-axis the area bounded by the y-axis, the line $2x - y - 2 = 0$ and the lines $y = 2$ and $y = 6$.

4. The equation of the line K is $3x + 2y - 6 = 0$. Using integration methods, find the volume of the cones generated by rotating the areas bounded by K and the axes about:
   (i) the x-axis   **(ii)** the y-axis.

5. Using integration methods, find the volume generated by rotating about the x-axis the circle $x^2 + y^2 = 9$.

6. A sphere has a radius of 6 cm.
A spherical cap of depth 3 cm, is removed from the sphere, as shown.
Using integration methods, find the volume of the spherical cap.

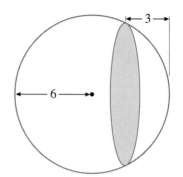

7. The diagram shows the circle $x^2 + y^2 = 4$ and the line $x = 1$. Find the volume generated by rotating the shaded region about the x-axis.

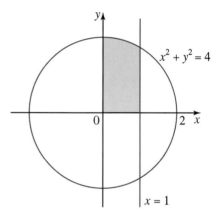

8. The diagram shows a graph of the circle $(x - 2)^2 + y^2 = 9$.
If $y^2 = a + bx - x^2$, find the value of a and b.
Find the volume of the solid generated by rotating about the x-axis the area bounded by the x-axis, the circle $(x - 2)^2 + y^2 = 9$ and the lines $x = 3$ and $x = 4$.

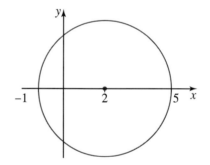

9. A triangle has vertices $(0, 0)$, (h, r), $(h, 0)$, as shown.
Find the equation of the line which contains the points $(0, 0)$ and (h, r). Hence, using integration methods, prove that the volume of a right-circular cone of base radius r and height h is $\frac{1}{3}\pi r^2 h$.

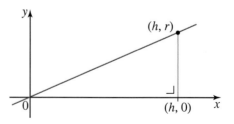

10. Using integration methods, prove that the volume of a hemisphere of radius r is $\frac{2}{3}\pi r^3$.

11. Using integration methods, find the volume of water needed to fill a hemispherical bowl of radius 9 cm to a depth of 6 cm.

12. The diagram shows the circle $x^2 + y^2 = 4$ and the line $x = 1$. The line intercepts the circle at the points a and b.

    (i)   Find the coordinates of a and b.

    (ii) Find the volume generated by rotating the shaded sector about the y-axis.

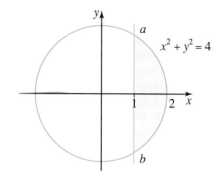

INDUCTION

Inductive Principle

If we find a pattern, how can we be sure that the pattern will always be true?
Consider the proposition that the expression $n^2 - n + 17$ is prime for all $n \in \mathbf{N}_0$.
($\mathbf{N}_0$ is the positive integers, 1, 2, 3, 4, 5, ...)

We can test this proposition by putting in $n = 1, 2, 3, 4, 5, \ldots$

$n = 1$: $1^2 - 1 + 17 = 17$, a prime number.

$n = 2$: $2^2 - 2 + 17 = 19$, a prime number.

$n = 3$: $3^2 - 3 + 17 = 23$, a prime number.

$n = 4$: $4^2 - 4 + 17 = 29$, a prime number.

If we put in 5, 6, 7, 8, ... we obtain a prime number.
This suggests that the proposition could be true.
However, if $n = 17$; $17^2 - 17 + 17 = 289 = 17^2$ which is **not** prime.
Hence, the proposition is false.

Proof by Induction

Many propositions, or statements, which we may develop from simple cases, can be proved using the **'principle of mathematical induction'**.

Proof by induction involves two steps:

> 1. Prove that the proposition is true for the smallest value of n given in the question (usually $n = 0$ or $n = 1$).
> 2. Assuming the proposition is true for $n = k$, show that the proposition is true for $n = k + 1$.

Note: If it is true for $n = 1$, then step 2 ensures that it is true for $n = 2$. If it is true for $n = 2$, then step 2 ensures that it is true for $n = 3$, and so on.

We will use 'proof by induction' to prove propositions in 3 areas:

1. Divisibility   **2. Series**   **3. Inequalities**

Note: Proof by induction applies only to propositions that are stated to be true for natural numbers. The proposition is often denoted by P(n). The assumption P(k) must **always** be used in proving that P($k + 1$) is true.

1. Divisibility

Example ▼

Prove by induction that $9^n - 5^n$ is divisible by 4 for all $n \in \mathbf{N}_0$.

Solution:

$$P(n): 9^n - 5^n \text{ is divisible by 4 for all } n \in \mathbf{N}_0.$$

Step 1: $P(1) = 9^1 - 5^1 = 9 - 5 = 4$, which is divisible by 4

∴ $P(1)$ is true.

Step 2: Assume $P(k)$ is true, i.e., $9^k - 5^k$ is divisible by 4.

Test $P(k+1)$: $\quad 9^{k+1} - 5^{k+1}$

$$= 9.9^k - 5.5^k$$
$$= (5+4)9^k - 5.5^k \quad \text{(split 9 up into 5 + 4)}$$
$$= 5.9^k + 4.9^k - 5.5^k$$
$$= 4.9^k + 5(9^k - 5^k)$$

4.9^k is divisible by 4 and we assumed $(9^k - 5^k)$ is divisible by 4.

∴ $P(k+1)$ is divisible by 4.

∴ $P(k+1)$ is true if $P(k)$ is true.

Hence, by the principle of mathematical induction, $P(n)$ is true.

Exercise 15.1 ▼

Prove by induction that:

1. $4^n - 1$ is divisible by 3 for all $n \in \mathbf{N}_0$.

2. $5^n - 1$ is divisible by 4 for all $n \in \mathbf{N}_0$.

3. $7^n - 2^n$ is divisible by 5 for all $n \in \mathbf{N}_0$.

4. $13^n - 5^n$ is divisible by 8 for all $n \in \mathbf{N}_0$.

5. $3^{2n} - 1$ is divisible by 8 for all $n \in \mathbf{N}_0$.

6. $2^{3n-1} + 3$ is divisible by 7 for all $n \in \mathbf{N}_0$.

7. $5^{2n} - 3^{2n}$ is divisible by 8 for all $n \in \mathbf{N}_0$.

8. $n^2 + 3n + 2$ is divisible by 2 (even) for all $n \in \mathbf{N}$.

9. $n^3 + 6n^2 + 8n$ is divisible by 3 for all $n \in \mathbf{N}_0$.

10. $5^n - 4n + 3$ is divisible by 4 for all $n \in \mathbf{N}_0$.

11. $5^{2(n+1)} - 4^{n+1}$ is divisible by 21 for all $n \in \mathbf{N}$.

12. $P(n) = 8^{2n} - 3^{2n}$

    (i) Evaluate P(0) and P(1).   **(ii)** Express $P(n+1)$ in the form $a \cdot 8^{2n} - b \cdot 3^{2n}$.

    (iii) Show that $P(n+1) - 9P(n) = 55.8^{2n}$.

    (iv) Hence, or otherwise, show that 5 is a factor of $P(n)$ for all $n \in \mathbf{N}$.

2. Series

Example ▼

Prove by induction that $1^2 + 2^2 + 3^2 + \cdots + n^2 = \dfrac{n}{6}(n+1)(2n+1)$.

Solution:

$$P(n): 1^2 + 2^2 + 3^2 + \cdots + n^2 = \frac{n}{6}(n+1)(2n+1)$$

Step 1: $P(1)$: LHS $= 1^2 = 1$ RHS $= \frac{1}{6}(2)(3) = 1$

                           $\therefore$ $P(1)$ is true.

Step 2: Assume $P(k)$ is true, i.e. $1^2 + 2^2 + 3^2 + \cdots + k^2 = \dfrac{k}{6}(k+1)(2k+1)$.

Test $P(k+1)$: $1^2 + 2^2 + 3^2 + \cdots + k^2 + (k+1)^2 = \left(\dfrac{k+1}{6}\right)(k+2)(2k+3)$

$$\begin{aligned}
\mathbf{LHS} &= 1^2 + 2^2 + 3^2 + \cdots + k^2 + (k+1)^2 \\
&= (1^2 + 2^2 + 3^2 + \cdots + k^2) + (k+1)^2 \\
&= \frac{k}{6}(k+1)(2k+1) + (k+1)^2 && \text{(using our assumption)} \\
&= \frac{k(k+1)(2k+1) + 6(k+1)^2}{6} && \text{(use common denominator 6)} \\
&= \left(\frac{k+1}{6}\right)\left[k(2k+1) + 6(k+1)\right] && \left(\text{take out common factor } \left(\frac{k+1}{6}\right)\right) \\
&= \left(\frac{k+1}{6}\right)\left[2k^2 + k + 6k + 6\right] \\
&= \left(\frac{k+1}{6}\right)\left[2k^2 + 7k + 6\right] \\
&= \left(\frac{k+1}{6}\right)(k+2)(2k+3) = \mathbf{RHS}
\end{aligned}$$

         $\therefore$ $P(k+1)$ is true if $P(k)$ is true.

Hence, by the principle of mathematical induction, $P(n)$ is true.

Note: This question could have been asked using sequence and series notation:

i.e. Prove by induction that $\sum_{r=1}^{n} r^2 = \frac{n}{6}(n+1)(2n+1)$.

Exercise 15.2 ▼

Prove by induction that:

1. $1 + 2 + 3 + \cdots + n = \frac{n}{2}(n+1)$, for all $n \in \mathbf{N}_0$.

2. $2 + 4 + 6 + \cdots + 2n = n(n+1)$, for all $n \in \mathbf{N}_0$.

3. $1 + 3 + 5 + \cdots + (2n-1) = n^2$, for all $n \in \mathbf{N}_0$.

4. $1^3 + 2^3 + 3^3 + \cdots + n^3 = \frac{n^2}{4}(n+1)^2$, for all $n \in \mathbf{N}_0$.

5. $1.2 + 2.3 + 3.4 + \cdots + n(n+1) = \frac{n}{3}(n+1)(n+2)$, for all $n \in \mathbf{N}_0$.

6. $\frac{1}{1.3} + \frac{1}{3.5} + \frac{1}{5.7} + \cdots + \frac{1}{(2n-1)(2n+1)} = \frac{n}{2n+1}$, for all $n \in \mathbf{N}_0$.

7. $\sum_{r=1}^{n}(3n-2) = \frac{n}{2}(3n-1)$.

8. $\sum_{r=1}^{n} n(n+3) = \frac{n}{3}(n+1)(n+5)$.

9. $a + (a+d) + (a+2d) + \cdots + [a+(n-1)d] = \frac{n}{2}[2a+(n-1)d]$, for all $n \in \mathbf{N}_0$.

10. $a + ar + ar^2 + \cdots + ar^{n-1} = \frac{a(1-r^n)}{1-r}$, $r \neq 1$, $n \in \mathbf{N}_0$.

11. $\sum_{r=1}^{n}(r+1)2^r = n2^{n+1}$.

Hint for questions 12 and 13: $5.4! = 5!$ $10.9! = 10!$ $(k+1)k! = (k+1)!$

12. $1.1! + 2.2! + 3.3! + \cdots + n.n! = (n+1)! - 1$, for all $n \in \mathbf{N}$, $n \geqslant 0$.

13. $\sum_{r=1}^{n}(r^2+1)r! = n(n+1)!$

3. Inequalities

Example ▼

Prove by induction that $(1 + r)^n \geqslant 1 + nr, \qquad r > -1$ and $n \in \mathbf{N}$.

Solution:

$$P(n): (1 + r)^n \geqslant 1 + nr, \qquad r > -1 \text{ and } n \in \mathbf{N}.$$

Step 1: $P(0): (1 + r)^0 \geqslant 1 + (0)r$

$$1 \geqslant 1 \qquad \text{which is true}$$

$\therefore$ $P(0)$ is true.

Step 2: Assume $P(k)$ is true, i.e. $(1 + r)^k \geqslant (1 + kr)$

Test $P(k + 1)$: $(1 + r)^{k+1} \geqslant 1 + (k + 1)r$

$$\begin{aligned}
\textbf{LHS} \quad &= (1 + r)^{k+1} \\
&= (1 + r)(1 + r)^k \\
&\geqslant (1 + r)(1 + kr) \qquad &\text{(using our assumption)} \\
&= 1 + kr + r + kr^2 \\
&= 1 + (k + 1)r + kr^2 \\
&\geqslant 1 + (k + 1)r \qquad &\text{(as } kr^2 \geqslant 0)
\end{aligned}$$

$\therefore$ $(1 + r)^{k+1} \geqslant 1 + (k + 1)r$

$\therefore$ $P(k + 1)$ is true if $P(k)$ is true.

Hence, by the principle of mathematical induction, $P(n)$ is true.

Exercise 15.3 ▼

Prove by induction that:

1. $2n^2 > (n + 1)^2, \qquad n \geqslant 3, n \in \mathbf{N}.$

2. $2^n > n, n \geqslant 1, \qquad n \in \mathbf{N}.$

3. $(a + b)^n \geqslant a^n + b^n$, for all $a, b > 0$, $a, b \in \mathbf{R}$ and $n \in \mathbf{N}_0.$

4. $n! > 2^n$, for $n \geqslant 4, n \in \mathbf{N}.$

5. $3^n > 2n + 1$ for $n \geqslant 2, n \in \mathbf{N}.$

6. $3^n > n^2$, for all $n \in \mathbf{N}_0.$

7. $4^n \geqslant 3n^2 + 1$, for all $n \in \mathbf{N}_0.$

8. $1 + \dfrac{1}{\sqrt{2}} + \dfrac{1}{\sqrt{3}} + \cdots + \dfrac{1}{\sqrt{n}} \geqslant \sqrt{n}.$

9. $\dfrac{1}{(1 + r)^n} \leqslant \dfrac{1}{1 + nr}, \qquad r > 0$, for all $n \geqslant 1, n \in \mathbf{N}.$

16

BINOMIAL THEOREM

Factorials

Definition:

The product of all the positive whole numbers from n down to 1 is called '**factorial n**' and is denoted by $n!$

Thus, $n! = n(n-1)(n-2) \ldots 3.2.1$

For example, $5! = 5.4.3.2.1 = 120$ $8! = 8.7.6.5.4.3.2.1 = 40{,}320$

By definition: $0! = 1$.

Note:
$8! = 8.7! = 8.7.6!$ (and so on) $n! = n(n-1)! = n(n-1)(n-2)!$ (and so on)

Also,

$7.6! = 7!$ $(n+1)n! = (n+1)!$

When simplifying factorials, it is good practice to start with the larger factorial and work down to the smaller one.

Note: Later on we will show that the number of arrangements of all n different objects is given by $n!$

Example ▼

(i)   If $\dfrac{4!n!}{(n-1)!3n} = k$, find the value of k.

(ii)   Solve: $\dfrac{(n-2)!}{n!} = \dfrac{1}{56}$

Solution:

(i)

$$\dfrac{4!n!}{(n-1)!3n}$$

$$= \dfrac{4.3.2.1.n(n-1)!}{(n-1)!3n}$$

$$= \dfrac{24n(n-1)!}{3n(n-1)!}$$

$$= 8$$

Thus, $k = 8$

(ii)

$$\dfrac{(n-2)!}{n!} = \dfrac{1}{56}$$

$$\dfrac{(n-2)!}{n(n-1)(n-2)!} = \dfrac{1}{56}$$

$$\dfrac{1}{n(n-1)} = \dfrac{1}{56}$$

$$n(n-1) = 56$$

$$n^2 - n - 56 = 0$$

$$(n-8)(n+7) = 0$$

$$n = 8 \quad \text{or} \quad n = -7$$

$n = -7$ is rejected as $n!$ is defined for natural numbers only.

Thus, $n = 8$.

Evaluate each of the following:

1. $10!$

2. $\dfrac{8!}{6!2!}$

3. $\dfrac{20!}{18!}$

4. $\dfrac{(5!)^2}{2!4!}$

5. If $\dfrac{(n+5)!}{(n+3)!} = n^2 + an + b$, find the value of a and the value of b.

6. If $\dfrac{(n+1)!}{(n-1)!} = n^2 + pn + q$, find the value of p and the value of q.

7. If $(n+1)! + n^2(n-1)! = (an+1)n!$, find the value of a.

8. If $\dfrac{4!n!}{(n-1)!12n} = k$, find the value of k.

9. If $\dfrac{5!(n+1)!}{3!(n-1)!n(n-1)} = an$ find the value of a.

Solve each of the following:

10. $9(n-4)! = (n-3)!$

11. $\dfrac{(n+1)!}{(n-1)!} = 30$

12. $\dfrac{(n-2)!(n+1)!}{n!(n-1)!} = \dfrac{7}{5}$

13. $\dfrac{(2n-1)!}{(2n)!} = \dfrac{3!}{5!}$

Combinatorial Numbers

1. $\dbinom{n}{r} = \dfrac{n!}{r!(n-r)!}$ (definition)

2. $\dbinom{n}{r} = \dfrac{n(n-1)(n-2) \dots (n-r+1)}{r!}$ (in practice)

Both give the same result; however, the second is easier to use in practical questions. For example:

1. $\dbinom{6}{2} = \dfrac{6!}{2!(6-2)!} = \dfrac{6!}{2!4!} = \dfrac{720}{2 \times 24} = 15$

2. $\dbinom{6}{2} = \dfrac{6 . 5}{2 . 1}$ $\quad \rightarrow$ start at 6, go down two terms
$\quad \quad \quad \quad \rightarrow$ start at 2, go down two terms

$\quad = 15$

Memory Aid: $\quad \dbinom{n}{r} = \dfrac{n!}{r!(n-r)!} = \dfrac{\text{top!}}{\text{bottom!}(\text{top} - \text{bottom})!}$

$\binom{n}{r}$ is pronounced '*n-c-r*' or '*n-choose-r*'.

Note: Later on we will show the number of ways of choosing r objects from n different objects is given by $\binom{n}{r}$.

Other results:

> **1.** $\binom{n}{0} = 1$ and $\binom{n}{n} = 1$
>
> **2.** $\binom{n}{r} = \binom{n}{n-r}$

Use result 2 if r is greater than $\dfrac{n}{2}$.

For example, $\binom{12}{9} = \binom{12}{12-9} = \binom{12}{3}$

Example ▼

Calculate: **(i)** $\binom{10}{3}$ **(ii)** $\binom{6}{0}$ **(iii)** $\binom{30}{28}$

Solution:

(i) $\binom{10}{3} = \dfrac{10 \cdot 9 \cdot 8}{3 \cdot 2 \cdot 1} = 120$ $\left(\boxed{} \; 10 \; \boxed{nCr} \; 2 \; \boxed{=} \right)$

(ii) $\binom{6}{0} = 1$ $\left(\boxed{} \; 6 \; \boxed{nCr} \; 0 \; \boxed{=} \right)$

(iii) $\binom{30}{28} = \binom{30}{30-28} = \binom{30}{2} = \dfrac{30 \cdot 29}{2 \cdot 1} = 435$ $\left(\boxed{} \; 30 \; \boxed{nCr} \; 28 \; \boxed{=} \right)$

The following occur quite frequently when we have to solve equations involving combinatorial numbers.

$$\binom{n}{1} = n \qquad\qquad \binom{n}{2} = \frac{n(n-1)}{2 \cdot 1} \qquad\qquad \binom{n}{3} = \frac{n(n-1)(n-2)}{3 \cdot 2 \cdot 1}$$

Example ▼

Solve: **(i)** $\binom{n+1}{2} = 21$, $\quad n \in \mathbf{N}$ **(ii)** $4\binom{n}{2} = \binom{n+2}{3}$, $\quad n \in \mathbf{N}$

Solution:

(i)
$$\binom{n+1}{2} = 21, \; n \in \mathbf{N}.$$
$$\frac{(n+1)n}{2 \cdot 1} = 21$$
$$n^2 + n = 42$$
$$n^2 + n - 42 = 0$$
$$(n+7)(n-6) = 0$$
$$n = -7 \quad \text{or} \quad n = 6$$
reject $n = -7$ as $-7 \notin \mathbf{N}$.
Thus, $n = 6$

(ii)
$$4\binom{n}{2} = \binom{n+2}{3}, \; n \in \mathbf{N}.$$
$$\frac{4(n)(n-1)}{2 \cdot 1} = \frac{(n+2)(n+1)(n)}{3 \cdot 2 \cdot 1}$$
$$2(n-1) = \frac{(n+2)(n+1)}{6}$$
$$12n - 12 = n^2 + 3n + 2$$
$$n^2 - 9n + 14 = 0$$
$$(n-7)(n-2) = 0$$
$$n = 7 \quad \text{or} \quad n = 2$$

Exercise 16.2 ▼

Evaluate each of the following:

1. $\binom{5}{2}$ **2.** $\binom{7}{3}$ **3.** $\binom{8}{6}$ **4.** $\binom{6}{0}$ **5.** $\binom{4}{1}$

6. $\binom{5}{5}$ **7.** $\binom{12}{5}$ **8.** $\binom{20}{17}$ **9.** $\binom{50}{49}$ **10.** $\binom{100}{98}$

11. Verify that: **(i)** $\left[\binom{8}{2}\right]^2 = 4\binom{9}{4} + 5\binom{8}{3}$ **(ii)** $\sqrt{\binom{8}{2} - \binom{3}{2}} = 5$

Solve each of the following, $n \in \mathbf{N}_0$:

12. $\binom{n}{2} = 15$ **13.** $\binom{n}{2} = 10$ **14.** $\binom{n+1}{2} = 15$ **15.** $\binom{n+2}{2} = 6$ **16.** $\binom{n+1}{2} = 4n$

17. $\binom{n+2}{2} = 36$ **18.** $\binom{n}{3} = 5n$ **19.** $\binom{n+1}{2} = \frac{1}{2}(n^2 + 6)$ **20.** $\binom{n+1}{2} - \binom{n}{1} = 28$

Use the following in questions 21 to 24:

$$\binom{n}{r} = \frac{n!}{r!(n-r)!} = \frac{\text{top!}}{\text{bottom!}(\text{top} - \text{bottom})!}$$

Prove each of the following:

21. $\binom{n}{r} = \binom{n}{n-r}$ **22.** $\binom{n}{r} + \binom{n}{r-1} = \binom{n+1}{r}$ **23.** $\binom{n}{r+1} = \frac{n-r}{r+1}\binom{n}{r}$ **24.** $r\binom{n}{r} = n\binom{n-1}{r-1}$

25. Show that $\binom{n+2}{n} = \binom{n+2}{2}$. Hence, or otherwise, solve $\binom{n+2}{n} = 45$.

Binomial Theorem

An expression with two terms, e.g. $a + b$, is called a **binomial**.

The Binomial Theorem is used to write down the expansion of a binomial to any power, e.g. $(a + b)^n$.

The expansion of $(a + b)^n$ is found as follows:

$$(a+b)^n = \binom{n}{0}a^n b^0 + \binom{n}{1}a^{n-1}b^1 + \binom{n}{2}a^{n-2}b^2 + \cdots + \binom{n}{n-1}a^1 b^{n-1} + \binom{n}{n}a^0 b^n$$

Notes:

1. The expansion contains $(n + 1)$ terms (one more than the power).
2. The powers of a decrease by 1 in each successive term.
3. The powers of b increase by 1 in each successive term.
4. In each term the sum of the indices of a and b is n.
5. The power of b is always the same as the lower number in the combination bracket.
6. If the binomial is a difference, $(a - b)$, the signs will be alternately $+, -, +, -, +, \ldots$

The Binomial Expansion of $(1 + a)^n$ is found as follows:

$$(1+a)^n = \binom{n}{0} + \binom{n}{1}a + \binom{n}{2}a^2 + \cdots + \binom{n}{n-1}a^{n-1} + \binom{n}{n}a^n$$

This form of the Binomial Theorem can be used to expand a binomial to any power when the first term of the binomial is 1.

Example ▼

Write out all terms in the expansion of $(a + b)^5$.

Solution:

The power is 5, thus there are 6 terms (always one more than the power).

Step 1: $\quad ab + \qquad ab + \qquad ab + \qquad ab + \qquad ab + \qquad ab$

$\qquad$ (write down 6 pairs of the variables)

Step 2: $\quad a^5 b^0 + \qquad a^4 b^1 + \qquad a^3 b^2 + \qquad a^2 b^3 + \qquad a^1 b^4 + \qquad a^0 b^5$

$\qquad$ (put in powers, starting with the highest power of a; sum of powers = 5 in each term)

Step 3: $\quad \binom{5}{0}a^5 b^0 + \binom{5}{1}a^4 b^1 + \binom{5}{2}a^3 b^2 + \binom{5}{3}a^2 b^3 + \binom{5}{4}a^1 b^4 + \binom{5}{5}a^0 b^5$

$\qquad$ (put in combinatorial numbers)

Step 4: $a^5 + 5a^4 b + 10a^3 b^2 + 10a^2 b^3 + 5ab^4 + b^5$

In practice the first three steps can be combined in one step.

Note: (any real number)^0 = 1, thus $a^0 = 1$, $b^0 = 1$, etc.

Expand, using the Binomial Theorem, $(1 + 2x)^5$. Hence, expand $(1 - 2x)^5$.

Solution:

$(1 + 2x)^5$ (the power is 5, thus there are 6 terms)

$$= \binom{5}{0} + \binom{5}{1}(2x) + \binom{5}{2}(2x)^2 + \binom{5}{3}(2x)^3 + \binom{5}{4}(2x)^4 + \binom{5}{5}(2x)^5$$

$$= (1) + (5)(2x) + (10)(4x^2) + (10)(8x^3) + (5)(16x^4) + (1)(32x^5)$$

$$= 1 + 10x + 40x^2 + 80x^3 + 80x^4 + 32x^5$$

The only difference between the expansions of $(1 + 2x)^5$ and $(1 - 2x)^5$ is that in the expansion of $(1 - 2x)^5$ the signs alternate $+, -, +, -, +, -$.

Thus $(1 - 2x)^5 = 1 - 10x + 40x^2 - 80x^3 + 80x^4 - 32x^5$

Expand, using the Binomial Theorem, $(x - 3y)^4$.

Solution:

$(x - 3y)^4$ (the power is 4, thus there are 5 terms)

$$= \binom{4}{0}x^4(-3y)^0 + \binom{4}{1}x^3(-3y)^1 + \binom{4}{2}x^2(-3y)^2 + \binom{4}{3}x^1(-3y)^3 + \binom{4}{4}x^0(-3y)^4$$

$$= (1)(x^4)(1) + (4)(x^3)(-3y) + (6)(x^2)(9y^2) + (4)(x)(-27y^3) + (1)(1)(81y^4)$$

$$= x^4 - 12x^3y + 54x^2y^2 - 108xy^3 + 81y^4$$

Expand, using the Binomial Theorem, $\left(p + \dfrac{2}{p}\right)^4$.

Show that one of the terms is independent of p.

Solution:

$\left(p + \dfrac{2}{p}\right)^4$ (the power is 4, thus there are 5 terms)

$$= \binom{4}{0}(p)^4\left(\frac{2}{p}\right)^0 + \binom{4}{1}(p)^3\left(\frac{2}{p}\right)^1 + \binom{4}{2}(p)^2\left(\frac{2}{p}\right)^2 + \binom{4}{3}(p)^1\left(\frac{2}{p}\right)^3 + \binom{4}{4}(p)^0\left(\frac{2}{p}\right)^4$$

$$= (1)(p^4)(1) + (4)(p^3)\left(\frac{2}{p}\right) + (6)(p^2)\left(\frac{4}{p^2}\right) + (4)(p)\left(\frac{8}{p^3}\right) + (1)(1)\left(\frac{16}{p^4}\right)$$

$$= p^4 + 8p^2 + 24 + \frac{32}{p^2} + \frac{16}{p^4}$$

The third term, 24, is independent of p (in other words, the term does not contain p or the power of p is 0, i.e. p^0)

Use the Binomial Theorem to expand each of the following:

1. $(a+b)^4$ **2.** $(x+y)^5$ **3.** $(p+q)^6$ **4.** $(x-y)^7$

5. $(1+2x)^4$ **6.** $(1-3x)^4$ **7.** $(1 \quad 2x)^6$ **8.** $(1-5x)^4$

9. $(3+y)^4$ **10.** $(2-x)^6$ **11.** $(2+3y)^4$ **12.** $(2x-3y)^5$

13. $\left(1+\dfrac{x}{2}\right)^6$ **14.** $\left(p+\dfrac{1}{p}\right)^5$ **15.** $\left(x+\dfrac{2}{x}\right)^8$ **16.** $\left(2a-\dfrac{1}{b}\right)^4$

17. $f(x)=(1+x)^4+(1-x)^4$. Express $f(x)$ as a series in ascending powers of x.

18. $(a+2b)^5+(a-2b)^5=pa^5+qa^3b^2+rab^4$. Find the values of p, q and r.

19. $\left(x+\dfrac{1}{x}\right)^4+\left(x-\dfrac{1}{x}\right)^4=px^4+q+\dfrac{r}{x^4}$. Find the values of p, q and r.

Write down and simplify the first three terms in the expansion of each of the following:

20. $(1+2a)^{12}$ **21.** $\left(1-\dfrac{a}{2}\right)^{10}$ **22.** $\left(x^2+\dfrac{2}{x}\right)^9$

23. Write out the binomial expansion of $\left(\dfrac{x}{2}+\dfrac{2}{x}\right)^4$.

Show that one of the terms is independent of x.

Evaluating Expansions of Sums and Differences

We can be asked to evaluate expansions such as $(1+\sqrt{5})^4$ and write the answer in the form $a+b\sqrt{5}$.

Example ▼

Expand $(3+\sqrt{2})^5$ by the Binomial Theorem, and write your answer in the form $a+b\sqrt{2}$.

Solution:

$(3+\sqrt{2})^5$ (the power is 5, thus there are 6 terms)

$= \binom{5}{0}(3)^5(\sqrt{2})^0 + \binom{5}{1}(3)^4(\sqrt{2})^1 + \binom{5}{2}(3)^3(\sqrt{2})^2 + \binom{5}{3}(3)^2(\sqrt{2})^3 + \binom{5}{4}(3)^1(\sqrt{2})^4 + \binom{5}{5}(3)^0(\sqrt{2})^5$

$= (1)(243)(1) + (5)(81)(\sqrt{2}) + (10)(27)(2) + (10)(9)(2\sqrt{2}) + (5)(3)(4) + (1)(1)(4\sqrt{2})$

$= 243 + 405\sqrt{2} + 540 + 180\sqrt{2} + 60 + 4\sqrt{2}$

$= 843 + 589\sqrt{2}$

$\left(\left(\sqrt{2}\right)^2 = 2, \quad (\sqrt{2})^3 = 2\sqrt{2}, \quad (\sqrt{2})^4 = 4, \quad (\sqrt{2})^5 = 4\sqrt{2}\right)$

Use the Binomial Theorem to evaluate each of the following, writing your answer in the form $a + b\sqrt{c}$:

1. $(1 + \sqrt{2})^4$ **2.** $(1 - \sqrt{3})^5$ **3.** $(1 + \sqrt{5})^6$ **4.** $(2 + \sqrt{6})^4$

5. $(1 + 3\sqrt{2})^4$ **6.** $(1 - 2\sqrt{3})^6$ **7.** $(2 + \sqrt{3})^6$ **8.** $(\sqrt{3} - \sqrt{2})^5$

9. $(1 + \sqrt{3})^4 + (1 - \sqrt{3})^4 = k$. Use the Binomial Theorem to find the value of k.

10. $(3 + \sqrt{2})^5 + (3 - \sqrt{2})^5 = k$. Use the Binomial Theorem to find the value of k.

11. Use the Binomial Theorem to show that $(1 + x)^6 + (1 - x)^6 = 2(1 + 15x^2 + 15x^4 + x^6)$.
Hence, evaluate $(1 + \sqrt{2})^6 + (1 - \sqrt{2})^6$.

12. Use the Binomial Theorem to expand $(a + b)^5$.
Hence, expand $(1 + 2x)^5 - (1 - 2x)^5$.
Hence, write $(1 + 2\sqrt{3})^5 - (1 - 2\sqrt{3})^5$ in the form $k\sqrt{3}$, $k \in \mathbf{N}$.

13. Use the Binomial Expansion to expand $(p + q)^4 + (p - q)^4$.
Hence, or otherwise, write $(x + \sqrt{x^2 + 1})^4 + (x - \sqrt{x^2 + 1})^4$ as a polynomial in x.
Hence, evaluate $(4 + \sqrt{17})^4 + (4 - \sqrt{17})^4$.

Unknown Coefficients or an Unknown Index

In some questions we have to find unknown coefficients or an unknown index (power).

When the index (power) is unknown we make use of the following:

$$\binom{n}{0} = 1 \qquad\qquad \binom{n}{1} = n \qquad\qquad \binom{n}{2} = \frac{n(n - 1)}{2 \cdot 1} \qquad\qquad \binom{n}{3} = \frac{n(n - 1)(n - 2)}{3 \cdot 2 \cdot 1}$$

Then equate the coefficients and solve the resultant equations.

Example ▼

The first three terms in the binomial expansion of $(1 + ax)^n$ are $1 + 2x + \frac{5}{3}x^2$.
Find the value of n and the value of a.

Solution:
The first three terms are:

$$(1 + ax)^n = \binom{n}{0} + \binom{n}{1}(ax) + \binom{n}{2}(ax)^2$$

$$= 1 + n(ax) + \frac{n(n - 1)}{2 \cdot 1} a^2 x^2$$

$$= 1 + nax + \frac{n(n - 1)}{2} a^2 x^2$$

$$\therefore \quad 1 + nax + \frac{n(n-1)}{2}a^2x^2 = 1 + 2x + \tfrac{5}{3}x^2$$

What we do next is equate the coefficients and solve the resultant equations.

$$na = 2 \ \text{①}$$

$$a = \left(\frac{2}{n}\right)$$

put this into ②

$$\frac{n(n-1)}{2}a^2 = \frac{5}{3} \quad \text{②}$$

$$\frac{n(n-1)}{2} \cdot \left(\frac{2}{n}\right)^2 = \frac{5}{3}$$

$$\frac{n(n-1)}{2} \cdot \frac{4}{n^2} = \frac{5}{3}$$

$$\frac{2(n-1)}{n} = \frac{5}{3}$$

$$6(n-1) = 5n$$

$$6n - 6 = 5n$$

$$n = 6$$

From ①, $a = \dfrac{2}{n} = \dfrac{2}{6} = \dfrac{1}{3}$

Thus, $n = 6$ and $a = \tfrac{1}{3}$.

Exercise 16.5 ▼

1. The first four terms in the expansion of $(1 - x)^n$ are $1 - 6x + ax^2 + bx^3$.
   Find the value of n, the value of a and the value of b.

2. The first three terms in the expansion of $(1 + ax)^n$ are $1 + 20x + 150x^2$.
   Find the value of n and the value of a.

3. The first three terms in the expansion of $(1 + ax)^n$ are $1 + 28x + 336x^2$.
   Find the value of n and the value of a.

4. The first three terms in the expansion of $(1 + kx)^n$ are $1 - 18x + 135x^2$.
   Find the value of n and the value of k.

5. The first four terms in the expansion of $(1 + kx)^n$ are $1 + 20x + 180x^2 + ax^3$.
   Find the value of n, the value of k and the value of a.

6. The first three terms in the expansion of $(1 + ax)^n$ are $1 - 5x + \tfrac{45}{4}x^2$.
   Find the value of n and the value of a.

7. The first three terms in the expansion of $(1 + ax)^n$ are $1 + 8x + 30x^2$.
   Find the value of n and the value of a.

8. The first four terms in the expansion of $\left(1 - \dfrac{3x}{2}\right)^n$ are $1 - 24x + ax^2 + bx^3$.

   Find the value of n, the value of a and the value of b.

9. The first three terms in the expansion of $(1 + kx)^n$ are $1 + 2x + \frac{15}{8}x^2$.
   Find the value of n and the value of k.

10. The first four terms in the expansion of $(1 + kx)^6$ are $1 + ax + 135x^2 + bx^3$.
    Find the values of k, the values of a and the values of b.

11. The first three terms of the expansion of $\left(a - \dfrac{x}{3}\right)^6$, $a > 0$, in ascending powers of x, are

    $64 + 16bx + \frac{1}{3}bcx^2$, $\quad a, b, c \in \mathbf{R}$. Find the value of a, of b and of c.

12. In the expansion of $(1 + x)^{n+1}$ the coefficient of x^4 is $6k$ and in the expansion of $(1 + x)^{n-1}$ the coefficient of x^2 is k. Find the value of n, $n > 2$.

Selecting a Particular Term

In many problems we require only a particular term. For example, the middle term, the fifth term or the term independent of x (no x term or the power of x is zero, i.e. x^0).

In these cases we make use of the '**general term**'.

General Term:

> The general term in the binomial expansion of $(a + b)^n$ is:
>
> $$u_{r+1} = \binom{n}{r} a^{n-r} b^r$$

$$\text{(sum of powers} = n - r + r = n)$$

$$u_{r+1} = \binom{n}{r} a^{n-r} b^r$$

$$\text{(same)}$$

Note: The number at the bottom of the combination bracket, r, is always **one less** than the term number, $r + 1$.

Example ▼

(i) Find, and simplify, the middle term in the binomial expansion of $\left(6x + \dfrac{y}{3}\right)^{10}$.

(ii) Find, and simplify, the third term in the expansion of $\left(2x - \dfrac{1}{x}\right)^8$.

Solution:

(i) $\left(6x + \dfrac{y}{3}\right)^{10}$

General term: $u_{r+1} = \dbinom{10}{r}(6x)^{10-r}\left(\dfrac{y}{3}\right)^r$

There are 11 terms in the expansion.
Thus, the middle term is u_6

$\therefore \quad u_6 = u_{r+1} \Rightarrow r = 5$

$\therefore \quad u_6 = \dbinom{10}{5}(6x)^{10-5}\left(\dfrac{y}{3}\right)^5$

$\qquad = \dbinom{10}{5}(6x)^5\left(\dfrac{y}{3}\right)^5$

$\qquad = (252)(7776x^5)\left(\dfrac{y^5}{243}\right)$

$\qquad = 8064x^5y^5$

(ii) $\left(2x - \dfrac{1}{x}\right)^8$

General term: $u_{r+1} = \dbinom{8}{r}(2x)^{8-r}\left(-\dfrac{1}{x}\right)^r$

$u_3 = u_{r+1} \Rightarrow r = 2$

$\therefore \quad u_3 = \dbinom{8}{2}(2x)^{8-2}\left(-\dfrac{1}{x}\right)^2$

$\qquad = \dbinom{8}{2}(2x)^6\left(-\dfrac{1}{x}\right)^2$

$\qquad = (28)(64x^6)\left(\dfrac{1}{x^2}\right)$

$\qquad = 1792x^4$

Example ▼

Find **(i)** the general term   **(ii)** the term independent of x, in the binomial expansion of $\left(2x - \dfrac{1}{x^2}\right)^9$.

Solution:

(i) $\left(2x - \dfrac{1}{x^2}\right)^9$

General term:

$u_{r+1} = \dbinom{9}{r}(2x)^{9-r}\left(\dfrac{-1}{x^2}\right)^r$

$\qquad = \dbinom{9}{r}(2^{9-r})(x^{9-r})(x^{-2r})(-1)^r$

$\qquad = (-1)^r\dbinom{9}{r}2^{9-r}x^{9-3r}$

(ii) For the term independent of x,
the power of $x = 0$

$\therefore \quad 9 - 3r = 0$

$\qquad r = 3 \text{ (4th term)}$

Thus, the required term

$= (-1)^3\dbinom{9}{3}2^{9-3}x^{9-9}$

$= (-1)(84)(2^6)(x^0)$

$= -5376 \qquad (x^0 = 1)$

229

(i) Write down the general term in the binomial expansion of $(2x + 5y^2)^n$.
(ii) If k is a constant and kx^3y^4 is a term in the binomial expansion of $(2x + 5y^2)^n$, find the value of n and the value of k.

Solution:

(i) $(2x + 5y^2)^n$
General term:

$$u_{r+1} = \binom{n}{r}(2x)^{n-r}(5y^2)^r$$

$$= \binom{n}{r}2^{n-r}x^{n-r}5^ry^{2r}$$

$$= \binom{n}{r}2^{n-r}5^rx^{n-r}y^{2r}$$

(ii) If kx^3y^4 is a particular term, then

$2r = 4$	and	$n - r = 3$
$r = 2$	and	$n - 2 = 3$
$r = 2$	and	$n = 5$

$$k = \binom{5}{2}2^35^2$$

$$= (10)(8)(25) = 2000$$

Find the:

1. 4th term of $(1 + 2x)^6$
2. 5th term of $(a + 2b)^9$
3. 3rd term of $(x - 2y)^{12}$
4. 7th term of $(1 + x^2)^8$
5. 4th term of $(2x - \frac{1}{2})^4$
6. 5th term of $\left(x + \dfrac{1}{x}\right)^8$
7. 6th term of $\left(x - \dfrac{1}{x^2}\right)^{10}$
8. 4th term of $\left(1 + \dfrac{x}{2}\right)^{10}$

9. Write down the first three terms in the expansion of $(1 + 3x)^7$, and find their sum when $x = \frac{2}{3}$.

10. When $\left(1 - \dfrac{x}{2y}\right)^5$ is expanded in ascending powers of x, find:

   (i) the coefficient of x^4, when $y = 1$
   (ii) the sum of the first three terms when $x = 0.1$, $y = 0.02$.

Find the middle term in each of the following:

11. $(1 + 2x)^{10}$
12. $(a + 2b)^8$
13. $(p - 2q)^{10}$
14. $(a - 3b)^6$
15. $\left(2 - \dfrac{x}{2}\right)^6$
16. $\left(p^2 + \dfrac{1}{p}\right)^6$
17. $\left(x^2 + \dfrac{2}{x}\right)^8$
18. $\left(x^3 - \dfrac{1}{2x}\right)^8$

Find the term independent of x in the binomial expansion of each of the following:

19. $\left(x + \dfrac{2}{x}\right)^4$
20. $\left(x - \dfrac{1}{x}\right)^8$
21. $\left(2x + \dfrac{1}{x^2}\right)^3$
22. $\left(x^2 - \dfrac{1}{x}\right)^6$

23. $\left(x + \dfrac{1}{x^2}\right)^9$ **24.** $\left(x - \dfrac{1}{x^2}\right)^{18}$ **25.** $\left(x^4 + \dfrac{1}{x}\right)^{30}$ **26.** $\left(x + \dfrac{1}{\sqrt{x}}\right)^{15}$

27. If k is a constant and kxy^6 is a term in the expansion of $(2x + 3y^2)^n$, find the value of n and the value of k.

28. If h is a constant and hx^4y^2 is a term in the expansion of $(3x - 4y^2)^n$, find the value of n and the value of h.

29. Write down the binomial expansion of $(1 + 2x)^n$ in ascending powers of x as far as the term containing x^3.
Given that the coefficient of x^3 is twice the coefficient of x^2 and that both are positive, find the value of n.

30. Write down the first three terms in the binomial expansion, in ascending powers of x, of $(1 + ax)^n$, where $a \neq 0$ and $n \in \mathbf{N}$.
Given that the coefficient of x in this expansion is twice the coefficient of x^2,

(i) show that $n = \dfrac{a + 1}{a}$

(ii) find the value of the coefficient of x^2 when $a = \frac{1}{7}$.

Sums of Binomial Coefficients

The binomial expansion

$$(1 + x)^n = \binom{n}{0} + \binom{n}{1}x + \binom{n}{2}x^2 + \cdots \binom{n}{n-1}x^{n-1} + \binom{n}{n}x^n$$

can be used to find the sums of binomial coefficients by letting $x = 1$ or $x = -1$ on both sides.

Other binomial series can also be used.

Example ▼

(i) Prove that: $\binom{n}{0} + \binom{n}{1} + \binom{n}{2} + \binom{n}{3} + \cdots + \binom{n}{n} = 2^n$.

Hence, prove that $\binom{n}{0} + \binom{n}{2} + \binom{n}{4} + \cdots = \binom{n}{1} + \binom{n}{3} + \binom{n}{5} + \cdots = 2^{n-1}$.

(ii) Evaluate: $\binom{12}{0} + \binom{12}{1} + \binom{12}{2} + \cdots + \binom{12}{11} + \binom{12}{12}$.

(iii) Evaluate the sum of the coefficients in the expansion of $(x + 3)^8$.

Solution:

(i) Consider the expansion of $(1+x)^n$.

$$(1+x)^n = \binom{n}{0} + \binom{n}{1}x + \binom{n}{2}x^2 + \binom{n}{3}x^3 + \cdots + \binom{n}{n}x^n$$

This is true for all x. Let $x = 1$ on both sides.

$$(1+1)^n = \binom{n}{0} + \binom{n}{1} + \binom{n}{2} + \binom{n}{3} + \cdots + \binom{n}{n}$$

$$\therefore \quad 2^n = \binom{n}{0} + \binom{n}{1} + \binom{n}{2} + \binom{n}{3} + \cdots + \binom{n}{n}$$

Let $x = -1$ on both sides.

$$(1-1)^n = \binom{n}{0} - \binom{n}{1} + \binom{n}{2} - \binom{n}{3} + \binom{n}{4} - \binom{n}{5} + \cdots$$

$$\therefore \quad 0 = \binom{n}{0} - \binom{n}{1} + \binom{n}{2} - \binom{n}{3} + \binom{n}{4} - \binom{n}{5} + \cdots$$

$$\binom{n}{0} + \binom{n}{2} + \binom{n}{4} + \cdots = \binom{n}{1} + \binom{n}{3} + \binom{n}{5} + \cdots$$

$$= \frac{1}{2}\left[\binom{n}{0} + \binom{n}{1} + \binom{n}{2} + \binom{n}{3} + \binom{n}{4} + \binom{n}{5} + \cdots\right]$$

$$= \tfrac{1}{2}(2^n) \quad \text{[by result above]}$$

$$= 2^{n-1}$$

(ii) $\binom{12}{0} + \binom{12}{1} + \binom{12}{2} + \cdots + \binom{12}{12} = 2^{12} = 4{,}096$

(iii) $(x+3)^8 = \binom{8}{0}x^8 + \binom{8}{1}x^7(3) + \binom{8}{2}x^6(3)^2 + \cdots + \binom{8}{8}(3)^8$

Let $x = 1$ on both sides.

$$(1+3)^8 = \binom{8}{0} + \binom{8}{1}(3) + \binom{8}{2}(3)^2 + \cdots + \binom{8}{8}(3)^8 = 4^8$$

Thus, the sum of the coefficients is $4^8 = 65{,}536$.

Exercise 16.7 ▼

Use the binomial expansion $(1+x)^n$ to verify:

1. $\binom{8}{0} + \binom{8}{1} + \binom{8}{2} + \cdots + \binom{8}{7} + \binom{8}{8} = 2^8$

2. $\binom{16}{0} + \binom{16}{1} + \binom{16}{2} + \cdots + \binom{16}{15} + \binom{16}{16} = 2^{16}$

3. $\dbinom{16}{0} + \dbinom{16}{2} + \dbinom{16}{4} + \cdots + \dbinom{16}{14} + \dbinom{16}{16} = 2^{15}$

4. $\dbinom{14}{1} + \dbinom{14}{3} + \dbinom{14}{5} + \cdots + \dbinom{14}{13} = \dbinom{14}{0} + \dbinom{14}{2} + \dbinom{14}{6} + \cdots + \dbinom{14}{14}$

5. $\dbinom{11}{0} - \dbinom{11}{1} + \dbinom{11}{2} - \dbinom{11}{3} + \cdots + \dbinom{11}{10} - \dbinom{11}{11} = 0$

6. Evaluate the sum of the coefficients in the expansion of $(x + 2)^7$.

7. Evaluate the sum of the coefficients in the expansion of $(x + y)^{12}$.

8. Evaluate the sum of the coefficients in the expansion of $(3x + 1)^9$.

CHAPTER 17

PROOFS

Algebra Proof

Factor Theorem

Let $f(x) = ax^3 + bx^2 + cx + d$, where $a, b, c, d \in \mathbf{R}$.
If k is a real number such that $f(k) = 0$, prove that $(x - k)$ is a factor of $f(x)$.

Proof:

If $\qquad f(x) = ax^3 + bx^2 + cx + d$

then $\qquad f(k) = ak^3 + bk^2 + ck + d$

$$
\begin{aligned}
\text{and} \quad f(x) - f(k) &= a(x^3 - k^3) + b(x^2 - k^2) + c(x - k) \\
&= a(x - k)(x^2 + kx + k^2) + b(x - k)(x + k) + c(x - k) \\
&= (x - k)[a(x^2 + kx + k^2) + b(x + k) + c]
\end{aligned}
$$

$\therefore \; (x - k)$ is a factor of $f(x) - f(k)$

but $f(k) = 0$

$\therefore \; (x - k)$ is a factor of $f(x)$.

Coordinate Geometry of the Line Proofs

Angle Between Two Lines

If θ is the angle between two lines with slopes m_1 and m_2, then:
$$\tan\theta = \frac{m_1 - m_2}{1 + m_1 m_2}$$

Proof:

Let $L_1: y = m_1 x + c_1$ and $L_2: y = m_2 x + c_2$ be two lines making angles α and β, respectively, with the x-axis. Let θ be one of the angles made by the intersection of the lines.

The slope of $L_1 = m_1 = \tan\alpha$
The slope of $L_2 = m_2 = \tan\beta$

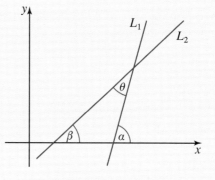

From the diagram, $\alpha = \theta + \beta$ (exterior angle)

$$\theta = \alpha - \beta$$
$$\tan\theta = \tan(\alpha - \beta)$$
$$= \frac{\tan\alpha - \tan\beta}{1 + \tan\alpha \tan\beta} = \frac{m_1 - m_2}{1 + m_1 m_2}$$

Perpendicular Distance from a Point to a Line

The perpendicular distance, d, from the point (x_1, y_1) to the line $ax + by + c = 0$ is given by:

$$\frac{|ax_1 + by_1 + c|}{\sqrt{a^2 + b^2}}$$

Proof:

Let L be the line $ax + by + c = 0$, intersecting the x-axis at q and the y-axis at r. Let p be the point (x_1, y_1) and let d be the perpendicular distance from p to L.

The coordinates of q are $\left(-\dfrac{c}{a}, 0\right)$ and

the coordinates of r are $\left(0, -\dfrac{c}{b}\right)$.

Method: We find the area of $\triangle pqr$ by two different methods and equate them.

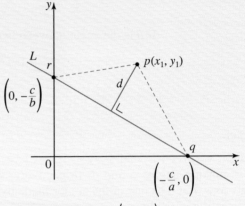

1. By formula.

Area of $\triangle pqr$

$= \frac{1}{2} | \text{ base } | \cdot | \text{ perpendicular height } |$

$= \frac{1}{2} | qr | \cdot d$

$= \frac{1}{2} d \sqrt{\left(\dfrac{c}{a}\right)^2 + \left(-\dfrac{c}{b}\right)^2}$

$= \frac{1}{2} d \sqrt{\dfrac{c^2}{a^2} + \dfrac{c^2}{b^2}}$

$= \frac{1}{2} d \sqrt{\dfrac{a^2 c^2 + b^2 c^2}{a^2 b^2}}$

$= \frac{1}{2} d \sqrt{\dfrac{c^2}{a^2 b^2}(a^2 + b^2)}$

$= \frac{1}{2} d \cdot \dfrac{c}{ab} \sqrt{a^2 + b^2}$

2. By the translation $\left(0, -\dfrac{c}{b}\right) \rightarrow (0, 0)$.

$\left(0, -\dfrac{c}{b}\right) \rightarrow (0, 0)$, thus

$\left(-\dfrac{c}{a}, 0\right) \rightarrow \left(-\dfrac{c}{a}, \dfrac{c}{b}\right)$, and

$(x_1, y_1) \rightarrow \left(x_1, y_1 + \dfrac{c}{b}\right)$

Area of $\triangle pqr = \frac{1}{2} | x_1 y_2 - x_2 y_1 |$

$= \frac{1}{2} \left| x_1 \left(\dfrac{c}{b}\right) - \left(-\dfrac{c}{a}\right)\left(y_1 + \dfrac{c}{b}\right) \right|$

$= \frac{1}{2} \left| \dfrac{cx_1}{b} + \dfrac{cy_1}{a} + \dfrac{c^2}{ab} \right|$

$= \frac{1}{2} \left| \dfrac{acx_1 + bcy_1 + c^2}{ab} \right|$

$= \frac{1}{2} \dfrac{c}{ab} | ax_1 + by_1 + c |$

Area of $\triangle pqr$ = Area of $\triangle pqr$

$\therefore \ \frac{1}{2} d \dfrac{c}{ab} \sqrt{a^2 + b^2} = \frac{1}{2} \dfrac{c}{ab} | ax_1 + by_1 + c |$

$d\sqrt{a^2 + b^2} = | ax_1 + by_1 + c |$

$d = \dfrac{| ax_1 + by_1 + c |}{\sqrt{a^2 + b^2}}$

Trigonometric Proofs

Cosine Rule

$$\text{In } \Delta abc, \qquad a^2 = b^2 + c^2 - 2bc \cos A$$

Proof:

In Δabc, let $|cd|$ be the length of the perpendicular from c to $[ab]$. Let $|cd| = h$ and $|ad| = x$, thus, $|db| = c - x$

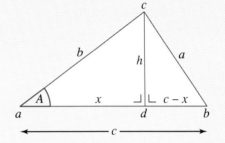

Using Pythagoras' Theorem:

On Δacd: $\qquad h^2 + x^2 = b^2 \Longrightarrow h^2 = b^2 - x^2$

On Δbcd: $\qquad h^2 + (c-x)^2 = a^2 \Longrightarrow h^2 = a^2 - (c-x)^2$

Thus, $\qquad a^2 - (c-x)^2 = b^2 - x^2 \qquad (h^2 = h^2)$

$$a^2 - c^2 + 2cx - x^2 = b^2 - x^2$$

$$a^2 = b^2 + c^2 - 2cx$$

$$a^2 = b^2 + c^2 - 2bc \cos A \qquad \text{(replace } x \text{ with } b \cos A\text{)}$$

In Δacd,

$$\cos A = \frac{x}{b}$$

$$b \cos A = x$$

Cos $(A + B)$

$$\boxed{\cos(A + B) = \cos A \cos B - \sin A \sin B}$$

Proof:

Let $p(\cos A, \sin A)$ and $q(\cos B, \sin B)$ be two points on the unit circle.

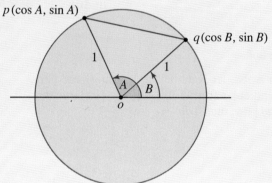

Using the distance formula:

$$|pq|^2 = (\cos A - \cos B)^2 + (\sin A - \sin B)^2$$
$$= \cos^2 A - 2\cos A \cos B + \cos^2 B + \sin^2 A - 2\sin A \sin B + \sin^2 B$$
$$= (\cos^2 A + \sin^2 A) + (\cos^2 B + \sin^2 B) - 2(\cos A \cos B + \sin A \sin B)$$
$$= 1 + 1 - 2(\cos A \cos B + \sin A \sin B)$$
$$= 2 - 2(\cos A \cos B + \sin A \sin B) \qquad \text{①}$$

Using the cosine rule on $\triangle opq$:

$$|pq|^2 = 1 + 1 - 2\cos(A - B)$$
$$= 2 - 2\cos(A - B) \qquad \text{②}$$

Equating ① and ② gives:

$$2 - 2\cos(A - B) = 2 - 2(\cos A \cos B + \sin A \sin B)$$
$$\cos(A - B) = \cos A \cos B + \sin A \sin B$$

Replace B with $-B$ on both sides.

$$\cos[A - (-B)] = \cos A \cos(-B) + \sin A \sin(-B)$$
$$\cos(A + B) = \cos A \cos B - \sin A \sin B$$

$[\cos(-B) = \cos B$ and $\sin(-B) = -\sin B]$

Differentiation Proofs

Addition Rule

If $u = u(x)$ and $v = v(x)$, then:

$$\frac{d}{dx}(u + v) = \frac{du}{dx} + \frac{dv}{dx}$$

Proof:

Let

$$f(x) = u(x) + v(x)$$

$$f(x + h) = u(x + h) + v(x + h)$$

$$f(x + h) - f(x) = u(x + h) + v(x + h) - u(x) - v(x)$$

$$= u(x + h) - u(x) + v(x + h) - v(x)$$

$$\frac{f(x + h) - f(x)}{h} = \frac{u(x + h) - u(x)}{h} + \frac{v(x + h) - v(x)}{h}$$

$$\lim_{h \to 0} \frac{f(x + h) - f(x)}{h} = \lim_{h \to 0} \frac{u(x + h) - u(x)}{h} + \lim_{h \to 0} \frac{v(x + h) - v(x)}{h}$$

$$= \frac{du}{dx} + \frac{dv}{dx}$$

$$\text{Thus, } f'(x) = \frac{du}{dx} + \frac{dv}{dx} = \frac{d}{dx}(u + v)$$

Product Rule

$$\boxed{\begin{array}{c} \text{If } u = u(x) \text{ and } v = v(x), \text{ then:} \\[2mm] \dfrac{d}{dx}(uv) = u\dfrac{dv}{dx} + v\dfrac{du}{dx} \end{array}}$$

Proof:

Let

$$y = uv$$

$$\ln y = \ln (uv)$$

$$\ln y = \ln u + \ln v$$

$$\frac{1}{y}\frac{dy}{dx} = \frac{1}{u}\frac{du}{dx} + \frac{1}{v}\frac{dv}{dx} \qquad \text{(implicit differentiation)}$$

$$\frac{dy}{dx} = y \cdot \frac{1}{u}\frac{du}{dx} + y \cdot \frac{1}{v}\frac{du}{dx} \qquad \text{(multiply both sides by } y\text{)}$$

$$= uv \cdot \frac{1}{u}\frac{du}{dx} + uv \cdot \frac{1}{v}\frac{du}{dx} \qquad (y = uv)$$

$$= v\frac{du}{dx} + u\frac{dv}{dx}$$

$$= u\frac{dv}{dx} + v\frac{du}{dx}$$

$$\therefore \quad \frac{d}{dx}(uv) = u\frac{dv}{dx} + v\frac{du}{dx}$$

Quotient Rule

If $u = u(x)$ and $v = v(x)$, then:

$$\frac{d}{dx}\left(\frac{u}{v}\right) = \frac{v\dfrac{du}{dx} - u\dfrac{dv}{dx}}{v^2}$$

Proof:

Let

$$y = \frac{u}{v}$$

$$\ln y = \ln\left(\frac{u}{v}\right)$$

$$\ln y = \ln u - \ln v$$

$$\frac{1}{y}\frac{dy}{dx} = \frac{1}{u}\frac{du}{dx} - \frac{1}{v}\frac{dv}{dx} \qquad \text{(implicit differentiation)}$$

$$\frac{dy}{dx} = y \cdot \frac{1}{u}\frac{du}{dx} - y \cdot \frac{1}{v}\frac{dv}{dx} \qquad \text{(multiply both sides by } y\text{)}$$

$$= \frac{u}{v} \cdot \frac{1}{u}\frac{du}{dx} - \frac{u}{v} \cdot \frac{1}{v}\frac{dv}{dx} \qquad \left(y = \frac{u}{v}\right)$$

$$= \frac{1}{v}\frac{du}{dx} - \frac{u}{v^2}\frac{dv}{dx}$$

$$= \frac{v}{v^2}\frac{du}{dx} - \frac{u}{v^2}\frac{dv}{dx} \qquad \left(\frac{1}{v} = \frac{v}{v^2}\right)$$

$$= \frac{v\dfrac{du}{dx} - u\dfrac{dv}{dx}}{v^2}$$

$$\therefore \quad \frac{d}{dx}\left(\frac{u}{v}\right) = \frac{v\dfrac{du}{dx} - u\dfrac{dv}{dx}}{v^2}$$

Differential Rule

$$\frac{d}{dx}(x^n) = nx^{n-1}, \quad n \in N_0$$

Proof:

$$P(n): \quad \frac{d}{dx}(x^n) = nx^{n-1}, \quad n \in N_0$$

Step 1: $P(1):$ $\quad \dfrac{dx}{dx} = 1$

Let $f(x) = x$

$$\frac{d}{dx}(x) = \lim_{h \to 0} \frac{f(x+h) - f(x)}{h} = \lim_{h \to 0}\left(\frac{x+h-x}{h}\right) = \lim_{h \to 0} 1 = 1$$

$\therefore$ $P(1)$ is true

Step 2: Assume $P(k)$ is true, i.e. $\dfrac{d}{dx}(x^k) = kx^{k-1}$

Test $p(k+1)$:

$$\frac{d}{dx}(x^{k+1}) = \frac{d}{dx}(x \cdot x^k)$$

$$= x\frac{d}{dx}(x^k) + x^k\frac{d}{dx}(x) \qquad \text{[using the product rule]}$$

$$= x \cdot kx^{k-1} + x^k(1) \qquad \begin{bmatrix} \text{using our assumption} \\ \text{and } P(1) \text{ is true} \end{bmatrix}$$

$$= kx^k + x^k$$

$$= (k+1)x^k$$

Thus, $P(k+1)$ is true if $P(k)$ is true.

Hence, by the principle of mathematical induction, $P(n)$ is true.

REVISION EXERCISE 1 ALGEBRA

Paper 1, Questions 1, 2 and 5

This revision exercise covers chapters 1, 2, 3, 4 and 5.

Exercise 1R.A ▼

1. If $x = \dfrac{2\sqrt{a}}{\sqrt{1-a}}$, express a in terms of x.

2. If $y = \sqrt{x+4} + 2$, express x in terms of y.

3. Solve the simultaneous equations $\dfrac{x}{3} - \dfrac{y}{6} = \dfrac{7}{6}$ and $\dfrac{3x+7y}{x+y} = 1$.

4. Solve the simultaneous equations $\dfrac{10}{y} + 1 = \dfrac{3}{x}$ and $2x - y + 1 = 0$.

5. Express $\dfrac{1-\sqrt{2}}{1+\sqrt{2}}$ in the form $a\sqrt{a} - b$, where $a, b, \in \mathbf{N}$.

6. If $a = 1 - \sqrt{3}$ and $b = 1 + \sqrt{3}$, express $\dfrac{1}{a} - \dfrac{1}{b}$ in the form $-\sqrt{p}$.

7. Simplify $\dfrac{\sqrt{3}-1}{\sqrt{3}+1} + \dfrac{\sqrt{3}+1}{\sqrt{3}-1}$.

8. Show that each of the following simplifies to a constant and find that constant:
   (i) $\dfrac{x+3}{x-1} + \dfrac{4}{1-x}$, $\quad x \ne 1$
   (ii) $\dfrac{4x-5}{2x-3} - \dfrac{2(x-2)}{3-2x}$, $\quad x \ne \frac{3}{2}$
   (iii) $\dfrac{p+2}{2} - \dfrac{p}{p+2} - \dfrac{p^3-2p^2}{2p^2-8}$, $\quad p \ne \pm 2$

9. Solve:
   (i) $|2x+3| = |x+7|$
   (ii) $3x - \sqrt{12x+1} = 5$
   (iii) $4x^2 - 5\sqrt{3}x + 3 = 0$
   (iv) $\sqrt{2(x-2)} = 4 - \sqrt{x}$
   (v) $2\sqrt{2x+1} = 1 - \sqrt{4x+3}$
   (vi) $\left|\dfrac{x+2}{x-1}\right| = 3$

10. Solve $x + \dfrac{24}{x} = 14$. Hence, or otherwise, solve $a(a+1) + \dfrac{24}{a(a+1)} = 14$.

11. Solve $x^2 - 9x + 20 = 0$. Hence, or otherwise, solve $y - 9\sqrt{y} + 20 = 0$.

12. Solve $x^2 - 5x - 14 = 0$. Hence, or otherwise, solve $(x^3 - 1)^2 - 5(x^3 - 1) - 14 = 0$.

13. Find the values of the integers a, b and c, if the equation $ax^2 + bx + c = 0$ has roots $-\frac{1}{2}$ and 5.

14. Let $g(x) = ax^3 + bx^2 + cx + d$, where a, b, c and d are constants.
If $(2x - 1)$, $(x + 2)$ and $(x - 3)$ are factors of $g(x)$, find the values of a, b, c and d.

15. $(x + 1)$ is a factor of $x^3 + 5x^2 + kx - 12$.
Find the value of k and the other two factors of the cubic expression.

16. If $P(x) = 6 + x - 4x^2 + x^3$, show that $(3 - x)$ is a factor of $P(x)$.
Find the other two factors of $P(x)$.

Solve each of the following inequalities for $x \in \mathbf{R}$:

17. $9(x + 1) - 1 \geqslant 2(5x + 6)$

18. $\frac{1}{2}(3x - 2) - \frac{1}{3}(x - 4) > x$

19. $\frac{1}{3}(x - 1) - \frac{1}{2}x < \frac{1}{4}(x + 1)$

20. $-1 \leqslant 2x + 1 \leqslant 9$

21. $4 \geqslant 1 - 3x \geqslant -5$

22. $2x - 3 \leqslant x - 1 < 3x + 2$

23. $(x + 1)^2 \leqslant 9$

24. $2x^2 - 3x < 0$

25. $4x^2 - 9 \geqslant 0$

26. $|x + 4| < |x + 3|$

27. $|x - 2| \geqslant 2|x + 1|$

28. $3|x - 1| > |x + 1|$

29. Solve the simultaneous equations $x - y = 0$ and $(x + 2)^2 + y^2 = 10$.

30. Solve the simultaneous equations $3x + y - 5 = 0$ and $5x^2 - 2xy + y^2 = 5$.

31. Verify that $(x^2 + 1)^2 = x^4 + 2x^2 + 1$. Hence, simplify $\dfrac{3}{\sqrt{x^4 + 2x^2 + 1} - x^2}$.

32. The diagram shows a graph of the function
$f(x) = x^3 - 4x^2 + ax + 30$
The graph cuts the x-axis at p, q and 5.
Calculate the value of a, the value of p and
the value of q.

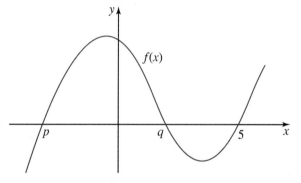

33. Find the real numbers a and b such that $x^2 + 4x - 6 = (x + a)^2 + b$ for all $x \in \mathbf{R}$.

34. If $2x^2 + 8x - 1 = p(x + q)^2 + r$ for all $x \in \mathbf{R}$, find the values of p, q and r.

35. If $a(x + 1)(x + 2) + b(x + 1) + c = 3x^2 + 5x + 7$ for all $x \in \mathbf{R}$, find the value of a, the value of b and the value of c.

36. Simplify $\left(x^2 + \sqrt{2} + \dfrac{1}{x^2}\right)\left(x^2 - \sqrt{2} + \dfrac{1}{x^2}\right)$, and express your answer in the form $x^n + \dfrac{1}{x^n}$.

37. Evaluate: **(i)** $27^{2/3}$ **(ii)** $32^{-4/5}$ **(iii)** $(\frac{4}{9})^{-3/2}$ **(iv)** $(64^{5/6}) \div (1\frac{7}{9})^{3/2}$

38. If $\dfrac{64^{-2/3}}{32^{-2/5}} = 2^n$, find the value of n.

39. If $3(2^{n+1}) - 2^n = k(2^n)$, find the value of k.

40. Solve for x,

    (i) $2^{2x-1} = (\frac{1}{8})^x$ **(ii)** $x^{1/2} + x^{-1/2} = 2(x^{1/2} - x^{-1/2})$ **(iii)** $x^{3/2} = 8$ **(iv)** $(x^{1/3} + 1)^{1/2} = 2$

41. If $x + \dfrac{1}{x} = a$, express   **(i)** $x^2 + \dfrac{1}{x^2}$ and   **(ii)** $x^3 + \dfrac{1}{x^3}$ in terms of a.

Exercise 1R.B ▼

1. If $x = \sqrt{p} + \dfrac{2}{\sqrt{p}} + 2$ where $p > 0$, express $x^2 - 4x$ in terms of p.

2. If $3(x^2 + 2x) + 7 = a(x^2 + 2) + bx(x - 3) + c$ for all $x \in \mathbf{R}$, find the values of a, b and c.

3. Solve the simultaneous equations:
$$x + y + z = 11, \qquad x - 2y - z = -16, \qquad x - 2y + 3z = 20$$
Hence, or otherwise, solve:
$$(2a + 1) + (b^2 - 1) + (c^3 + 1) = 11, \qquad (2a + 1) - 2(b^2 - 1) - (c^3 + 1) = -16,$$
$$(2a + 1) - 2(b^2 - 1) + 3(c^3 + 1) = 20.$$

4. Solve the simultaneous equations:
$$\frac{x + y}{2} = \frac{y + z}{4} = \frac{x + z}{3} \text{ and } x + y + z = 27$$

5. Show that each of the following simplifies to a constant and find that constant:

    (i) $\left(\dfrac{a^2 + b^2}{a^2 - b^2}\right)^2 - \left(\dfrac{2ab}{a^2 - b^2}\right)^2, \qquad a \neq b$ **(ii)** $\dfrac{\dfrac{1}{x+1} + \dfrac{1}{x-1}}{\dfrac{x+1}{x-1} - \dfrac{x-1}{x+1}}, \qquad x \neq \pm 1, 0$

6. Let $p(x) = 2x^3 + mx^2 + nx - 3$ where m and n are constants.
    Given that $(x + 1)$ and $(2x - 1)$ are factors of $p(x)$, find the value of m and the value of n.
    Hence, or otherwise, find the third linear factor of $p(x)$.

7. $f(x) = px^3 + qx^2 - 2x + 1$ and $g(x) = px^3 + qx^2 - 5x + 2q$, where p and q are constants.
    If $(x + 1)$ is a common factor of $f(x)$ and $g(x)$, find the value of p and the value of q.

8. $p(x) = x^3 - 4x^2 + x + 6$. Express $p(x)$ as the product of three linear factors.
    $q(x) = x^3 - 3x^2 + 2x + a$. If $p(x)$ and $q(x)$ have a common factor, find the three possible values of a.

9. One root of the equation $kx^2 - 9x + 2 = 0$, $k \neq 0$, is double the other root. Find the value of k.

10. If α and β are the roots of the equation $2x^2 - 3x - 7 = 0$, find the value of:

    (i) $\alpha^2\beta + \alpha\beta^2$ **(ii)** $\alpha^2 + \beta^2$ **(iii)** $\dfrac{1}{\alpha^2} + \dfrac{1}{\beta^2}$.

    The equation $px^2 + qx + r = 0$, $p, q, r \in \mathbf{Z}$, has roots $2\alpha + \beta$ and $2\beta + \alpha$.
    Find the value of p, the value of q and the value of r.

11. α and β are the roots of the equation $x^2 - px + q = 0$.
    (a) Write $\alpha^2 + \beta^2$ in terms of p and q.
    (b) Show that $(\alpha^2 + 1)(\beta^2 + 1) = (q - 1)^2 + p^2$.

12. If $3^{2x} = 81$ and $2^{x-y} = 64$, find the value of x and the value of y.

13. Solve the simultaneous equations $2^{3x-y} = 32$ and $\dfrac{3^x}{3^{4y}} = \dfrac{1}{9}$.

14. If $2^x + 2^x = 2^{x+2}(k-2)$ for all $x \in \mathbf{R}$, find the value of k.

15. If $y = 2^x$, express (i) 2^{x+3} (ii) 2^{2x} (iii) 2^{2x+1} in terms of y.
Hence, solve $2^{2x+1} - 2^{x+3} - 2^x + 4 = 0$.

16. Solve each of the following equations:

(i) $3^{2x} - 12(3^x) + 27 = 0$
(ii) $3^x - 10 + 3^{2-x} = 0$
(iii) $4^x - 3(2^x) + 2 = 0$
(iv) $2^{2x+2} - 33(2^x) + 8 = 0$

17. Show that each of the following reduces to a constant and find that constant:

(i) $\dfrac{8^{n+2} - 6 \cdot 2^{3n+3}}{2^n \cdot 4^{n+2}}$

(ii) $\dfrac{27^{n+3} - 3 \cdot 3^{3n+6}}{3^{n+1} \cdot 9^{n+3}}$

(iii) $\dfrac{1}{b^{-1} - a^{-1}} - \dfrac{1}{b^{-1} + a^{-1}} - \dfrac{2a^{-1}}{b^{-2} - a^{-2}}$

18. $u^n = 2(3^n) + 4^n$ for all $n \geqslant 1$, $n \in \mathbf{N}_0$. Prove that $u_{n+2} + 12u_n = 7u_{n+1}$.

19. If for all integers n, $u_n = 3^{n-1} - 2^{n-1}$, verify that $u_{n+2} - 5u_{n+1} + 6u_n = 0$.

20. Given that $u_n = \frac{1}{2}(4^n - 2^n)$ for all integers n, show that $u_{n+1} = 2u_n + 4^n$.

21. Let $f(x) = \left(\dfrac{b^n - a^n}{b - a}\right)x + ab\left(\dfrac{a^{n-1} - b^{n-1}}{b - a}\right)$, for $a \neq b$. Show that $f(a) = a^n$.

Solve each of the following inequalities for $x \in \mathbf{R}$:

22. $\dfrac{2}{x-3} < 1$

23. $\dfrac{5x}{x-2} < 1$

24. $\dfrac{4-x}{x} > 0$

25. $\dfrac{3x^2 - 1}{x^2 + 1} \geqslant 1$

26. $\dfrac{4 - 3x}{1 - x} < 2$

27. $\dfrac{2x - 3}{x - 5} > \dfrac{3}{2}$

28. $f(x) = \left|\dfrac{2x - 3}{x + 3}\right|$. Write down the values of $x \in \mathbf{N}$ for which $f(x) < 1$.

29. If $x = \dfrac{y}{\sqrt{1 + y^2}}$, express y in terms of x.
Hence, find the range of values of x for which $y \in \mathbf{R}$.

30. Find the range of values of k for which the equation $k(x^2 + 1) = x(x + 6) + 1$ has real roots.

31. Express each of the equations in the form $ax^2 + bx + c = 0$ and find the values of k for which each equation has equal roots:

(i) $k = \dfrac{x^2 - 2x}{2x^2 + 1}$

(ii) $\dfrac{1}{k} = \dfrac{2x^2 + 1}{2 + 10x - x^2}$

32. Prove that the equation $x^2 + (p + r)x + (pr - q^2) = 0$ has real roots, $p, q, r \in \mathbf{R}$.

33. Show that the roots of the equation $x^2 + 2(k+1)x + (k^2 + 2k - 3) = 0$ can never be equal for all values of $k \in \mathbf{R}$. Find the value of k for which the roots are equal in magnitude but opposite in sign. Using this value of k, find the roots of the equation.

34. Prove that the equation $2p^2x^2 + pqx - q^2 = 0$, has real roots for all $p, q \in \mathbf{R}$.
If the roots are α and β, express the roots in terms of p and q.
Construct a quadratic equation with roots 2α and 2β.

35. If $x \in \mathbf{R}$ and $x > 0$, prove that $x + \dfrac{1}{x} \geqslant 2$.

36. If $a \neq 1$, show that $\dfrac{a}{(a+1)^2} \leqslant \dfrac{1}{4}$.

37. Solve: (i) $\log_2 x + \log_2(x+2) = 3$, $\quad x > 0$ (ii) $\log_{10}(x^2 + 9) - 2\log_{10} x = 1$, $\quad x > 0$
  (iii) $\log_4(3x+1) = \log_2(x-1)$, $\quad x > 1$ (iv) $\log_3 x + 3\log_x 3 = 4$, $\quad x > 0$

38. Solve for x and y:
$\log_2(x - 5y + 4) = 0$ and $\log_2(x+1) - 2\log_2 y = 1$.

39. Let $g(x) = x^n + 3$, for all $x \in \mathbf{R}$, where $n \in \mathbf{N}$.
Show that if n is odd then $g(x) + g(-x)$ is constant.

Exercise 1R.C ▼

1. The roots of $x^2 - px + q = 0$ are double the roots of $x^2 - (b+c)x + bc = 0$.
Show that $pq = 8bc(b+c)$.

2. α and β are the roots of the equation $ax^2 + bx + c = 0$. Show that $\alpha^3 + \beta^3 = \dfrac{3abc - b^3}{a^3}$.

3. (i) The roots of the equation $px^2 + qx + r = 0, p \neq 0$, are α and $k\alpha$.
   Prove that $kq^2 = (1+k)^2 pr$.
   (ii) If $(px + q)$ is a factor of $2px^2 + (2q - p)x + r, p \neq 0$, show that $q = -r$.

4. $f(x) = x^2 + 2kx + (k + 2)$, $\quad x \in \mathbf{R}$ and k is a constant.
   (i) If α and β are the roots of the equation $f(x) = 0$, express, in terms of k:
   (a) $\alpha + \beta$ **(b)** $\alpha\beta$ **(c)** $\alpha^2 + \beta^2$
   (ii) Show that $\left(1 + \dfrac{\alpha}{\beta}\right) + \left(1 + \dfrac{\beta}{\alpha}\right) = \left(1 + \dfrac{\alpha}{\beta}\right)\left(1 + \dfrac{\beta}{\alpha}\right)$.
   (iii) If $k \neq 2$, form a quadratic equation, with coefficients in terms of k,
   whose roots are $\left(1 + \dfrac{\alpha}{\beta}\right)$ and $\left(1 + \dfrac{\beta}{\alpha}\right)$.
   (iv) Find the values of k for which the roots of the equation $f(x) = 0$ differ by 4.

5. Find the quadratic equation with roots $\dfrac{1}{\alpha}$ and $\dfrac{1}{\beta}$ given that $\alpha + \beta = 5$ and $\alpha\beta = k$, where $k \neq 0$.
Find the range of values of k for which the equation will have real roots.

6. (i) Factorise $\alpha^3 + \beta^3$. If $\alpha^3 + \beta^3 = 56$ and $\alpha + \beta = 2$, calculate the value of $\alpha\beta$.
   (ii) The roots of the equation $x^2 - px + q = 0$ are α and β.
   If $\alpha^3 + \beta^3 = 1$, prove $p^3 = 3pq + 1$.

7. $p(x) = x^3 + px^2 + qx + r$, is a cubic polynomial, such that:
$p(1) = 0$, $p(4) = 0$ and $f(-1) + f(2) = -38$.
Find the value of p, the value of q and the value of r.

8. If $x^3 + ax^2 + bx + c = (x + k)^3$ for all $x \in \mathbf{R}$, show that:

    (i) $a = 3k$ **(ii)** $b = 3k^2$ **(iii)** $ab = 9c$

9. If $(x + k)(x - t)^2 = x^3 + 3px + c$, for all $x \in \mathbf{R}$, show that:

    (i) $k = 2t$ **(ii)** $p = -t^2$ **(iii)** $c = 2t^3$

10. If $(x - p)(x^2 + qx + r) = x^3 - ax + b$ for all $x \in \mathbf{R}$, show that:

    (i) $p = q$ **(ii)** $r = q^2 - a$ **(iii)** $q(a - q^2) = b$

11. If $x^2 - kx + 9$ is a factor of $x^3 + ax + b$, express a in terms of k and b in terms of k. Hence find the values of k for which $a + b = 27$.

12. $x^2 + a^2$ is a factor of $4x^3 + px^2 + qx + 2$. Verify that $pq = 8$.

13. If $(x - 1)^2$ is a factor of $ax^3 + bx^2 + 1$, find the value of a and the value of b.

14. If $x^2 + qx + 3$ is a factor of $ax^3 + bx^2 + cx + 3d$, show that $b = aq + d$ and $c = 3a + qd$.

15. If $x^2 + 2x + a$ is a factor of $x^3 + px^2 + qx + r$, show that $r = (p - 2)(q - 2p + 4)$.

16. $x^2 + ax + b$ is a factor of $x^3 + qx^2 + rx + s$. Prove that $r - b = a(q - a)$ and $s = b(q - a)$.

17. If $(x - p)^2$ is a factor of $x^3 + ax + b$, prove that $4a^3 + 27b^2 = 0$.

18. $(ax + b)^2$ is a factor of $a^2x^3 + px^2 - q^3$.

    Show that: **(i)** $p = \frac{3}{2}ab$ **(ii)** $b^3 = 2aq^3$.

19. If for all integers n, $u_n = 2(n - 1)$, show that $(u_{n+3}^2 - u_{n+1}^2) - (u_{n+2}^2 - u_n^2) = 16$.

    Note: $u_{n+3}^2 = (u_{n+3})^2$ etc.

20. If for all integers n, $u_n = 8(3^n)$, verify that $u_{n+2} - 8u_{n+1} + 15u_n = 0$.

    Find the value of q such that $u_n = 8(q^n)$, $q \neq 3$, satisfies $u_{n+2} - 8u_{n+1} + 15u_n = 0$.

21. If $u_n = (n + 2)n!$, show that $u_{n+1} = (n + 1)u_n + (n + 1)!$

22. If $p, q > 0$, show that: **(i)** $\dfrac{p}{q} + \dfrac{q}{p} \geqslant 2$ **(ii)** $\dfrac{1}{p} + \dfrac{1}{q} \geqslant \dfrac{2}{p+q}$.

23. Show that $(a^2 + b^2)(x^2 + y^2) \geqslant (ax + by)^2$, for all $a, b, x, y \in \mathbf{R}$.

24. Factorise: **(i)** $a^3 + b^3$ **(ii)** $a^2b + ab^2$.

    Hence, or otherwise, if $a, b > 0$ and $a \neq b$, show that:

    $a^3 + a^2b + ab^2 + b^3 \geqslant 2a^2b + 2ab^2$.

25. **(i)** Factorise $a^2 - b^2$ and, hence, express $a^4 - b^4$ as a product of three factors.

    (ii) Factorise $a^5 - a^4b - ab^4 + b^5$.

    Use your results from **(i)** and **(ii)** to show that $a^5 + b^5 > a^4b + ab^4$, where $a, b > 0$ and $a \neq b$.

26. Prove that $p^4 + q^4 \geqslant 2p^2q^2$, $p, q \in \mathbf{R}$.

    Hence, prove that $p^4 + q^4 + r^4 \geqslant p^2q^2 + q^2r^2 + r^2p^2$, $p, q, r \in \mathbf{R}$.

    By expanding $(pq - rs)^2$, prove that $p^4 + q^4 + r^4 + s^4 \geqslant 4pqrs$, $p, q, r, s \in \mathbf{R}$.

27. Simplify $(a + b + c)(a + b - c)$.

If $a, b, c \in \mathbf{Z}$, show that one of the roots of the equation $(a + b + c)x^2 - 2(a + b)x + (a + b - c) = 0$ is independent of a, b and c and the other is not.

28. $(p + r - t)x^2 + 2rx + (t + r - p) - 0$ is a quadratic equation, where p, r, and t are integers.

Show that:

(i) the roots are rational   **(ii)** one of the roots is an integer.

29. (i)   Show that if the roots of $x^2 + bx + c = 0$ differ by 1, then $b^2 - 4c = 1$.

(ii)   The roots of the equation $x^2 + (4k - 5)x + k = 0$ are consecutive integers.

Using the result from part **(i)**, or otherwise, find the value of k and the roots of the equation.

30. Show that $x = 1$ is a root of $x^3 + (2p - 1)x^2 + (q - 2p)x - q = 0$. Given that the other two roots are equal, prove that $p^2 = q$.

31. Solve the simultaneous equations: $2^x + 3^y = 7$ and $5.2^x - 2.3^y = 14$.

32. The equation $x^2 - px + q = 0$ has roots α and β. Explain why $\alpha^2 - p\alpha + q = 0$.

Given that $u_n = \alpha^n + \beta^n$, verify that $u_{n+2} - pu_{n+1} + qu_n = 0$.

Hence, calculate u_3 in terms of p and q.

REVISION EXERCISE 2   THE LINE AND LINEAR TRANSFORMATIONS

Paper 2, Question 3

This revision exercise covers Chapter 6.

Exercise 2R.A ▼

1. Are $(102, -79)$ and $(-80, 79)$ on the same side of the line $x + y - 4 = 0$?

2. Find the equation of the line through the point of intersection of the lines $3x - 2y - 7 = 0$ and $2x + 5y + 1 = 0$ which has slope of $-\frac{1}{2}$.

3. θ is the acute angle between the lines $3x - 2y - 1 = 0$ and $x - y = 0$. Find $\tan \theta$.

4. Find k if the points $(k, 2k)$ and $(k - 3, 2k + 1)$ are equidistant from the origin.

5. Find the equation of the line which is perpendicular to $3x + y - 5 = 0$ and contains the point of intersection of $3x - 5y - 7 = 0$ and $2x - 7y - 3 = 0$.

6. Calculate the perpendicular distance between the parallel lines $3x - 4y + 10 = 0$ and $3x - 4y - 15 = 0$.

7. Find the coordinates of the point that divides the line segment from $a(-3, 1)$ to $b(6, 7)$,
   (i) internally   **(ii)** externally in the ratio $2 : 1$.

8. $p(1, 2)$ and $q(7, -2)$ are two points. The point r is on $[pq]$ produced, such that $|pr| : |qr| = 3 : 1$. Find the coordinates of r.

9. Under axial symmetry in the line L, the image of the point $(1, 5)$ is $(3, 1)$. Find the equation of the line L.

10. The line B contains the points $(6, -2)$ and $(-4, 10)$.
    The line A with equation $ax + 6y + 21 = 0$ is perpendicular to B.
    Find the value of the real number a.

11. The equation of the line L is $14x + 6y + 1 = 0$.
    Find the equation of the line perpendicular to L that contains the point $(3, -2)$.

12. Show that the line $6x - 8y - 71 = 0$ contains the midpoint $[ab]$, where a has coordinates $(8, -6)$ and b has coordinates $(5, -2)$.

13. The parametric equations $x = 3 - 4t$ and $y = 1 + 2t$ represent a line, where $t \in \mathbf{R}$.
Find the Cartesian equation of the line.

14. A triangle has vertices $(1, -1)$, $(5, 1)$ and $(-\frac{5}{2}, -5)$. Find the area of the triangle.

15. Find the equation of the line through the point of intersection of the lines $L: x - 2y + 6 = 0$ and $K: 3x + 10y - 2 = 0$ and which contains the point $(\frac{1}{4}, 0)$.

16. Find the acute angle between the lines $x - 2y - 5 = 0$ and $3x - y - 6 = 0$.

17. Find the equation of the line through the point of intersection of the lines $2x + 3y - 9 = 0$ and $5x - 6y + 7 = 0$ and which is perpendicular to the line $2x - 3y - 4 = 0$.

18. The area of the triangle with vertices $(-1, 3)$, $(1, -1)$ and $(k - 2, k + 1)$ is 10.
Find the values of k.

Exercise 2R.B ▼

1. Find the equation of the line pq, where p has coordinates $(7, -6)$ and q has coordinates $(-3, 2)$.
Find the point of intersection of pq and the line $2x - 3y + 1 = 0$.
Determine the ratio in which the line $2x - 3y + 1 = 0$ divides $[pq]$.

2. L and K are two lines whose parametric equations are:
$$L: x = t + 1, \ y = t - 5 \qquad K: x = \frac{3 + t}{2 - t}, \ y = \frac{1 - 3t}{2 - t}.$$
Find the coordinates of $L \cap K$.

3. $opqr$ is a parallelogram where o is the origin $(0, 0)$.
The coordinates of p are $(k, 0)$, the coordinates of q are $(4, 2)$ and the point r is on the line $y = 2x$.
Find:
(i)   the value of k
(ii) the coordinates of r
(iii) the area of parallelogram $opqr$.

4. $p(7, 3)$ and $q(-1, -5)$ are two points. r is the midpoint of $[pq]$.
Find the values of t if the line containing the point r and $s(t^2, t)$ is perpendicular to pq.

5. A line L contains the point $(2, 5)$ and has slope m. Find the equation of L in terms of m.
Find the values of m if the area of the triangle formed by L and the positive x- and y-axes is 36 square units.

6. $a(-1, 3)$, $b(x, y)$ and $c(7, -2)$ are three points. The line L contains the point b.
Find the equation of L if the area of $\triangle abc$ is 20 square units.

7. f is the transformation $(x, y) \rightarrow (x', y')$ where $x' = -5x - 6y$, $\quad y' = 4x + 3y$.
(i) $L: x - 9y - 2 = 0$ is a line. Find $f(L)$, the image of L under f.
(ii) M is a line containing the point $(1, k)$, where $k \in \mathbf{Z}$.
Given that $f(M)$ is $5x' - 2y' + 3k = 0$, find the value of k.

8. $a(1, -2)$ and $c(-4, 8)$ are two points.

f is the transformation $(x, y) \rightarrow (x', y')$ where $x' = 2x - 3y$ and $y' = 6x + y$.

   (i) b divides $[ac]$ in the ratio $3 : 2$. Find the coordinates of b.

   (ii) Find $f(a), f(b)$ and $f(c)$.

   (iii) Verify that $|f(a)f(b)| : |f(b)f(c)| = |ab| : |bc|$.

9. f is the transformation $(x, y) \rightarrow (x', y')$ where $x' = 3x - y$, $y' = x + 2y$.

$p(0, 0)$, $q(1, 0)$ and $r(0, 2)$ are three points.

   (i)   Find $f(p), f(q)$ and $f(r)$.

Investigate if:

   (ii) $|qr| = |f(q)f(r)|$

   (iii) area of $\triangle pqr$ = area of $\triangle f(p)f(q)f(r)$.

10. The parametric equations of the lines L and K are

$$L: x = t + \frac{1}{2}, \ y = 2t + 7 \quad \text{and } K: x = \frac{1-t}{3}, \ y = t - 5.$$

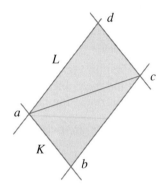

   (i)   Show that their Cartesian equations are $L: 2x - y + 6 = 0$ and $K: 3x + y + 4 = 0$.

   (ii) Find the coordinates of a, the point of intersection of L and K.

   (iii) If L and K contain adjacent sides of a parallelogram $abcd$ and the midpoint of $[ac]$ is $(0, 3\frac{1}{2})$, find the coordinates of vertices c, b and d.

Exercise 2R.C ▼

1. $L: 3x - 4y - 12 = 0$ is a line.

Find the equations of the two lines through the point $(2, 5)$ which make an angle of θ with L, given that $\theta = \tan^{-1} \frac{1}{2}$.

2. $p(1, 4)$ and $q(7, 1)$ are two points on the line L.

Find the equation of the line L. r is a point on $[pq]$ such that $|pr| : |rq| = 2 : 1$.

Find the equation of the line K which contains the point r and is perpendicular to L.

M is the line with negative slope, which contains the point r and makes an angle of $45°$ with L.

Find the equation of M.

Find the area of the triangle formed by K, M and the y-axis.

3. L is the line $x - 2y + 1 = 0$. The point $(-3, k)$ is a distance $3\sqrt{5}$ from the line L.

Find two possible values of k.

4. $rstu$ is a quadrilateral where r is $(-1, -5)$ and s is $(13, 9)$.

$q(3, -1)$ lies between r and s.

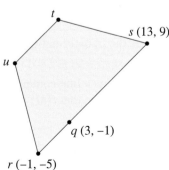

   (i)   The coordinates of u are $(-2k, 3k)$ where $k \in \mathbf{R}$ and $k > 0$.

The area of a triangle rqu is 28 square units.

Find the value of k.

   (ii) The slope of ts is $-\frac{3}{11}$.

sr is parallel to tu.

Find the coordinates of t.

5. N is the line $tx + (t-2)y + 4 = 0$ where $t \in \mathbf{R}$.

    (i) Write down the slope of N in terms of t.

    (ii) Given that the angle between N and the line $x - 3y + 1 = 0$ is $45°$, find the two possible values of t.

6. A line containing the point $(-4, -2)$ has slope m, where $m \neq 0$.
This line intercepts the x-axis at $(x_1, 0)$ and the y-axis at $(0, y_1)$.
Given that $x_1 + y_1 = 3$, find the slopes of the two lines that satisfy this condition.
Find the measure of the acute angle between these two lines and give your answer to the nearest degree.

7. **(i)** Show that the point $(1, 5)$ is on the line $2x - 5y + 23 = 0$.

    (ii) If $2x - 5y + 23 = 0$, express y in terms of x.

    (iii) A triangle abc lies entirely in the first quadrant and has an area of $4\frac{1}{2}$ square units. The equation of one side of the triangle is $2x - 5y + 23 = 0$ and the vertices of a and b are $(1, 5)$ and $(3, 4)$, respectively. Find the coordinates of the point c.

8. f is the transformation $(x, y) \rightarrow (x', y')$, where $x' = 2x + y$, $y' = x + 3y$.
L: $x + 2y = 0$ and K: $x - y = 0$ are two lines.

    (i) Show that $f(L) = L$.

    (ii) Investigate if $f(K) = K$.

9. f is the transformation $(x, y) \rightarrow (x', y')$ where $x' = 3x - 4y$, $y' = 4x + 3y$.
L: $x - y - 5 = 0$ and K: $x - 4y - 14 = 0$.

    (i) Investigate if the acute angle between L and K is equal in measure to the acute angle between $f(L)$ and $f(K)$.

    (ii) M: $2x - y - 8 = 0$ and N: $x - 2y + 3 = 0$ are two lines. Verify: **(a)** $M \perp N$ **(b)** $f(M) \perp f(N)$.

10. f is the transformation $(x, y) \rightarrow (x', y')$ where $x' = 4x - y$, $y' = 2x + y$.
For the points $a(0, 0)$, $b(-2, -5)$ and $c(4, 9)$, find $f(a)$, $f(b)$ and $f(c)$.

    (i) L is the line ac. The image of L under f is the line $f(L)$.
Find the equation of $f(L)$.

    (ii) $f(M)$ is the image of the line M under f.
$f(M)$ is perpendicular to $f(L)$ and $f(b) \in f(M)$.
Find the equation of the line M.

11. f is the transformation $(x, y) \rightarrow (x', y')$ where $x' = 3x + y$ and $y' = x - 2y$.
S is the square whose vertices are $(0, 0)$, $(1, 0)$, $(1, 1)$ and $(0, 1)$.

    (i) Find the image under f of each of the four vertices of S.

    (ii) Express x and y in terms of x' and y'.

    (iii) By considering the lines $ax + by + c = 0$ and $ax + by + d = 0$, or otherwise, prove that f maps every pair of parallel lines to another pair of parallel lines.
(You may assume that f maps every line to a line.)

    (iv) Show both S and $f(S)$ on a diagram.

    (v) Find the area of $f(S)$.

12. If $a = (4, -2)$ and $b = (1, 3)$, show that $x = 4 - 3t$, $y = 5t - 2$, $0 \leqslant t \leqslant 1$, $t \in \mathbf{R}$, are parametric equations of the line segment $[ab]$.

f is the transformation $(x, y) \rightarrow (x', y')$ when $x' = x - 2y$, $y' = 2x + y$.

Verify that $f([ab])$ is a line segment and find a pair of parametric equations to describe this image.

Find the coordinates of c, the midpoint of $[ab]$.

Investigate whether $f(c)$ is the midpoint of $[f(a)f(b)]$.

13. Find the Cartesian equation of the line L: $x = t$, $y = 2t$, $0 \leqslant t \leqslant 1$, $t \in \mathbf{R}$.

Find the coordinates of the points a, b and c on the line L corresponding to the values of $0, 1, 2$ for t, respectively. Verify that b is the midpoint of $[ac]$.

Find the image of this line segment under the transformation f,

$(x, y) \rightarrow (x', y')$, where $x' = 3x - y$, $y' = x - y$, giving your answer in parametric form.

Investigate whether $f(b)$ is the midpoint of $[f(a)f(b)]$.

14. L_1 and L_2 are two lines with slopes m_1 and m_2, respectively.

If θ is an angle between L_1 and L_2, prove that:

$$\tan \theta = \frac{m_1 - m_2}{1 + m_1 m_2}.$$

15. The line M is $ax + by + c = 0$.

Prove that the perpendicular distance from the point (x_1, y_1) to the line M is given by:

$$\frac{\left| ax_1 + by_1 + c \right|}{\sqrt{a^2 + b^2}}.$$

16. If p is the length of the perpendicular from the origin to the line $\dfrac{x}{a} + \dfrac{y}{b} = 1$, prove that $\dfrac{1}{p^2} = \dfrac{1}{a^2} + \dfrac{1}{b^2}$.

REVISION EXERCISE 3   TRIGONOMETRY

Paper 2, Questions 4 and 5

This revision exercise covers Chapters 7 and 8.

Exercise 3R.A ▼

1. In the triangle abc, $|ab| = 9$, $|ac| = 8$ and $|\angle cab| = 40°$.

Find the area of triangle abc, correct to two places of decimals.

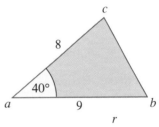

2. Show that the area of the triangle pqr, correct to one decimal place, is 2.7 m^2, if $|pr| = \sqrt{8}$ m, $|\angle rpq| = 30°$ and $|\angle pqr| = 45°$.

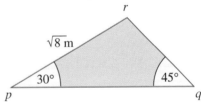

3. Find the values of θ for which $\cos\theta = \dfrac{\sqrt{3}}{2}$, where $0° \leqslant \theta \leqslant 360°$.

4. Find the value of θ for which $\tan\theta = -\dfrac{1}{\sqrt{3}}$, where $0° \leqslant \theta \leqslant 180°$.

5. Show that:

   (i) $\cos 2\theta = 2\cos^2\theta - 1$

   (ii) $\tan\left(\dfrac{\pi}{4} + A\right) = \dfrac{1 + \tan A}{1 - \tan A}$

   (iii) $\dfrac{2\tan A}{1\tan^2 A} = \sin 2A$

   (iv) $\dfrac{1 - \tan^2 A}{1 + \tan^2 A} = \cos 2A$

   (v) $(\cos A + \sin A)^2 = 2\sin A + 1$.

6. Express $\sin A$ in terms of t if $\tan A = \dfrac{t}{2}$, $0° < A < 90°$ and $t > 0$.

7. Find the value of k for which $\sin 75° - \sin 15° = \dfrac{1}{\sqrt{k}}$, $k \in \mathbf{N}_0$.

8. Find the value of k, if $\quad k = \dfrac{\cos\left(\dfrac{\pi}{4} + \theta\right) - \cos\left(\dfrac{\pi}{4} - \theta\right)}{\sin\left(\dfrac{\pi}{4} + \theta\right) - \sin\left(\dfrac{\pi}{4} - \theta\right)}\quad$ where $\sin\theta \neq 0$.

9. The length of an arc of a circle is 10 cm. The radius of the circle is 4 cm.
The measure of the angle at the centre of the circle subtended by the arc is θ.
(i) Find θ in radians.
(ii) Find θ in degrees, correct to the nearest degree.

10. The area of a sector of a circle is 27 cm^2. The length of the radius of the circle is 6 cm.
Find, in radians, the measure of the angle in the sector.

11. p, q and r are points of a circle, centre c.
The radius of the circle measures 3 cm.

$|\angle pqr| = 60°$. Find the length of the minor arc pr.

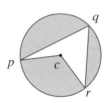

12. If $\sqrt{3} \sin\theta - \cos\theta = 0$, find the value of $\tan\theta$.

13. Find, correct to one decimal place, the size of the greatest angle of the triangle which has sides of length 4, 5 and 6.

14. If $\tan A = \frac{3}{4}$ and $\sin B = \frac{24}{25}$, $0° \leqslant A \leqslant 90°$, $0° \leqslant B \leqslant 90°$, express:
(i) $\sin(A + B)$ \qquad\qquad **(ii)** $\cos(A + B)$ \qquad\qquad **(iii)** $\tan(A - B)$ in the form $\dfrac{p}{q}$, $\quad p, q \in \mathbf{Z}$.

15. If $\sin A = \frac{3}{5}$, $90° < A < 180°$, calculate the value of $\sin 2A$ without using tables or a calculator.

16. Evaluate each of the following:
(i) $\displaystyle\lim_{x \to 0} \frac{\sin 3x}{x}$ \qquad\qquad **(ii)** $\displaystyle\lim_{x \to 0} \frac{x}{\sin 5x}$ \qquad\qquad **(iii)** $\displaystyle\lim_{x \to 0} \frac{\sin 2x}{\sin x}$

(iv) $\displaystyle\lim_{\theta \to 0} \frac{\sin 7\theta}{\sin 2\theta}$ \qquad\qquad **(v)** $\displaystyle\lim_{\theta \to 0}\left(\frac{\sin 6\theta}{6\theta} + \frac{\sin 3\theta}{3\theta}\right)$ \qquad\qquad **(vi)** $\displaystyle\lim_{\theta \to 0}\left(\frac{\sin 4\theta}{\theta} + \frac{3\theta}{\sin 2\theta}\right)$

Exercise 3R.B ▼

1. Solve: $3 - 3\cos\theta = 2\sin^2\theta$, $\quad 0 \leqslant \theta \leqslant 360°$.

2. Solve: $\cos^2 A + \cos A = 0$, $\quad 0 \leqslant A \leqslant 2\pi$.

3. **(i)** Write $\cos 2x$ in terms of $\sin x$.
(ii) Hence, find all the solutions of the equation $\cos 2x - \sin x = 1$ in the domain $0° \leqslant x \leqslant 360°$.

4. **(i)** Express $\sin 5x + \sin 3x$ as a product of sine and cosine.
(ii) Find all the solutions of the equation $\sin 5x + \sin 3x = 0$ in the domain $0° \leqslant x \leqslant 180°$.

5. **(i)** Solve: $3\tan^2\theta + 5 = 7\sec\theta$, $\quad 0 \leqslant \theta \leqslant 360°$.
(ii) Solve: $5\cos^2\theta + \sin^2\theta - 4 = 0$, $\quad 0 \leqslant \theta \leqslant 360°$.

6. Find the two solutions of the equation $4\sin^2 x - 3\cos x - 3 = 0$, where $0° \leqslant x \leqslant 180°$. Give your answers, where necessary, correct to the nearest degree.

7. Find x if $\dfrac{1}{\sqrt{3}}\sin x = \cos\dfrac{x}{2}$, where $0 \leqslant x \leqslant 2\pi$.

8. $x = 0°$ and $x = 60°$ are two solutions of the equation $a\sin^2 2x + \cos 2x - b = 0$ where $a, b \in \mathbf{N}$. Find the value of a and the value of b. Using these values of a and b, find all the solutions of the equation where $0° \leqslant x \leqslant 360°$.

9. Prove that $\tan(A + B) = \dfrac{\tan A + \tan B}{1 - \tan A \tan B}$.

   Find, in the form $p \pm \sqrt{q}$, $\quad p \in \mathbf{Z}, q \in \mathbf{N}$:   **(i)** $\tan 75°$ **(ii)** $\tan 15°$.

10. If $\tan A = \frac{1}{2}$, find $\tan 2A$ without evaluating A, where A is an acute angle.

    Express $\tan B$ in the form $\dfrac{a}{b}$, where $a, b \in \mathbf{N}_0$, given that $\tan(2A + B) = \frac{63}{16}$.

11. **(i)** Show that $\dfrac{1 - \tan^2 A}{1 + \tan^2 A} = \cos 2A$.

    (ii) Hence, or otherwise, find the values of the integers l and k such that:

    $$\dfrac{1 - \tan^2(135° - A)}{1 + \tan^2(135° - A)} = l\sin kA \text{ for all values of } A \text{ for which } \tan(135° - A) \text{ is defined.}$$

12. If $\tan(45° - A) = \dfrac{1 - \tan A}{1 + \tan A}$, show that $\dfrac{\cos 2A}{1 + \sin 2A} = \tan(45° - A)$.

    Deduce that $\tan 22\frac{1}{2}° = \dfrac{1}{\sqrt{2} + 1}$.

13. In the triangles pqs and qrs, $|pq| = 3.5$, $|qr| = 2$, $|ps| = 6.5$, $|\angle qsr| = 30°$ and $|\angle sqr| = 52°$. Calculate:

    (i) $|qs|$, correct to two places of decimals

    (ii) $|\angle pqs|$, correct to the nearest degree.

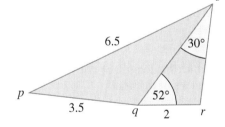

14. In a triangle pqr, $|\angle pqr| = 30°$, $|qr| = 15$ and $|rp| = 5\sqrt{3}$. Find two values for $|\angle pqr|$ and sketch the two resulting triangles. Calculate the ratio of the areas of the two triangles.

15. xyz is a triangle where $|xy| = 8$ cm and $|yz| = 6$ cm. Given that the area of triangle xyz is 12 cm^2, find:

    (i) the two possible values of $|\angle xyz|$

    (ii) the two possible values of $|xz|$, correct to one decimal place.

16. In triangle pqr, $|pq| = 5$, $|pr| = 4$ and $|qr| = 6$.
θ is the largest angle.

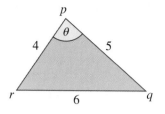

  (i) Calculate the value of $\cos \theta$.

  (ii) If $\sin \theta = \dfrac{a\sqrt{7}}{b}$, find the value of a and the value of b.

17. The points a, b and c lie on horizontal ground such that $|ab| = 3p$, $|bc| = 5p$, $|\angle abc| = 120°$ and $|\angle abd| = |\angle cbd|$.

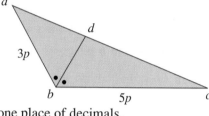

Show that:

  (i) $|ac| = 7p$ **(ii)** $|ad| = \frac{21}{8}p$

A vertical pole $[ae]$ is placed at a.
The angle of elevation of e from b is $30°$.
Calculate the angle of elevation of e from d, correct to one place of decimals.

18. The chord $[pq]$ of a circle of radius 6 cm is subtended by an angle at the centre of $\dfrac{5\pi}{6}$, as shown in the diagram.

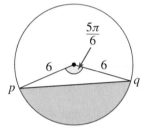

Calculate the area of the shaded region, leaving your answer in terms of π.

19. p, q, r are points of a circle, centre k. The length of the radius of the circle is 2 cm. The length of the minor arc pq is $\dfrac{5\pi}{3}$ cm.

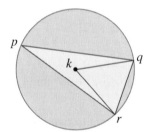

  (i) Find the length of the chord $[pq]$, correct to two places of decimals.

  (ii) If $|pq| = |pr|$, find $|rq|$.

20. The diagram shows two circles each of radius 10 cm, which intersect at a and b.
If $|\angle aob| = 60°$ where o is the centre of the circle, find the area of the shaded region.

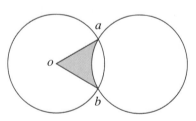

Write your answer in the form $a\left(\dfrac{\sqrt{3}}{2} - \dfrac{\pi}{b}\right)$.

21. If $0 \leqslant A \leqslant \dfrac{\pi}{2}$ and $0 \leqslant B \leqslant \dfrac{\pi}{2}$, show that:

$$\frac{\cos(A - B) - \cos(A + B)}{\sin(A + B) - \sin(A - B)} = \tan A.$$

22. Show that: $\dfrac{\sin 4\theta(1 - \cos 2\theta)}{\cos 2\theta(1 - \cos 4\theta)} = \tan \theta.$

23. If $\sin(A + B) = 2 \sin(A - B)$, show that $\tan A = 3 \tan B$.

Hence, or otherwise, solve the equation $\sin\left(A + \dfrac{\pi}{6}\right) = 2 \sin\left(A - \dfrac{\pi}{6}\right)$, $\qquad 0 \leqslant A \leqslant 2\pi$.

24. Show that: $\sqrt{\dfrac{1 - \cos \theta}{1 + \cos \theta}} = \dfrac{\tan \theta}{\sec \theta + 1}$, for $0 \leqslant \theta \leqslant \dfrac{\pi}{2}$.

25. Evaluate: **(i)** $\tan(\sec^{-1} \sqrt{2})$ **(ii)** $\tan(\sin^{-1} \tfrac{3}{5} + \sin^{-1} \tfrac{5}{13})$.

Exercise 3R.C ▼

1. Show that the area, A, of the shaded segment of the circle, of radius r, is given by:

$A = \tfrac{1}{2} r^2 (\theta - \sin \theta)$ (θ in radians).

Hence, evaluate the area of the shaded segment,

when $r = 3\sqrt{2}$ and $\theta = \dfrac{\pi}{3}$, giving your answer in the

form $9\left(\dfrac{\pi}{a} - \dfrac{\sqrt{a}}{b}\right)$, where a and b are prime numbers.

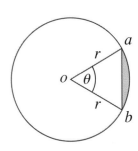

2. A is an obtuse angle such that:

$$\sin\left(A + \dfrac{\pi}{6}\right) + \sin\left(A - \dfrac{\pi}{6}\right) = \dfrac{4\sqrt{3}}{5}.$$

(i)   Find $\sin A$ and $\tan A$.

(ii)   Given that $\tan(A + B) = \dfrac{1}{2}$, find $\tan B$ and express your answer in the form $\dfrac{p}{q}$, where $p, q \in \mathbf{Z}$

and $q \neq 0$.

3. Using the formula for $\sin(A + B)$, show that $\sin 2A = 2 \sin A \cos A$.

Hence, or otherwise, show that $\sin 3A = 3 \sin A - 4 \sin^3 A$.

Using the result for $\sin 3A$, or otherwise, show that:

$$\sin 3\left(A - \dfrac{\pi}{2}\right) = 4 \cos^3 A - 3 \cos A.$$

4. Express $\sin(135° - A)$ in terms of $\sin A$ and $\cos A$.

5. Express $\sin(135° - A) \cos(135° + A)$ in the form $k(1 + \sin pA)$, where $k, p \in \mathbf{R}$.

6. Find the values of A for which $\sin(135° - A)\cos(135° + A) = -\tfrac{3}{4}$, where $0° \leqslant A \leqslant 180°$.

7. In the triangle pqr, $|\angle qrp| = 90°$ and $|rp| = h$.

s is a point on $[qr]$ such that $|\angle spq| = 2B$ and

$\qquad |\angle rps| = 45° - B, \qquad 0° < B < 45°$.

(i)   Show that $|sr| = h \tan(45° - B)$.

(ii)   Hence, or otherwise, show that $|qs| = 2h \tan 2B$.

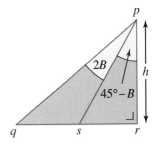

8. The angles of elevation of the top of a tower h metres high, from two points on level ground which are x metres apart, are α and β as shown.

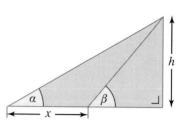

Prove that: $\quad h = \dfrac{x \tan \alpha \tan \beta}{\tan \beta - \tan \alpha}$.

Hence calculate the height of the tower in the form $a\sqrt{b}$, when $\alpha = 30°$, $\beta = 60°$ and $x = 20$ m.

9. p, q and r are points on level ground. $[sr]$ is a vertical tower of height h. The angles of elevation of the top of the tower from p and q are α and β, respectively.

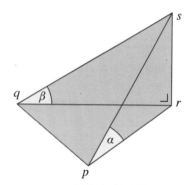

(i) If $|\alpha| = 60°$ and $|\beta| = 30°$,

express $|pr|$ and $|qr|$ in terms of h.

(ii) Find $|qp|$ in terms of h, if $\tan \angle qrp = \sqrt{8}$.

10. (i) Prove that: $\quad \tan 2A = \dfrac{2 \tan A}{1 - \tan^2 A}$.

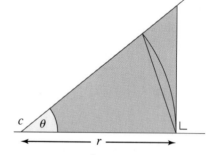

(ii) A triangle is inscribed in a sector of a circle, centre c, radius r, $\theta < 90°$. A right-angled triangle circumscribes the sector (see diagram).

If the area of the sector is $\frac{1}{2}r^2\theta$, prove that $\sin \theta < \theta < \tan \theta$.

11. The diagram shows a circle of centre o and radius a.

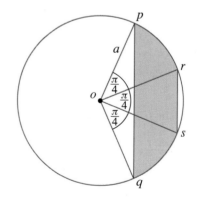

$[pq]$ and $[rs]$ subtend angles of $\dfrac{3\pi}{4}$ and $\dfrac{\pi}{4}$ at o, respectively.

Verify that the area of the shaded region is $\frac{1}{4}\pi a^2$.

12. Verify that $\cos(180° - \theta) = -\cos\theta$.

In the diagram, $[ab]$ is a diameter of the circle of centre o and radius r.

$bc \perp od$ and $\angle boc = \theta$.

Express $|oc|$ in terms of r and θ.

By applying the cosine rule to triangle oac, or otherwise, show that $|ac|^2 = r^2(1 + 3\cos^2\theta)$.

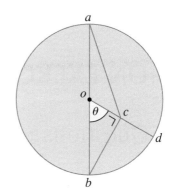

13. A chain passes around two circular wheels as shown. One wheel has a radius 75 cm and the other has radius 15 cm. The centres, e and f, of the wheels are 120 cm apart.

The chain consists of the common tangent $[ab]$, the minor arc bc, the common tangent $[cd]$ and the major arc da.

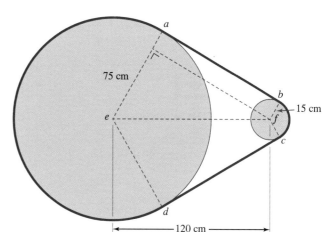

(i) Find the measure of $\angle aef$.

(ii) Find $|ab|$ in surd form.

(iii) Find the length, l, of the chain, giving your answer in the form $k\pi + l\sqrt{3}$ where $k, l \in \mathbf{Z}$.

14. A vertical radio mast $[pq]$ stands on flat horizontal ground. It is supported by three cables that join the top of the mast, q, to the points a, b and c on the ground. The foot of the mast, p, lies inside the triangle abc.
Each cable is 52 m long and the mast is 48 m high.

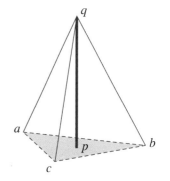

(i) Find the (common) distance from p to each of the points a, b and c.

(ii) Given that $|ac| = 38$ m and $|ab| = 34$ m, find $|bc|$ correct to one decimal place.

15. Express $\sin 2A + \sin 2B$ as a product of sine and cosine.
If $A + B + C = 180°$, show that $\sin(A + B) = \sin C$.
Hence, show that $\sin 2A + \sin 2B - \sin 2C = 4\cos A \cos B \sin C$.
Note: $\cos(A + B) = -\cos C$.

16. A triangle has sides of length a, b and c, with angle A being the angle opposite the side of length a, as shown.

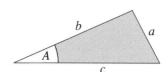

(i) Derive the formula $a^2 = b^2 + c^2 - 2bc \cos A$.

(ii) If $90° < A < 180°$, show that $a^2 > b^2 + c^2$.

17. (i) Derive the formula $\cos(A + B) = \cos A \cos B - \sin A \sin B$.

(ii) Show that $\cos(A + B)\cos B + \sin(A + B)\sin B = \cos A$.

REVISION EXERCISE 4   DIFFERENTIATION

Paper 1, Questions 6 and 7

This revision exercise covers
Chapters 9, 10, 11, 12 and 13.

| *Exercise 4R.A* ▼ |

Differentiate each of the following:

1. $\dfrac{2x}{x+1}$ **2.** $(4x-1)^3$ **3.** $x^3 + 2\sqrt{x}$ **4.** $4e^{2x+1}$

5. $x \sin x$ **6.** $(x+2)\ln x$ **7.** $e^x \sin 2x$ **8.** $\sqrt{x^2+1}$

9. $e^x \ln x$ **10.** $e^{x \sin x}$ **11.** $(\sin 3x)^2$ **12.** $\tan 4x^2$

13. $(\tan 4x^2)^3$ **14.** $\dfrac{3x}{\sqrt{2x^2-1}}$ **15.** $\sin^{-1} 2x$ **16.** $\tan^{-1}\left(\dfrac{1}{x}\right)$

17. Find the equation of the tangent to the curve $y = x(x^3 - 2)$ at the point where $x = 1$.

18. Find the equation of the tangent to the curve $x^2 - xy + y^2 = 1$ at the point $(1, 0)$.

19. Take $x_1 = 3$ as the first approximation of a real root of the equation $x^3 - 6x^2 + 24 = 0$.
Find, using the Newton–Raphson method, x_2, the second approximation and write your answer as a fraction.

20. Let $\theta = 5t^3 - 2t^2$, where t is in seconds and θ is in radians.
Find the rate of change of θ when $t = 2$ seconds.

Evaluate each of the following limits:

21. $\displaystyle\lim_{x \to 4} \dfrac{x^2 + x - 20}{x - 4}$ **22.** $\displaystyle\lim_{x \to \infty} \dfrac{5x + 2}{4x - 3}$ **23.** $\displaystyle\lim_{x \to -1} \dfrac{2x^2 + 7x + 5}{x + 1}$

24. $\displaystyle\lim_{x \to 3} \dfrac{x^3 - 27}{x - 3}$ **25.** $\displaystyle\lim_{x \to 2} \dfrac{8 - x^3}{4 - x^2}$ **26.** $\displaystyle\lim_{x \to 3} \dfrac{x - 3}{1 - \sqrt{4 - x}}$

27. Show that $\displaystyle\lim_{x \to 0} \dfrac{3 - \sqrt{x+9}}{x} = -\dfrac{1}{6}$.

28. Shown opposite is part of the graph of the periodic function $y = f(x)$.
State its period and range.
Evaluate:

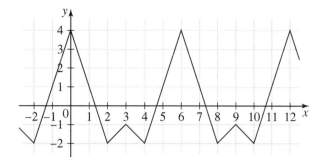

(i) $f(2)$

(ii) $f(3)$

(iii) $f(6)$

(iv) $f(-9)$

(v) $f(27)$

(vi) $f(-36)$

Find the number of times $f(x)$ reaches its minimum value in the domain $18 \leqslant x \leqslant 42$.

Exercise 4R.B ▼

Find the derivatives of the functions:

1. $y = \ln(1 + \tan x)$

2. $y = \tan^{-1}(\sin x)$

3. $y = x \sin^{-1} x$

4. $y = x^2 \ln(2x + 1)$

5. Show that the equation $x^3 = 7x - 1$ has a root between 2 and 3.
Taking 2.5 as a first approximation, apply the Newton–Raphson formula once to obtain a better approximation, giving your answer correct to 3 significant figures.

6. Take $x_1 = 1$ as the first approximation of a real root of the equation $x^3 - 2 = 0$. Find, using the Newton–Raphson method, x_2 and x_3, the second and third approximations. Write your answers as fractions.

7. Find the slope of the tangent to the curve $x^2 - y^2 - x = 1$ at the point $(2, 1)$.

8. Find the equation of the tangent to the curve $y^3 - xy - 6x^3 = 0$ at the point $(1, 2)$.

9. If $y = e^{2x}$, show that $\dfrac{d^2 y}{dx^2} - 4y = 0$.

10. (i) If $u = \sqrt{e^x}$, find $\dfrac{du}{dx}$.

  (ii) If $y = \ln\left(\dfrac{\sqrt{e^x}}{e^x + 1}\right)$, find the value of $\dfrac{dy}{dx}$ at $x = 0$.

11. Find from first principles the derivative of x^2 with respect to x.

12. Let $f(x) = \dfrac{(x-2)^2}{x+1}$. Find the values of x for which $f'(x) > 0$.

13. $f(x) = 2x^2 + \dfrac{k}{x}$. If $f'(-2) = -16$, find   (i) the value of k (ii) the local minimum value of $f(x)$.

263

14. Find the value of the constant k, if $y = kx^2$ is a solution of the equation
$$x\frac{dy}{dx} + \frac{1}{2}\left(\frac{dy}{dx}\right)^2 + y = 0, \text{ where } x \in \mathbf{R} \text{ and } k \neq 0.$$

15. Find from first principles the derivative of x^3 with respect to x.

16. $f(x) = \cos 4x$ and $g(x) = 2\sin^2 2x$. Show that $f'(x) + g'(x) = 0$.

17. Given $y = \sin^{-1}(2x - 1)$, find $\dfrac{dy}{dx}$ and calculate its value at $x = \frac{1}{2}$.

18. $f(x) = \dfrac{1 + \tan x}{1 - \tan x}$. Verify that $f'(x) = \dfrac{2}{1 - \sin 2x}$.

19. Let $f(x) = \sin^4 x + \cos^4 x$. Find the derivative of $f(x)$ and express it in the form $k\sin px$, where $k, p \in \mathbf{Z}$.

20. $y = \dfrac{\sin x}{2 + \cos x}$. If $\dfrac{dy}{dx} = \dfrac{a + b\cos x}{(2 + \cos x)^2}$, find the value of a and the value of b.

21. Find from first principles the derivative of $\sin x$ with respect to x.

22. If $x = \dfrac{1 - t^2}{1 + t^2}$ and $y = \dfrac{2t}{1 + t^2}$, find, as a fraction, the value of $\dfrac{dy}{dx}$ when $t = \frac{3}{4}$.

23. Let $x = t^2 e^t$ and $t + 2\ln t$, $\quad t > 0$. Show that $\dfrac{dy}{dx} = \dfrac{1}{x}$.

24. Let $x = t - \sin t \cos t$ and $y = 4\cos t$, $\quad 0 < t < \dfrac{\pi}{2}$. Show that $\dfrac{dy}{dx} = -\dfrac{2}{\sin t}$.

25. Let $x = 4\cos\theta + 3\sin\theta$ and $y = 3\cos\theta - 4\sin\theta$, where $-\pi < \theta < \pi$. Evaluate $\dfrac{dy}{dx}$ when $\theta = \dfrac{\pi}{2}$.

26. (i) If $y = e^\theta \cos\theta$ and $x = e^\theta \sin\theta$, evaluate $\dfrac{dy}{dx}$ at $\theta = \dfrac{\pi}{2}$.

(ii) If $x = a(\theta - \sin\theta)$, $y = a(1 - \cos\theta)$, prove that: $\quad 1 + \left(\dfrac{dy}{dx}\right)^2 = \dfrac{2}{1 - \cos\theta}$.

27. The parametric equations of a curve are $x = \dfrac{1 + \sin t}{\cos t}$, $\quad y = \dfrac{1 + \cos t}{\sin t}$, $\quad 0 < t < \dfrac{\pi}{2}$.

Find **(i)** $\dfrac{dx}{dt}$ and $\dfrac{dy}{dt}$ **(ii)** the slope of the tangent to the curve at the point where $t = \tan^{-1}(\frac{3}{4})$.

28. The parametric equations of a curve are $x = \cos^3 t$ and $y = \sin^3 t$, $\quad 0 \leq t \leq \dfrac{\pi}{2}$.

(i) Find $\dfrac{dx}{dt}$ and $\dfrac{dy}{dt}$ in terms of t.

(ii) Hence, find integers a and b such that $\left(\dfrac{dx}{dt}\right)^2 + \left(\dfrac{dy}{dt}\right)^2 = \dfrac{a}{b}(\sin 2t)^2$.

29. Find from first principles the derivative of $\dfrac{1}{x}$ with respect to x.

30. If $y = \tan^{-1} x$, show that $\dfrac{d^2y}{dx^2}(1 + x^2) + 2x\dfrac{dy}{dx} = 0$.

31. Let $x + y = 15$, calculate the maximum value of $2x + 3y + xy$.

32. If $x + y = 10$, calculate the minimum value of $x^2 + y^2$.

33. Let $f(x) = x^4 + 4x^3$.
Find the coordinates of the points on the curve $y = f(x)$ for which $f'(x) = 0$.
Find the coordinates of the points of inflection.

34. Let $f(x) = \dfrac{e^x}{x^2 - 3}$; show that $f'(x) = \dfrac{e^x(x + 1)(x - 3)}{(x^2 - 3)^2}$.
Find the coordinates of the two points where the slope of the tangent to $f(x)$ is 0.

35. Let $f(x) = xe^{-x}$.
Find the coordinates of the local maximum point and the point of inflection.

36. A ball is thrown vertically upwards. The height h metres of the ball, t seconds after it is thrown, is given by the formula $h = 3(10t - t^2)$.
(i) Find the speed of the ball after 1 second.
(ii) After how many seconds is the ball instantaneously at rest?
(iii) Find the maximum height the ball reaches.

37. The distance, s metres, travelled in t seconds by a train after its brakes are applied is given by $s = 16t - 0.4t^2$.
(i) Find its speed after 5 seconds.
(ii) How long does it take to stop the train?
(iii) Verify that the train is decelerating.

38. If $V = \frac{1}{2}\pi h^3$ and $\dfrac{dV}{dt} = -5$, evaluate $\dfrac{dh}{dt}$ at $h = 8$.

39. Given that $p = s^2 + 5s - 3$ and $s = 4t + 1$, find:
(i) $\dfrac{dp}{ds}$ **(ii)** $\dfrac{ds}{dt}$ **(iii)** $\dfrac{dp}{dt}$.

40. Given that $V = (y + 1)^3$ and $y = (2x - 1)^2$, express $\dfrac{dV}{dy}$ in terms of x.

41. A circle has radius r cm, circumference C cm, and area A cm^2. Show that $\dfrac{dA}{dC} = r$.

42. The path of a football is given by the equation $y = x - \dfrac{x^2}{40}$, $x \geqslant 0$.
If $\dfrac{dx}{dt} = 10\sqrt{2}$ for all t, find $\dfrac{dy}{dt}$ when $x = 10$.

43. A point $p(x, y)$ moves along the curve $y = 2x^{3/2}$, $x > 0, y > 0$.
The rate of change of x with respect to time is e^x m/s.
Find the corresponding rate of change of y with respect to time when:
(i) $x = 1$ **(ii)** $y = 16$.

44. The volume, V, of water in a container is given by $V = 6\,h^2$ cm^3, where h cm is the depth of the water. Water is pouring into the container at a steady rate of 24 cm^3/s.
Find the rate, in cm/s, at which the depth of water is rising when $h = 4$ cm.

45. A spherical snowball, of volume V and radius r, rolls down a snow-covered hill.
If $\dfrac{dV}{dt} = 4\pi$ cm^3/s, find the value of $\dfrac{dr}{dt}$ when $r = 5$ cm.

46. The side of a cube is increasing at $\frac{1}{2}$ cm/s. Find the rate of increase of the volume when the length of a side is 4 cm.

Exercise 4R.C ▼

1. $f(x) = \dfrac{1}{x+1}$ where $x \in \mathbf{R}$, $x \neq -1$.

   (i) Find the equations of the asymptotes of the graph of $f(x)$.

   (ii) Prove that the graph of $f(x)$ has no turning points or points of inflection.

   (iii) If the tangents to the curve at $x = x_1$ and $x = x_2$ are parallel and if $x_1 \neq x_2$, show that $x_1 + x_2 + 2 = 0$.

2. Given that $f(x) = \dfrac{x}{x+2}$, $\quad x \in \mathbf{R}$ and $x \neq -2$:

   (i) Find the equations of the asymptotes of the graph of $f(x)$.

   (ii) Prove that the graph of $f(x)$ has no turning points or points of inflection.

   (iii) Find the range of values of x for which $f'(x) \leqslant 1$, where $f'(x)$ is the derivative of $f(x)$.

3. If $y = (x^2 + 1)^n$, show that $(x^2 + 1)\dfrac{dy}{dx} - 2nxy = 0$.

4. If $y = \sin(\ln x)$, show that $x^2\dfrac{d^2y}{dx^2} + x\dfrac{dy}{dx} + y = 0$.

5. If $y = e^{-2x}(1 + 2x)$, show that: **(i)** $\dfrac{dy}{dx} = -2y$ **(ii)** $4y + 4\dfrac{dy}{dx} + \dfrac{d^2y}{dx^2} = 0$.

6. If $y = \ln e^{-x}\sqrt{\dfrac{1+2x}{1-2x}}$, show that $\dfrac{dy}{dx} = \dfrac{1+4x^2}{1-4x^2}$.

   (Hint: $\ln\dfrac{ab}{c} = \ln a + \ln b - \ln c$ and $\ln\sqrt{x} = \frac{1}{2}\ln x$).

7. Let $y = \ln x$. Find $\dfrac{dy}{dx}$. The tangent to the curve $y = \ln x$ at the point $(k, \ln k)$ passes through the origin, $(0, 0)$. Find the value of k.

8. The parametric equations of a curve are given by:

   $x = \sin 4\theta + 2\sin 2\theta$, $\qquad y = \cos 4\theta - 2\cos 2\theta$, $\qquad -\dfrac{\pi}{6} < \theta < \dfrac{\pi}{6}$.

   Find: **(i)** $\dfrac{dx}{d\theta}$ **(ii)** $\dfrac{dy}{d\theta}$. Verify that $\dfrac{dy}{dx} = -\tan\theta$.

9. The concentration C of an antibiotic in the bloodstream after a time of t hours is given by:
$$C = \frac{5t}{1 + \left(\dfrac{t}{k}\right)^2} \text{ units, where } k > 0.$$

If the maximum concentration is reached at $t = 6$ hours, find the value of k.

10. (i) Solve the equation $3x^2 - 5kx = 0$.

    (ii) Let $f(x) = x^3 + kx^2 + 4$, $k \in \mathbf{R}$ and $k < 0$.

        (a) Show that the coordinates of the local maximum and minimum points of $f(x)$ are $(0, 4)$ and
$$\left(-\frac{2k}{3}, \frac{4k^3 + 108}{27}\right), \text{ respectively.}$$

        (b) Taking $x_1 = 1$ as the first approximation to one of the roots of $f(x) = 0$, the Newton–Raphson method gives the second approximation as $x_2 = \frac{6}{5}$.
        Find the value of k.

11. Let $f(x) = x^3 - kx^2 + 8$, $k \in \mathbf{R}$ and $k > 0$.

Show that the coordinates of the local minimum point of $f(x)$ are $\left(\dfrac{2k}{3}, 8 - \dfrac{4k^3}{27}\right)$.

Taking $x_1 = 3$ as the first approximation of one of the roots of $f(x) = 0$, the Newton–Raphson method gives the second approximation as $x_2 = \frac{10}{3}$.
Find the value of k.

12. Let $f(x) = xe^{-ax}$, $x \in \mathbf{R}$, a constant and $a > 0$.
Show that $f(x)$ has a local maximum and express the coordinates of this local maximum point in terms of a.
Find, in terms of a, the coordinates of the point at which the second derivative of $f(x)$ is zero.

13. $f(x) = \dfrac{\ln x}{x}$ where $x > 0$.

    (i)   Show that the maximum of $f(x)$ occurs at the point $\left(e, \dfrac{1}{e}\right)$.

    (ii)   Hence, show that $x^e \leqslant e^x$ for all $x > 0$.

14. $[pq]$ is a chord of the loop of the curve $y^2 = x^2(6 - x)$, so that the chord is parallel to the y-axis. Calculate the maximum value of $|pq|$.

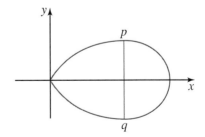

15. The parametric equations of a curve are given by:
$$x = \theta - 2\cos\theta, \qquad y = 2\sin\theta - 2\cos\theta.$$
Find the equation of the tangent to the curve at the point where $\theta = 0$.

16. Let $f(x) = \sin\theta + 2\cos\theta$, where $0 < \theta < \dfrac{\pi}{2}$.

Verify that $f(x)$ has a maximum value of $\sqrt{5}$.

17. Differentiate: **(i)** $e^{3x}\cos 2x$ **(ii)** $e^{3x}\sin 2x$.

Let $f(x) = pe^{3x}\cos 2x + qe^{3x}\sin 2x$, $p, q \in \mathbf{Q}$.

If $f'(x) = e^{3x}\cos 2x$, find the value of p and the value of q.

18. The curve $y = e^x(ax^2 + b)$ has a minimum turning point at $(1, -4e)$.
Find the value of a and the value of b.

19. Let $y = px + \dfrac{q}{x}$, $p, q \in \mathbf{R}$.

Verify that: $x^2\left(\dfrac{d^2y}{dx^2}\right) + x\left(\dfrac{dy}{dx}\right) - y = 0$.

20. If $y = px^2 + qx$ and $\dfrac{d^2y}{dx^2} - 4\left(\dfrac{dy}{dx}\right)^2 + 32y = 0$, find the values of p and of q, $p, q \neq 0$.

21. If $y = Axe^{-2x}$, prove that:

$$\dfrac{d^2y}{dx^2} + 4\dfrac{dy}{dx} + 4y = 0.$$

22. If $y = e^{-ax}\cos nx$, show that $\dfrac{d^2y}{dx^2} + 2a\dfrac{dy}{dx} + (a^2 + n^2)y = 0$.

23. If $\sin y = \frac{1}{2}(1 - x^2)$ for $-\sqrt{3} < x < \sqrt{3}$,

calculate the value of a and the value of b when

$$\left(\dfrac{dy}{dx}\right)^2 = \dfrac{a}{3 - x^2} - \dfrac{b}{1 + x^2}, \qquad a, b \in \mathbf{N}_0.$$

24. The parametric equations of a curve are

$$x = t - \dfrac{1}{t}, \qquad y = t + \dfrac{1}{t}, \qquad \text{where } t \neq 0.$$

(i)   Find the value of $\dfrac{dy}{dx}$ at the point where $t = 2$.

(ii) a is the point on the curve where $t = k$ and b is the point on the curve where $t = -\dfrac{1}{k}$.

Show that the line ab is parallel to the y-axis.

25. x_n is the nth approximation to the positive root of $x^2 - 2 = 0$ and x_{n+1} is the next approximation.

Using the Newton–Raphson method, $x_{n+1} = x_n - \dfrac{f(x_n)}{f'(x_n)}$, show that:

$$x_{n+1} = \dfrac{1}{2}\left(x_n + \dfrac{2}{x_n}\right).$$

If $x_0 = 1$, find x_2 correct to three places of decimals.

26. Let $f(x) = \dfrac{c^x + e^{-x}}{2}$.

    (i)   Show that $f''(x) = f(x)$, where $f''(x)$ is the second derivative of $f(x)$.

    (ii)   Show that $\dfrac{f'(2x)}{f'(x)} = 2f(x)$, when $x \neq 0$ and where $f'(x)$ is the first derivative of $f(x)$.

27. Let $f(x) = x^2 + px + q$, where $p,\, q \in \mathbf{R}$.

    $x = -3$ is a root of $f(x)$. If the minimum value of $f(x)$ is -4, find the values of p and q.

28. The function $f(x) = ax^3 + bx^2 + cx + d$ has a maximum point at $(0, 4)$ and a point of inflection at $(1, 0)$.

    Find the values of a, b, c and d.

29. The graph of the function $f : x \rightarrow ax^3 + bx^2 + cx + d$, $x \in \mathbf{R}$, has a local maximum point at $x = r$, a local minimum point at $x = s$ and a point of inflection at $x = t$.

    Prove that $r + s = 2t$.

30. Given that $x = e^\theta \cos\theta$ and $y = e^\theta \sin\theta$, where $\dfrac{-3\pi}{4} < \theta < \dfrac{\pi}{4}$, show that:

    (i) $\left(\dfrac{dx}{d\theta}\right)^2 + \left(\dfrac{dy}{d\theta}\right)^2 = 2e^{2\theta}$
                       (ii) $\dfrac{dy}{dx} = \tan\!\left(\theta + \dfrac{\pi}{4}\right)$.

REVISION EXERCISE 5   INTEGRATION

Paper 1, Question 8

This revision exercise covers Chapter 14.

Exercise 5R.A ▼

Find:

1. $\displaystyle\int 3x^2 \, dx$

2. $\displaystyle\int (4x - 3) \, dx$

3. $\displaystyle\int (x^2 + 2) \, dx$

4. $\displaystyle\int \left(4x + 1 + \frac{1}{x^3}\right) dx$

5. $\displaystyle\int x(2x - 5) \, dx$

6. $\displaystyle\int x\left(x - \frac{1}{x}\right) dx$

7. $\displaystyle\int \sqrt{x}\,(x^2 + 1) \, dx$

8. $\displaystyle\int (2x + 3)(x - 1) \, dx$

9. $\displaystyle\int (2x - 1)^2 \, dx$

10. $\displaystyle\int \left(x + \frac{1}{x}\right)^2 dx$

11. $\displaystyle\int (1 + \sqrt{x})^2 \, dx$

12. $\displaystyle\int (1 + x)^3 \, dx$

13. $\displaystyle\int \left(\frac{x^4 + 2x^2 + 1}{x^2}\right) dx$

14. $\displaystyle\int \left(\frac{x + 1}{\sqrt{x}}\right) dx$

15. $\displaystyle\int \left(\frac{2x^2 + 1}{x}\right) dx$

16. $\displaystyle\int \left(\frac{3}{x^2} + \frac{5x}{\sqrt{x}}\right) dx$

17. $\displaystyle\int e^{3x} \, dx$

18. $\displaystyle\int e^{5x-2} \, dx$

19. $\displaystyle\int \cos 4x \, dx$

20. $\displaystyle\int \sin 5x \, dx$

21. $\displaystyle\int 6\cos(6x + 5) \, dx$

22. $\displaystyle\int (\cos 3x + \sin 2x) \, dx$

23. $\displaystyle\int (4 + \cos 2x) \, dx$

24. $\displaystyle\int (4 - 2\sin 2x) \, dx$

Evaluate each of the following:

25. $\displaystyle\int_1^2 2x \, dx$

26. $\displaystyle\int_1^3 (3x^2 + x) \, dx$

27. $\displaystyle\int_{-2}^2 (x^2 + 7) \, dx$

28. $\displaystyle\int_0^{\pi/2} \cos\theta \, d\theta$

29. $\displaystyle\int_0^1 2e^{2x} \, dx$

30. $\displaystyle\int_{\pi/6}^{\pi/4} 2\sin 2\theta \, d\theta$

Evaluate each of the following:

1. $\displaystyle\int_0^1 3x^2(1+x^3)^3 \, dx$

2. $\displaystyle\int_0^2 (1-2x)(3+x-x^2)^3 \, dx$

3. $\displaystyle\int_1^2 x\sqrt{x-1} \, dx$

4. $\displaystyle\int_0^3 \frac{1}{\sqrt{5x+1}} \, dx$

5. $\displaystyle\int_0^2 \frac{x^2}{\sqrt{x^3+1}} \, dx$

6. $\displaystyle\int_0^{\sqrt{5}} \frac{x}{\sqrt{x^2+4}} \, dx$

7. $\displaystyle\int_3^4 \frac{x-3}{x^2-6x+10} \, dx$

8. $\displaystyle\int_0^1 \frac{x}{x^2+4} \, dx$

9. $\displaystyle\int_0^1 \frac{1-x}{\sqrt{1+6x-3x^2}} \, dx$

10. $\displaystyle\int_{-1}^1 2e^{x+1} \, dx$

11. $\displaystyle\int_0^1 xe^{x^2/2} \, dx$

12. $\displaystyle\int_0^1 (x+1)e^{x(x+2)} \, dx$

13. $\displaystyle\int_0^{\pi/6} 2\cos 4\theta \cos 2\theta \, d\theta$

14. $\displaystyle\int_0^{\pi/3} \sin 2\theta \cos\theta \, d\theta$

15. $\displaystyle\int_{-\pi/2}^{\pi/2} \cos^2 3\theta \, d\theta$

16. $\displaystyle\int_0^{\pi/4} (\cos x + \sin x)^2 \, dx$

17. $\displaystyle\int_0^6 \frac{x}{x+3} \, dx$

18. $\displaystyle\int_1^3 \frac{x \, dx}{\sqrt{x-1}}$

19. $\displaystyle\int_0^{3\sqrt{3}/2} \frac{dx}{\sqrt{9-x^2}}$

20. $\displaystyle\int_0^{8\sqrt{3}} \frac{2 \, dx}{x^2+64}$

21. $\displaystyle\int_0^{1/2} \frac{8 \, dx}{1+4x^2}$

22. $\displaystyle\int_0^{1/4} \frac{2 \, dx}{\sqrt{1-4x^2}}$

23. $\displaystyle\int_0^{1/\sqrt{3}} \frac{dx}{\sqrt{4-9x^2}}$

24. $\displaystyle\int_3^8 \frac{x}{\sqrt{1+x}}$

25. Verify that $\displaystyle\int_0^1 2xe^{x^2} \, dx = \int_0^{\pi/2} e^{\sin x} \cos x \, dx$.

26. (a) Factorise $x^3 + 1$ **(b)** Evaluate $\displaystyle\int_0^1 \frac{x^3+1}{x+1} \, dx$.

27. (i) Evaluate $\displaystyle\int_0^{\pi/2} \cos^2 x \sin x \, dx$, using the substitution $u = \cos x$.

   (ii) By writing $\cos^3 x = \cos x(1 - \sin^2 x)$, or otherwise, evaluate $\displaystyle\int_0^{\pi/2} \cos^3 x \, dx$.

28. Evaluate $\displaystyle\int_0^{\pi/2} e^{\cos x} \sin x \, dx$, using the substitution $u = \cos x$.

29. Express $x^2 + 6x + 13$ in the form $(x+a)^2 + b^2$ and, hence, evaluate $\displaystyle\int_{-3}^{-1} \frac{dx}{x^2+6x+13}$.

30. Express $3 + 2x - x^2$ in the form $p^2 - (x-q)^2$ and, hence, evaluate $\displaystyle\int_1^2 \frac{dx}{\sqrt{3+2x-x^2}}$.

31. (i) Find the constant of integration given that $\displaystyle\int (6t^2 + 12t + 1)dt = 5$, when $t = -2$.

   (ii) Find the function of $y = f(x)$, given that $f'(x) = 3x^2 - 2$ and that the graph of $y = f(x)$ passes through the point $(-2, 6)$.

32. Evaluate: **(i)** $e^{\ln 3}$ **(ii)** $\displaystyle\int_0^{\ln 2} \frac{e^x}{e^x+3}\, dx$ **(iii)** $\displaystyle\int_0^{\ln 3} \frac{e^x}{(e^x+1)^2}\, dx.$

33. Given that $k > 1$ and $\displaystyle\int_1^k \frac{1}{\sqrt{x}}\, dx = 1$, find the value of k, $k \in \mathbf{R}$.

34. If $\displaystyle\int_0^k \cos x\, dx = \int_k^{\pi/2} \cos x\, dx$, find the value of k, $0 < k < \dfrac{\pi}{2}$.

35. Calculate the area bounded by the curve $y = 5x - x^2$ and the x-axis.

36. Find the area bounded by the curve $y = x^2 - 2x - 3$, the x-axis and the lines $x = 1$ and $x = 5$.

37. The diagram shows part of the graph of the curve $f(x) = 8x - x^2$ and the line $g(x) = 2x$. Calculate the area of the shaded region.

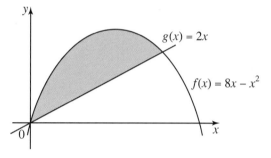

38. Calculate the area enclosed by the curve $y = 5 + x - x^2$ and the line $y = x + 4$.

39. Determine the area enclosed by the curve $y = x^2 + 1$ and the line $y = 5$.

40. Find the coordinates of the point where the graph of the curve $y = \dfrac{2x}{x^2+1}$ meets the x-axis.

Find the area of the bounded region enclosed by the curve $y = \dfrac{2x}{x^2+1}$, the x-axis, the line $x = 1$ and the line $x = 2\sqrt{2}$.

41. The diagram shows parts of the graphs of the curves $f(x) = x^2 - 2x - 3$ and $g(x) = 6 + 4x - 2x^2$. Calculate the area of the shaded region.

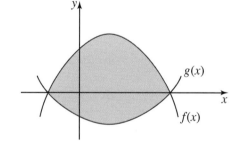

42. The diagram shows part of the curve with equation $y = \dfrac{x-2}{x^2-4x+5}$ and the line $y = \tfrac{1}{2}$.

The curve meets the x-axis at the point p.
The curve and the line meet at the point q.

(i) Find the coordinates of p and q.

(ii) Calculate the area of the shaded region.

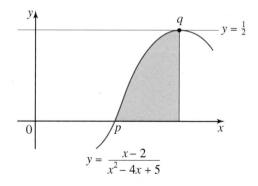

Evaluate each of the following:

1. $\displaystyle\int_0^1 \frac{x+1}{\sqrt{x^2+2x+1}}\,dx$ **2.** $\displaystyle\int_1^0 \frac{x^2-16}{2x+8}\,dx$ **3.** $\displaystyle\int_0^{1/3} \frac{1}{1+9x^2}\,dx$

4. $\displaystyle\int_0^{3/4} \frac{dx}{\sqrt{9-4x^2}}$ **5.** $\displaystyle\int_0^3 \frac{x}{\sqrt{x+1}}\,dx$ **6.** $\displaystyle\int_0^1 \frac{x^2}{x+1}\,dx$

7. $\displaystyle\int_1^4 \frac{dx}{\sqrt{x}(1+\sqrt{x})}$ (Hint: let $u=\sqrt{x}$)   **8.** $\displaystyle\int_e^{e^2} \frac{dx}{x\ln x}$ (Hint: let $u=\ln x$)

9. Evaluate: **(i)** $e^{\ln 4}$ **(ii)** $\displaystyle\int_0^{\pi/4} e^{\ln(\cos x)}\,dx$ **(iii)** $\displaystyle\int_0^{\ln\sqrt{3}} \frac{e^x}{1+e^{2x}}\,dx$.

10. Evaluate: **(i)** $\displaystyle\int_0^{\sqrt{3}} \sqrt{4-x^2}\,dx$ **(ii)** $\displaystyle\int_0^1 \frac{x^2}{\sqrt{4-x^2}}\,dx$.   (Hint: let $x=2\sin\theta$ in each case)

11. Evaluate: $\displaystyle\int_0^1 \frac{dx}{1+e^{-x}}$.   (Hint: $e^{-x}=\dfrac{1}{e^x}$: avoid negative powers of e)

12. Graph the function $y=\dfrac{1}{x}$ in the domain $\frac{1}{2} \leqslant x \leqslant 5$.

Find the area of the bounded region enclosed by the line $y=2x-1$, the line $x=4$ and the curve $y=\dfrac{1}{x}$, where $x>0$.

13. Find the value of the real number p given that $\displaystyle\int_2^p \frac{dx}{x^2-4x+5}=\frac{\pi}{4}$.

14. The diagram shows parts of the graph of the functions $y=x^2$ and $y=\sqrt{x}$.
The points of intersection of the curves are o and p.
Find the coordinates of p.
Find the area of the region bounded by the two curves.

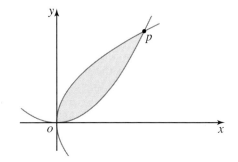

15. The diagram shows a graph of the curve $y=2x-x^2$ and the line $y=-2x$. The curve meets the x-axis at the origin o and the point p.
The curve and the line meet at the point q.
(i) Find the coordinates of p and q.
(ii) Find the area of the region enclosed by the curve and the x-axis.
(iii) Find the area of the region enclosed by the curve and the line, the shaded region in the diagram.

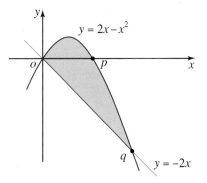

16. Find the volume of the solid generated by rotating about the y-axis the area bounded by the y-axis, the line $x - 2y - 4 = 0$ and the lines $y = -2$ and $y = 0$.

17. The area bounded by the line $y = ax$ and the lines $x = 0$ and $x = 4$ is rotated about the x-axis. If the volume of the solid generated is $\frac{256}{3}\pi$, find the values of a.

18. When the area bounded by the lines $y = x + k$, $x = 1$ and $x = 5$ is rotated about the x-axis, the solid generated has a volume equal to $\frac{64}{3}\pi$. Find the two values of k.

19. If $a > 0$ and $\displaystyle\int_0^b \frac{1}{1+x}\,dx = \frac{1}{2}\int_0^a \frac{1}{1+x}\,dx$, express b in terms of a.

20. The diagram shows a sketch of the function $f(x) = x^2 - 9$.
If the area of $oac = aby$, find the value of b, $\qquad b > 0$.
Express your answer in the form $k\sqrt{k}$.

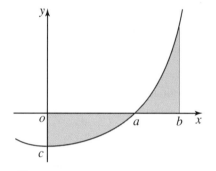

21. Find the value of k if the areas of the regions A and B are equal.

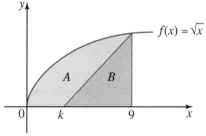

22. The diagram shows a part of the graph of the curve $y = \ln x$ and the line $y = 1$.
The curve meets the x-axis at the point a.
The curve and the line meet at the point b.
Find the coordinates of a and b.
Express x in terms of y.
Hence, or otherwise, calculate the area of
(i) A **(ii)** B.

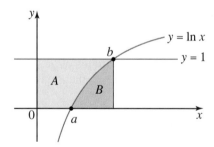

23. The diagram shows part of the graph of the curve $f(x) = x^2 + 2x + 2$. If the area of the region bounded by the curve, the x-axis, the y-axis and the line $x = 2k$ is four times that of the region bounded by the curve, the x-axis, the y-axis and the line $x = k$, find the value of k, $\qquad k > 0$.
Write your answer in the form $\sqrt{a}$.

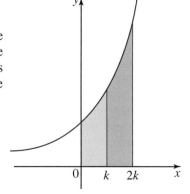

24. The region bounded by the curve $y = x^2$ and the line $y = 4$ is divided into two regions of equal area by the line $y = k$.
Show that $k^3 = 16$.

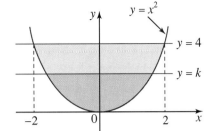

25. a is a real number such that $0 < a < 8$.
The line $y = ax$ intersects the curve $y = x(8 - x)$ at $x = 0$ and $x = p$.

(i) Show that $p = 8 - a$.

(ii) Show that the area between the curve and the line is $\dfrac{p^3}{6}$ square units.

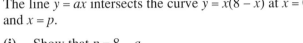

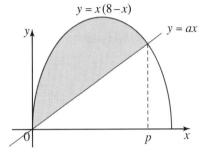

26. A line contains the points $(0, r)$ and (h, R), as shown. Find the equation of this line. By rotating the line about the x-axis, between the lines $x = 0$ and $x = h$, prove that the volume of a frustrum is given by $\frac{1}{3}\pi h(R^2 + Rh + r^2)$.

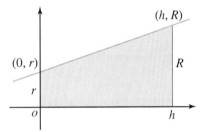

REVISION EXERCISE 6   INDUCTION AND THE BINOMIAL THEOREM

Paper 1, Questions 4 and 5

This revision exercise covers Chapters 15 and 16.

Exercise 6R.A ▼

1. Find the coefficient of a^3 in the expansion of $(2 + a)^5$.

2. If $\binom{18}{r} = \binom{18}{r+2}$, find $\binom{r}{5}$.

3. Solve $\binom{n+2}{2} = 36$, for $n \in \mathbf{N}$.

4. Write down and simplify the first three terms in the binomial expansion of $(1 - 2x)^8$.

5. $f(x) = (1 + x)^5 - (1 - x)^5$.
Express $f(x)$ as a series in ascending powers of x.

6. Expand $(2 + \sqrt{3})^5$ by the Binomial Theorem, and write your answer in the form $a + b\sqrt{3}$, $a, b \in \mathbf{R}$.

7. Use the Binomial Theorem to expand $(1 + 2x)^5$.
If $(1 + 2\sqrt{3})^5 = a + b\sqrt{3}$, find the values of a and b.

8. Verify that $(a + b)^6 + (a - b)^6 = 2(a^6 + 15a^4b^2 + 15a^2b^4 + b^6)$.
Hence, show that $(\sqrt{3} + \sqrt{2})^6 + (\sqrt{3} - \sqrt{2})^6 = 970$.

9. Write down the middle term of the expansion $(x - 2y)^{12}$ and find its value when $x = \frac{2}{3}$ and $y = \frac{1}{3}$.

10. Find the coefficients of x^4 in the expansion of $\left(x - \dfrac{1}{2x}\right)^{10}$.

11. Find the fifth term of $\left(x - \dfrac{1}{\sqrt{x}}\right)^{20}$.

12. Find the value of the term which is independent of x in the expansion of $\left(x^2 - \dfrac{1}{x}\right)^9$.

13. Find the term independent of x in the expansion of $\left(a - \dfrac{1}{a^2}\right)^{12}$.

14. The first two terms in the expansion of $(2 + ax)^n$ are $64 - 288x$.
Find the value of n and the value of a.

15. In the expansion of $(1 - 2x)^{11}$, the coefficient of x^3 is k times the coefficient of x^2. Find the value of k.

16. $(n + 2)! - n! = (n^2 + pn + q)n!$ Find the value of p and the value of q.

17. If $\dbinom{20}{r + 11} = \dbinom{20}{3r + 1}$, find two values of r.

18. Calculate the value of k if the coefficient of x^3 in the expansion of $(k + 2x)^4$ is 160.

Exercise 6R.B ▼

1. Find the term independent of x in the expansion of $\left(2x - \dfrac{1}{x^2}\right)^9$ and simplify.

2. Write the binomial expansion of $(a + b)^4$ in ascending powers of b.

    (i) Find $\left(x + \dfrac{1}{x}\right)^4 - \left(x - \dfrac{1}{x}\right)^4$ in its simplest form.

    (ii) Show that $(x + \sqrt{1 - x^2})^4 + (x - \sqrt{1 - x^2})^4 = 2(1 + 4x^2 - 4x^4)$.

3. Let $y = x + \dfrac{1}{x}$. If $y^3 + ky = x^3 + \dfrac{1}{x^3}$, find the value of k.

4. $u_n = n!$. If $u_{n+2} + u_{n+1} + u_n = (n^2 + kn + k)n!$, find the value of k.

5. Use the Binomial Theorem to expand $(1 + 2x)^6$ and $(1 - 2x)^6$.
If $(1 + 2\sqrt{5})^6 + (1 - 2\sqrt{5})^6 = k$, find the value of k, $k \in \mathbf{N}$.

6. The constant term in the expansion of $\left(px + \dfrac{q}{x}\right)^{10}$ is 8064. Evaluate pq.

7. If k is a positive integer and 720 is the coefficient of x^3 in the binomial expansion of $(k + 2x)^5$, find the value of k.

8. In the binomial expansion of $(1 + kx)^6$, the coefficient of x^4 is 240. Find the two possible real values of k.

9. If the first two terms in the expansion of $(1 + ax)^5 + (1 - ax)^5$ are $2 + 5x^2$, find two possible values for a.

10. The coefficient of x^3 in the expansion of $(1 + 2x)^n$ is $56n$, where $n \in \mathbf{N}_0$. Find the value of n.

11. The first three terms in the expansion of $(1 + ax)^n$ are $1 + 10x + 40x^2$. Find the value of n and the value of a.

12. The first three terms in the expansion of $(1 + ax)^n$ are $1 - 24x + 240x^2$. Find the value of n and the value of a.

13. The first three terms in the binomial expansion of $(1 + ax)^n$ are $1 + 2x + \frac{7}{4}x^2$.
    (i) Find the value of a and the value of n.
    (ii) Hence, find the middle term in the expansion.

14. The first four terms in the expansion of $\left(1+\dfrac{x}{n}\right)^n$ are $1+ax+\frac{7}{16}x^2+bx^3$.

Find the value of n, the value of a and the value of b.

15. Write down the binomial expansion of $\left(1+\dfrac{x}{2}\right)^n$ in ascending powers of x as far as x^3. Given that the coefficient of x^2 is equal to the coefficient of x^3 and that both coefficients are positive, find the value of n.

16. Write u_{r+1}, the general term of the binomial expansion of $(3+2x)^n$ in terms of x, r and n. If the coefficients of x^5 and x^6 are equal, find the value of n.

17. Expand $(1+x)^{10}$, using the Binomial Theorem.
Prove that:

(i) $\dbinom{10}{0}+\dbinom{10}{1}+\dbinom{10}{2}+\cdots+\dbinom{10}{10}=2^{10}$

(ii) $\dbinom{10}{0}+\dbinom{10}{2}+\dbinom{10}{4}+\dbinom{10}{6}+\dbinom{10}{8}+\dbinom{10}{10}=\dbinom{10}{1}+\dbinom{10}{3}+\dbinom{10}{5}+\dbinom{10}{7}+\dbinom{10}{9}$

18. Evaluate:

(i) $\displaystyle\sum_{r=0}^{6}\dbinom{6}{r}2^{6-r}3^r$ **(ii)** $\displaystyle\sum_{r=0}^{4}\dbinom{4}{r}\left(\dfrac{1}{2}\right)^r$

19. Write out the first three terms and the last three terms in the binomial expansion of $(1+x)^n$, $n\in\mathbf{N}$. Show that:

(i) $\displaystyle\sum_{r=0}^{n}\dbinom{n}{r}=2^n$ **(ii)** $\displaystyle\sum_{r=0}^{10}\dbinom{n}{2r}=2^{n-1}$

20. Prove that:

(i) $\dbinom{10}{r}\div\dbinom{10}{r-1}=\dfrac{11-r}{r}$ **(ii)** $\dbinom{n}{r}\div\dbinom{n}{r-1}=\dfrac{n-r+1}{r}$

(iii) $\dbinom{n}{3}+\dbinom{n+1}{3}+\dbinom{n+2}{3}=\dfrac{n(n^2+1)}{2}$ **(iv)** $\dbinom{n}{r}+\dbinom{n}{r+1}=\dbinom{n+1}{r+1}$

Prove by induction that:

22. 11^n-6 is divisible by 5 for all $n\in\mathbf{N}_0$.
   (i) 3.4^n is divisible by 6 for all $n\in\mathbf{N}_0$.
   (ii) 4^n+2 is divisible by 6 for all $n\in\mathbf{N}_0$.

24. 8^n-7n+6 is divisible by 7 for all $n\in\mathbf{N}_0$.

25. $n(n+1)(n+2)$ is divisible by 3 for all $n\in\mathbf{N}_0$.

26. $4+7+10+\cdots+(3n+1)=\dfrac{n}{2}(3n+5)$.

27. $1+2+4+\cdots+2^n=2^{n+1}-1$.

28. $2.5 + 5.8 + 8.11 + \cdots + (3n - 1)(3n + 2) = n(3n^2 + 6n + 1)$.

29. $(n + 1)! \geqslant 3^n$, for $n \in \mathbf{N}$, $n \geqslant 5$.

30. $3^n > n^2$, for $n \geqslant 2$, $n \in \mathbf{N}$.

Exercise 6R.C ▼

1. If $\binom{n}{r} > \binom{n}{r-1}$, where $n > r$, prove that $n + 1 > 2r$.

2. Write down the first four terms, in ascending powers of x, in the binomial expansion of $(1 + x)^8$. Hence, find the expansion of $(2 - 3x)(1 + x)^8$, up to and including the term in x^3.

3. Write down, in ascending powers of a, the expansion of $(1 + a)^4$. Hence, expand $[1 + (x + x^2)]^4$, up to the term containing x^2.

4. Write down, in ascending powers of x, the expansion of $(1 - x)^7$. Hence, expand $(1 + x + x^2)(1 - x)^7$, in ascending powers of x, up to the term containing x^3.

5. Write down the first three terms in the expansion of $\left(1 - \dfrac{x}{2}\right)^6$ in ascending powers of x.

In the expansion of $(a + bx)\left(1 - \dfrac{x}{2}\right)^6$ the coefficients of x and x^2 are -13 and $\frac{57}{2}$, respectively.

Find the value of a and the value of b.

6. The binomial expansion of $(a + b)^n$, where n is a positive integer, is written in descending powers of a. Denoting the first, second and third terms by p, q and r, respectively, write down expressions for p, q and r in terms of a, b and n.

Hence, show that $\dfrac{q^2}{pr} = \dfrac{2n}{n - 1}$.

7. Write down the rth and $(r + 1)$th terms of the binomial expansion of $(a + b)^{20}$, where a and b are **positive** numbers.

Show that the ratio of the $(r + 1)$th term to the rth term may be written in the form:

$\dfrac{b(21 - r)}{ar}$.

Prove by induction that:

8. $3 + 3^2 + 3^3 + \cdots + 3^n = \frac{3}{2}(3^n - 1)$.

9. $3^{2n+4} - 2^{2n}$ is divisible by 5, $\quad n \in \mathbf{N}_0$.

10. $9.4^{2n} - 5^{n-1}$ is divisible by 11, $\quad n \in \mathbf{N}_0$.

11. $x + x^2 + x^3 + \cdots + x^n = \dfrac{x(x^n - 1)}{x - 1}$, where $x \neq 1$, $n \in \mathbf{N}_0$.

12. $n! \geqslant 2^n$, for $n \geqslant 4$, $n \in \mathbf{N}$.

13. $\dfrac{1}{1.3} + \dfrac{1}{3.5} + \dfrac{1}{5.7} + \cdots + \dfrac{1}{(2n-1)(2n+1)} = \dfrac{n}{2n+1}$.

14. $n^3 \geqslant 2n^2$, $\qquad n \geqslant 2$, $n \in \mathbf{N}$.

ANSWERS

1. $12x^3$ **2.** $2x^2$ **3.** 0 **4.** b^2 **5.** $x(x+3)$ **6.** $3y(x-2y)$

7. $ab(a+b)$ **8.** $(3x-4y)(3x+4y)$ **9.** $(11p-q)(11p+q)$

10. $(1-5a)(1+5a)$ **11.** $(x-4)(x+2)$ **12.** $(3x-2)(x+5)$

13. $(3x-1)(2x-3)$ **14.** $(3a+2b)(9a^2-6ab+4b^2)$ **15.** $(1-4x)(1+4x+16x^2)$

16. $(5-2p)(25+10p+4p^2)$ **17.** $(1+5x)(1-5x+25x^2)$ **18.** $(6-x)(36+6x+x^2)$

19. $(10x+y)(100x^2-10xy+y^2)$ **20.** $a+4$ **21.** $\dfrac{x}{x+2}$ **22.** $a+b$ **23.** 1

24. $a+4$ **25.** $\dfrac{x}{y}$ **26.** $\dfrac{2a}{b}$ **27.** $\dfrac{2x}{(x+3)(x-2)}$ **28.** $\dfrac{1}{x+1}$

29. $\dfrac{1}{a+2}$ **30.** $\dfrac{3}{2x-3}$ **31.** $\dfrac{a-b}{ab}$ **32.** $\dfrac{1}{x+2}$ **33.** 1

34. 2 **35.** 2 **36.** 1 **37.** 4 **38.** 0 **39.** xy

40. $a+b$ **41.** $\dfrac{1}{x+3}$ **42.** $x+2$ **43.** 2 **44.** 4 **45.** 1

46. $a=1, b=-2$ **48.** $2x^3+6a^2x\,;\;2x(x^2+3a^2)$

1. $\dfrac{b+3c}{2}$ **2.** $\dfrac{t}{p-r}$ **3.** $\dfrac{b^2}{a-bd}$ **4.** $\dfrac{q^2-qr}{2r}$ **5.** $\dfrac{x-1}{x-2}$

6. $\dfrac{y^2+2}{5}$ **7.** $\dfrac{x^2+1}{x^2-1}$ **8.** $\dfrac{uv}{u+v}$ **9.** $\dfrac{gt^2}{k^2}$ **10.** $\dfrac{p^2+4}{p^2}$

11. $\dfrac{a+b}{p+q}$ **12.** y^3-1 **13.** $\pm\sqrt{\dfrac{y^3(1-r)}{a}}$ **14.** $\pm\sqrt{\dfrac{q^2-2p^2q^2}{p^2+2}}$ **15.** $\dfrac{p^2+1}{2p}$

Exercise 1.3 ▼

1. $a = 4, b = 2$

2. $2a + b = 4$; $3a - 4b = 17$; $a = 3, b = -2$

3. $p = 5, q = -2, r = -3$

4. $a = 8, b = -6, c = -8$

5. $p = 3, q = -4$

6. $a = 3, b = -5$

7. $p = 3, q = -4, r = 5$

8. $p = 2, q = 3, r = -5$

9. $a = 1, b = 3, c = -3$

Exercise 1.4 ▼

1. $2\sqrt{3}$ **2.** $3\sqrt{2}$ **3.** $2\sqrt{5}$ **4.** $6\sqrt{2}$ **5.** $4\sqrt{3}$ **6.** $3\sqrt{5}$ **7.** $5\sqrt{5}$

8. $3\sqrt{7}$ **9.** $10\sqrt{5}$ **10.** $2\sqrt{5}$ **11.** $2\sqrt{3}$ **12.** $3\sqrt{3}$ **13.** $\frac{2}{3}$ **14.** $\frac{6}{7}$

15. $\frac{10}{9}$ **16.** $\frac{3}{2}$ **17.** $\frac{5}{4}$ **18.** $\frac{11}{5}$ **19.** $4\sqrt{3}$ **20.** $3\sqrt{2}$ **21.** $3\sqrt{5}$

22. $4\sqrt{7}$ **23.** $2\sqrt{2}$ **24.** $3\sqrt{5}$ **25.** $\dfrac{5\sqrt{2}}{2}$ **26.** $\dfrac{4\sqrt{3}}{3}$ **27.** $\dfrac{3\sqrt{2}}{2}$ **28.** $\dfrac{3\sqrt{5}}{2}$

29. $\dfrac{4\sqrt{2}}{3}$ **30.** $\dfrac{5\sqrt{5}}{3}$ **31.** 4 **32.** $7 - 4\sqrt{3}$ **33.** $28\sqrt{5}$ **34.** $\frac{1}{60}\sqrt{5}$

36. $\dfrac{b-a}{ab}$; $-2\sqrt{2}$ **37.** 2

Exercise 1.5 ▼

1. $x = 1, y = 3$

2. $x = -2, y = -5$

3. $x = 2, y = 3$

4. $x = -3, y = 8$

5. $x = 9, y = 4$

6. $x = 3, y = 4$

7. $x = 10, y = 5$

8. $x = 15, y = 4$

9. $x = \frac{4}{5}, y = -\frac{6}{5}$

10. $x = 2, y = -1, z = 4$

11. $x = -1, y = -2, z = -1$

12. $x = -1, y = 2, z = 2$

13. $x = 2, y = 4, z = 6$

14. $x = -2, y = 3, z = 5$

15. $x = 1, y = -2, z = 3$

16. $x = 2, y = -3, z = 4$

17. $x = -2, y = -1, z = 4$

18. $x = 1, y = -2, z = -3$

19. $x = 4, y = -1, z = 5$; $a = \pm 2, b = 1, c = 3$

20. $a = 2, b = -3, c = 5$

21. $p = 2, q = -1, r = -3$

1. $-4, \frac{3}{2}$ **2.** $0, 3$ **3.** ± 2 **4.** $-4, -\frac{2}{3}$ **5.** $-3, \frac{1}{5}$

6. $3, 3$ **7.** $0, \frac{3}{2}$ **8.** $-\frac{1}{2}, \frac{2}{3}$ **9.** $\frac{2}{3}, \frac{2}{3}$ **10.** $-\frac{3}{2}, \frac{3}{4}$

11. $-\frac{2}{3}, \frac{3}{5}$ **12.** $-\frac{5}{2}, \frac{5}{2}$ **13.** $-3 \pm \sqrt{5}$ **14.** $2 \pm \sqrt{3}$ **15.** $4 \pm \sqrt{3}$

16. $1 \pm \sqrt{3}$ **17.** $2 \pm 3\sqrt{2}$ **18.** $-5 \pm 4\sqrt{3}$ **19.** $2, 3$ **20.** $\frac{2}{3}, 1$

21. $-1, 2$ **22.** $-2, 3$ **23.** $-1, \frac{8}{5}$ **24.** $-4, 8$ **25.** $4 \pm 2\sqrt{5}$

26. $-4, 5; -1, -1, \frac{1}{2}, 2$ **27.** $-6, \frac{2}{3}; -7, -\frac{7}{3}, 1, 3$ **28.** $-4, 6; 3 \pm \sqrt{5}, -2, -2$

29. $2, 4; 2 \pm \sqrt{3}, 1$ **30.** **(i)** $\pm 2, \pm 3$ **(ii)** $\pm 1, \pm 4$

1. $-3, 5$ **2.** $-1, 5$ **3.** $-8, 2$ **4.** $-1, 2$ **5.** $-1, \frac{5}{3}$

6. $-\frac{1}{2}, \frac{5}{2}$ **7.** $\frac{1}{2}$ **8.** $0, -2$ **9.** $\frac{1}{3}, 1$ **10.** $1, 3$

11. $0, \frac{2}{5}$ **12.** $\frac{1}{3}, 3$ **13.** $-\frac{5}{3}, 1$ **14.** $-4, -\frac{2}{5}$ **15.** $\frac{4}{3}, 4$

16. $-1, 5$ **17.** $-3, \frac{1}{5}$ **18.** $-\frac{4}{5}, 0$ **19.** $1, 4$ **20.** 3

21. $4, 9$ **22.** 5 **23.** 3 **24.** 5 **25.** $2, 3$

26. 6 **27.** $2, 5$ **28.** 16 **29.** 4 **30.** 9

31. $0, 3$ **32.** $1, 9$ **33.** $6, 2$ **34.** **(i)** $-1, 7$ **(ii)** $\frac{1}{3}, 3$

1. $x = -1, y = 3$ or $x = 3, y = 1$ **2.** $x = 7, y = 6$ or $x = -6, y = -7$

3. $x = 0, y = -5$ or $x = 2, y = 1$ **4.** $x = 4, y = 2$

5. $x = 5, y = 2$ or $x = 4, y = 1$ **6.** $x = 2, y = 6$ or $x = 6, y = 2$

7. $x = 1, y = 1$ or $x = 2, y = -1$ **8.** $x = 1, y = 2$ or $x = 3, y = -4$

9. $x = 1, y = 2$ or $x = 2, y = 1$ **10.** $x = 2, y = -1$ or $x = 3, y = 2$

11. $x = 4, y = -1$ **12.** $x = 7, y = 3$ **13.** $x = 2, y = 1$ or $x = -\frac{4}{5}, y = -\frac{13}{15}$

14. $x = -2, y = -4$ or $x = 1, y = \frac{7}{2}$ **15.** $x = -1, y = -\frac{2}{3}$ or $x = -\frac{7}{2}, y = 1$

Exercise 2.4 ▼

1. (i) -2 **(ii)** 5 **(iii)** -10 **(iv)** -6 **(v)** -30 **(vi)** -16 **(vii)** 22
(viii) 8 **(ix)** $-\frac{2}{5}$ **(x)** $-\frac{6}{5}$ **(xi)** -5 **(xii)** $\frac{3}{5}$

2. (i) 12 **(ii)** 9 **(iii)** 22 **(iv)** 100 **(v)** $-\frac{16}{3}$ **(vi)** $-\frac{22}{3}$ **(vii)** -2
(viii) $-\frac{4}{3}$ **(ix)** $x^2 - 8x - 12 = 0$ **(x)** $x^2 - 22x + 9 = 0$
(xi) $x^2 - 10x + 18 = 0$ **(xii)** $x^2 - 14x - 14 = 0$ **(xiii)** $x^2 - 2x - 6 = 0$
(xiv) $3x^2 + 4x - 1 = 0$ **(xv)** $3x^2 + 22x + 3 = 0$ **(xvi)** $x^2 - 10x + 18 = 0$

3. (i) -3 **(ii)** $\frac{3}{2}$ **(iii)** -9 **(iv)** $6; p = 18, q = 39.$

4. (i) (a) 7 **(b)** $12\frac{1}{2}$ **(ii)** $2x^2 - 14x + 25 = 0$ **6.** 16 **9.** $-64, 27$

10. ± 10 **13.** $-4, \frac{1}{2}$

14. (i) (a) $-2k - 2$ **(b)** $2k + 5$ **(c)** $-8k^2 - 28k - 20$ **(ii) (b)** $q = 25 - 4k^2$; **(c)** $\pm\frac{5}{2}$

Exercise 2.5 ▼

1. $(x + 1), (x + 2)$ **2.** $(x + 1), (x + 5)$ **3.** $(3x - 1), (x + 2)$ **4.** $(x - 2), (x - 4)$

6. $k = 19; (3x - 1), (2x + 3)$ **7.** $k = 7; (x + 1), (x + 2)$ **8.** $p = 2, q = -10$ **9.** $a = 5, b = 19$

10. $a = 9, b = 7$ **11.** $h = 5, k = 3$ **12.** $(x + 3)(x - 2); p = 3, q = 12$

13. $p = -5, q = 19$ **14.** $p = -12, q = 16$

Exercise 2.6 ▼

1. $(x - 3)(x - 2)(x + 4); 3, 2, -4$ **2.** $(2x - 1)(x - 1)(x + 1); \frac{1}{2}, 1, -1$ **3.** $-1, 3$

4. $-3 \pm 2\sqrt{2}$ **5.** $k = 7; 2, 3$ **6.** $a = 2, b = 9; k = \frac{3}{2}$

7. $k = -4$ or $\frac{1}{2}$ **8.** $p = -1, q = 14, r = -8; 1, 2, 4$ **9.** $-4p, -p, 2p$

1. $-1 \leqslant x \leqslant 2$ **2.** $x < -2$ or $x > 4$ **3.** $\frac{1}{2} < x < 5$

4. $-\frac{5}{3} \leqslant x \leqslant 1$ **5.** $-\frac{3}{2} \leqslant x \leqslant 1$ **6.** $x \leqslant 0$ or $x \geqslant 2$

7. $0 < x < \frac{2}{3}$ **8.** $-2 \leqslant x \leqslant 2$ **9.** $x \leqslant -5$ or $x \geqslant 5$

10. $-\frac{2}{3} \leqslant x \leqslant \frac{2}{3}$ **11.** $x < -\frac{1}{3}$ or $x > \frac{1}{3}$ **12.** $x \leqslant \frac{1}{2}$ or $x \geqslant \frac{5}{2}$

13. $-3 \leqslant x \leqslant -1$ **14.** $x \leqslant -1$ or $x \geqslant 5$ **15.** $-2 \leqslant x \leqslant 5$

16. $0 \leqslant x \leqslant 4$ **17.** $x \leqslant \frac{5}{2}$ or $x \geqslant \frac{7}{2}$ **18.** $-\frac{1}{3} \leqslant x \leqslant 3$

19. $x \leqslant 0$ or $x \geqslant 6$ **20.** $x \leqslant -\frac{3}{2}$ or $x \geqslant -1$ **21.** $-\frac{5}{3} < x < 1$

22. $x < 1$ or $x > 2$ **23.** $2 < x < 5$ **24.** $-3 < x < 10$

25. $x < 2$ or $x > \frac{7}{2}$ **26.** $1 \leqslant x \leqslant \frac{5}{3}$ **27.** $-3 < x < 4$

28. $-5 \leqslant x \leqslant -\frac{1}{2}$ **29.** $-\frac{5}{2} < x < 3$ **30.** $-2 < x < 0$

31. $x < -9$ or $x > 5$ **32.** $x < 0$ or $x > 2$ **33.** $2 < x < 3$

34. $-1 < x < 5$ **35.** $-4 < x < 0$ **36.** $x \leqslant \frac{1}{4}$ or $x \geqslant \frac{5}{2}$

11. (i) **(a)** ± 2 **(b)** $k \leqslant -2$ or $k \geqslant 2$ **(c)** $-2 < k < 2$

  (ii) **(a)** ± 8 **(b)** $k \leqslant -8$ or $k \geqslant 8$ **(c)** $-8 < k < 8$

  (iii) **(a)** $-\frac{1}{4}$ **(b)** $k \geqslant -\frac{1}{4}$ **(c)** $k < -\frac{1}{4}$

  (iv) **(a)** $\frac{3}{2}$ **(b)** $k \leqslant \frac{3}{2}$ **(c)** $k > \frac{3}{2}$

  (v) **(a)** $0, \frac{4}{3}$ **(b)** $0 \leqslant k \leqslant \frac{4}{3}$ **(c)** $k < 0$ or $k > \frac{4}{3}$

  (vi) **(a)** $-\frac{1}{3}, 1$ **(b)** $-\frac{1}{3} \leqslant k \leqslant 1$ **(c)** $k < -\frac{1}{3}$ or $k > 1$

14. $2, 2p + 3$

1. 9   **2.** 32   **3.** 16   **4.** $\frac{1}{7}$ **5.** $\frac{1}{4}$ **6.** 1000   **7.** $\frac{7}{2}$

8. $\frac{27}{8}$ **9.** $\frac{1}{9}$ **10.** $\frac{1}{8}$ **11.** $\frac{1}{2}$ **12.** $\frac{9}{8}$ **13.** $\frac{4}{3}$ **14.** $\frac{1}{32}$

15. 32   **16.** 3   **17.** 2   **18.** -1 **19.** $a = 2, b = 5$ **20.** $x + 1$

21. x **22.** 0   **23.** 0   **24.** 4   **25.** $\frac{27}{2}$ **26.** 6

1. $\frac{5}{2}$ **2.** 4   **3.** 2; 4   **4.** $\frac{5}{4}$ **5.** 3   **6.** $\frac{13}{2}$ **7.** $\frac{3}{2}$

8. 1, 3   **9.** $-\frac{1}{3}, 2$ **10. (i)** 3^3 **(ii)** $2^5; x = 2, y = -1$ **11.** $x = 1, y = 1$

12. $x = 21, y = 6$ **13.** $x = 1, y = 0$

14. (i) 2 **(ii)** 1 **(iii)** 0 **(iv)** -2 **(v)** -1 **(vi)** no solution **(vii)** no solution **(viii)** -3

15. (i) y^2 **(ii)** $2y; 1, 3$ **16.** 0; 2   **17.** 0, 1   **18.** 1, 2   **19.** 2, 3   **20.** $-1, 1$

21. 1, 2   **22.** 0, -1 **23.** 1, 2   **24.** $-2, 2$ **25.** $k = 7; 5$

4. 29; 157   **5.** $n < 22$ **6.** 1, 2, 3, 4, 5

3. (i) 3 **(ii)** 2 **(iii)** 4 **(iv)** 3 **(v)** 4 **(vi)** 5 **(vii)** 1 **(viii)** 0 **(ix)** -1 **(x)** -2 **(xi)** $\frac{5}{2}$
(xii) $\frac{3}{4}$ **(xiii)** $\frac{3}{2}$ **(xiv)** 1 **(xv)** $-\frac{1}{3}$ **(xvi)** $\frac{3}{2}$

4. (i) 2 **(ii)** 3 **(iii)** 4 **(iv)** 81 **(v)** 0

5. (a) (i) 2 **(ii)** 4 **(iii)** -2 **(iv)** 1 **(b)** 16   **6.** 0

7. (a) (i) $\frac{4}{3}$ **(ii)** $\frac{3}{5}$ **(b)** 1   **8.** $p = 2q^3$ **9.** $y = \dfrac{x^2}{5}$ **10. (b)** $3r$

1. 4   **2.** 8   **3.** ± 5 **4.** 3   **5.** 8   **6.** 10   **7.** 6

8. 7   **9.** $\frac{2}{7}$ **10.** 4, 6   **11.** 18   **12.** 2   **13.** 3   **14.** $-\frac{1}{2}$

15. $x = 2, y = 1$ **16.** $x = 3, y = 2$ **17.** $x = 2, y = \frac{5}{2}$ **18.** $x = 1, y = 1$ or $x = -3, y = 9$

19. $x = 1, y = 4$ **20.** $x = 4, y = -1$ **21.** 3   **22.** 2, 4   **23.** 3, 27   **24.** 4, 16

25. 125, $\frac{1}{25}$ **26.** 2, $\frac{1}{16}$ **27.** 10   **28.** $p = \sqrt{q}; \frac{3}{4}$ **29.** $\dfrac{a}{2}, 2a$

30. $x = 8, y = 2$ or $x = 2, y = 8$ **31. (i)** $2k$ **(ii)** $2k + 1$ **(iii)** $\frac{1}{2}k$ **(iv)** $\dfrac{1}{k}$ **(v)** $-\dfrac{1}{k}$

32. 7.122   **33.** 4.052   **34.** 2.161   **35.** 4.954   **36.** 3.878   **37.** 4.358

38. 1.756   **39.** 1.635   **40. (i)** 1 **(ii)** 3 **(iii)** -2 **(iv)** $\frac{1}{2}$

42. (i) $\ln 2$ (ii) $\ln 5$ (iii) no solution   (iv) $-\ln 3$ (v) no solutions   (vi) $\frac{1}{2}\ln 3$ or $\ln\sqrt{3}$

    (vii) e (viii) e^2 (ix) $\sqrt{e}$ or $e^{1/2}$ (x) e^{-1} or $\dfrac{1}{e}$ (xi) e^{-3} or $\dfrac{1}{e^3}$ (xii) $e^{-1/2}$ or $\dfrac{1}{e^{1/2}}$ or $\dfrac{1}{\sqrt{e}}$

43. (i) $\ln 2, \ln 3$ (ii) $\ln 3, \ln 5$ (iii) $\ln 4$ (iv) $-\ln 3, \ln 2$

44. $y^2 + (k-2)y + (-3k-2) = 0$; $-2, -6$; $\ln 2, \ln 4$

45. (i) e, e^2 (ii) $\sqrt{e}, e^3$

Exercise 6.1 ▼

1. (i) $2\sqrt{10}$ (ii) $(3, 1)$ (iii) 3; $3x - y - 8 = 0$ (iv) -14 (v) $h = 6$; $k = 2$
    (vi) $(6, 10)$ (vii) $(1, 11)$ (viii) $3x - y + 16 = 0$ **4.** 5 **5.** $k = 2$

6. $(2, -1)$; $5x + 2y - 8 = 0$; $(0, 4)$ **7.** (i) $x - y - 5 = 0$ (ii) $x + y + 1 = 0$

10. $(-8, 3)$ **11.** $h = 2$; $k = -1$ **12.** $s(4, 2)$ or $s(2, -6)$ **13.** $5x - 2y - 19 = 0$

14. (i) $3x - 2y - 24 = 0$ (ii) $3x - 2y + 18 = 0$ **15.** $(8, 3)$ **16.** $x - y - 2 = 0$; $x + y - 6 = 0$

17. ± 2 **18.** $-2, 14$ **19.** $1, 7$ **20.** $5, 15$ **21.** 6

22. (i) $x - 3y + 1 = 0$ (ii) $2x + y - 12 = 0$ (iii) $q(5, 2), s(1, 3)$

23. (i) $p\left(-\dfrac{c}{a}, 0\right)$; $q\left(0, -\dfrac{c}{b}\right)$ (ii) $\sqrt{\dfrac{c^2(a^2 + b^2)}{a^2 b^2}}$ or $\left|\dfrac{c}{ab}\right|\sqrt{a^2 + b^2}$; $\dfrac{c^2}{2ab}$

24. $a^2 x + y = 2ab$ or $ax + \dfrac{y}{a} = 2b$ **25.** $a = 4, b = 8$

Exercise 6.2 ▼

1. 7 **2.** 13 **3.** 24 **4.** 20 **5.** $\frac{27}{2}$ **6.** 12 **7.** 10

8. 12 **9.** 6 **10.** 7 **11.** 9 **12.** 37 **13.** 36 **14.** 72

15. Area $= 0$, $\therefore$ a, b and c are collinear   **16.** 5 or $-\frac{23}{5}$ **17.** ± 2 **18.** ± 2 **19.** 5

20. $(-29, 0)$ or $(3, 0)$ **21.** $a_1 = \frac{9}{2}$ or $-\frac{7}{2}$; $a_2 = 3$ or $-\frac{7}{3}$

Exercise 6.3 ▼

7. $p(2, -3)$ **8.** $r(7, -1)$ **9.** $b(-3, 11)$ **10.** $c(24, 16)$

11. $a(21, 0)$, $b(0, -14)$ **12.** (i) $(8h, -9k)$ (ii) $(32h, -57k)$

Exercise 6.4

1. $(3, 2)$ **2.** $(4, 1)$ **3.** $(1, 0)$ **4.** $(-2, 1)$ **5.** $p = 4, q = 9$

6. $h = -25, k = -51$ **7.** $(2, -4)$ **8.** $(5, -9)$ **9.** $(3, -1)$ **10.** $(1, -2)$

11. $(3, 2)$ **12.** $(-2, -1)$ **13.** $(-3, 2)$ **14.** $(2, 10)$

15. (i) $(\frac{5}{3}, -\frac{1}{3})$ **(ii)** $(2, -1)$ **(iii)** $(1, 1)$; $(\frac{5}{3}, -\frac{1}{3})$ is on $2x + y - 3 = 0$

Exercise 6.5

1. 5 **2.** 1 **3.** 2 **4.** 2 **5.** $\sqrt{5}$ **6.** $4\sqrt{2}$

8. 1 **9.** 1 **10.** $\frac{15}{13}$ **11.** $\frac{3}{2}$ **12.** $\sqrt{5}$

13. (ii) no **(iii)** $(30, 16)$ and $(0, 0)$ are on the same side; $(-19, -11)$ and $(0, 0)$ are on opposite sides

14. $a = 0$ or $a = 4$ **15.** $35; -25$ **16.** $3x - 4y + 11 = 0$ or $3x - 4y - 9 = 0$

17. $x + y - 2 = 0$ or $x - y = 0$ **18.** $mx - y + (2m + 1)$; $y - 1 = 0$ or $4x + 3y + 5 = 0$

19. $x - y - 3 = 0$ or $7x + y - 29 = 0$ **20.** $3x - 2y + 8 = 0$ or $3x - 2y - 18 = 0$

Exercise 6.6

1. $45°; 135°$ **2.** $42°; 138°$ **3.** $18°; 162°$ **4.** $71°, 109°$ **5.** 3 **6.** $45°$

7. $135°$ **8.** $45°$ **10.** $mx - y + (3 - 2m) = 0$ **11.** $x + 3y - 11 = 0$ or $3x - y - 3 = 0$

12. $5x + 7y - 41 = 0$ or $7x - 5y - 13 = 0$ **13. (i)** $30°$ **(ii)** $45°$

14. $x - 2y + 2 = 0$ or $11x + 2y - 2 = 0$ **15. (i)** -3 **(ii)** $45°$ **(iii)** $-\frac{1}{2}; 2$ **(iv)** $q(6, 4); s(0, 2)$

Exercise 6.7

1. $3x - y - 1 = 0$ **2.** $4x + 12y - 1 = 0$ **3.** $x - 3y + 8 = 0$

4. $25x - 15y - 2 = 0$ **5. (i)** $(-1, 5)$ **(iii) (a)** 0 **(b)** 7 **6. (i)** 1 **(ii)** -2

7. 2 **8. (i)** 1 **(ii)** $\frac{1}{3}; -\frac{3}{5}$ **9.** $(-2, 3)$ **10. (i)** $u = \lambda$ **(ii)** $3u = 5\lambda$

11. $2u + 5\lambda = 0$

1. $x - y - 2 = 0$ **2.** $2x + 3y - 1 = 0$ **3.** $3x - 2y - 1 = 0$

4. $3x + 2y - 7 = 0$ **5.** $x - 14y + 11 = 0$ **6.** $x + 3y - 5 = 0$

7. $11x - 14y + 9 = 0$ **8.** $5x + 4y - 15 = 0$ **9.** 1 square unit

10. $135°$ **11.** yes   **12.** $(1, 0); \frac{1}{5}; x + y - 1 = 0$

14. $-1 \leqslant t \leqslant 2$.

Exercise 6.9 ▼

1. **(i)** $(0, 0), (4, 3), (4, 1), (7, 5)$ **(iii)** **(a)** yes   **(b)** yes   **(iv)** $r(3, 2)$

2. **(ii)** **(a)** yes   **(b)** no   **(c)** yes   **(iii)** yes

3. **(i)** $(0, 0), (-9, 17), (-2, 16), (14, -2)$ **(ii)** **(a)** no   **(b)** yes   **(c)** yes   **(iii)** no   **(iv)** $k(2, 5)$

4. **(i)** $(-1, 1)$ **(ii)** $x = \dfrac{x' + y'}{5}; y = \dfrac{-2x' + 3y'}{5}$ **(iii)** $f(L) = 12x' - 13y' + 35 = 0$

     $f(K) = x' - 3y' + 1 = 0$ **(iv)** $(-1, 1) \rightarrow (-4, -1)$ **(vi)** $x + 3y - 2 = 0$

5. **(ii)** yes   **(iv)** $x = \dfrac{3x' - y'}{10}; y = \dfrac{2x' + y'}{5}$ **(v)** $f(L) = x' + 3y' + 40 = 0; \quad f(K) = x' + 3y' - 10 = 0$

6. **(iii)** $x = \dfrac{x' + 3y'}{7}; y = \dfrac{2x' - y'}{7}$ **(iv)** $(-4, 6), (-12, 11), (10, -8),$

     $x' + 10y' - 28 = 0, x' + 2 = 0$; yes   **(vi)** $k = 7$

7. If $f(L) \| f(K)$, then $p = \sqrt{-1} = i$, but we are given $p \in \boldsymbol{R} \therefore \quad f(L) \nparallel f(K)$.

8. **(i)** $x = -3x' + 2y'; y = 5x' - 3y'$ **(ii)** $f(P) = (-3a + 5b)x' + (2a - 3b)y' + c = 0$

     $f(Q) = (-3a + 5b)x' + (2a - 3b)y' + d = 0, \therefore \quad f(P) \| f(Q)$

9. **(i)** $bx - ay + d = 0$ **(ii)** yes   **(iii)** $b = 2a$

10. $p = 2, q = 3, r = 4, s = -5$; no

11. **(i)** $x' = 10 - 27t; y' = 3 - 8t$ **(ii)** $(10, 3), (-17, -5)$

12. **(i)** $p(1, 1); q(7, -2)$ **(ii)** **(a)** $x' = 4t - 1; y' = 3t + 3; 0 \leqslant t \leqslant 3$

                       (b) $3x' - 4y' + 15 = 0; -1 \leqslant x' \leqslant 11; 3 \leqslant y' \leqslant 12$

Exercise 7.1 ▼

1. 180°　　**2.** 30°　　**3.** 45°　　**4.** 120°　　**5.** 108°　　**6.** 240°　　**7.** 225°

8. 80°　　**9.** 50°　　**10.** 330°　　**11.** $\dfrac{\pi}{6}$　　**12.** $\dfrac{\pi}{4}$　　**13.** $\dfrac{\pi}{3}$　　**14.** $\dfrac{\pi}{2}$

15. $\dfrac{2\pi}{3}$　　**16.** $\dfrac{5\pi}{6}$　　**17.** $\dfrac{7\pi}{6}$　　**18.** $\dfrac{4\pi}{3}$　　**19.** $\dfrac{3\pi}{4}$　　**20.** $\dfrac{5\pi}{2}$　　**21.** $\dfrac{13\pi}{6}$

22. $\dfrac{2\pi}{5}$　　**23.** $\dfrac{8\pi}{5}$　　**24.** $\dfrac{7\pi}{12}$　　**25.** $\dfrac{\pi}{8}$　　**26.** (i) 8 cm　(ii) 40 cm^2

27. (i) 4.8 cm　(ii) 9.6 cm^2　　　　**28.** (i) 10π cm　(ii) 60π cm^2

29. (i) 2.25 cm^2　(ii) 6.5 cm　　　　**30.** (i) $\dfrac{8\pi}{3}$ cm^2　(ii) $\left(\dfrac{8\pi}{3}+4\right)$ cm

31. $\dfrac{4\pi}{3}$　　　　　　　　**32.** 80π cm^2　　　　　　**33.** 8 cm

Exercise 7.2 ▼

1. 1　　**2.** $\frac{1}{4}$　　**3.** $\frac{5}{4}$　　**4.** $\frac{1}{4}$　　**5.** 1　　**6.** $\frac{1}{2}$　　**7.** 1

8. 4　　**9.** $-\frac{1}{2}$　　**10.** 2　　**11.** $-\dfrac{1}{\sqrt{2}}$　　**12.** $-\sqrt{3}$　　**13.** $-\dfrac{\sqrt{3}}{2}$　　**14.** $\dfrac{1}{\sqrt{2}}$

15. $\dfrac{\sqrt{3}}{2}$　　**16.** $-\sqrt{3}$　　**17.** $-\dfrac{1}{\sqrt{2}}$　　**18.** $-\frac{1}{2}$　　**19.** $\frac{1}{2}$　　**20.** $\dfrac{1}{\sqrt{3}}$　　**21.** 1

22. $-\dfrac{2}{\sqrt{3}}$　　**23.** -2　　**24.** $-\sqrt{3}$　　**25.** $\dfrac{2}{\sqrt{3}}$　　**26.** (i) 180°　(ii) 90°　(iii) 90°, 270°

Exercise 7.3 ▼

1. $R = 66°$, $q = 13.92$ cm, $r = 12.79$ cm　　　**2.** 9.17 cm　　**3.** (i) 7.5　(ii) 3　(iii) 15

5. 27　　**6.** 4　　**7.** 28.96°, 46.57°, 104.48°　　　**8.** 30° or 150°　　　**9.** 7 or 8

10. $|\angle acb| = \dfrac{\pi}{3}$ and $|\angle abc| = \dfrac{5\pi}{12}$　　or　　$|\angle acb| = \dfrac{2\pi}{3}$ and $|\angle abc| = \dfrac{\pi}{12}$

11. 9.9 cm　　**12.** 23 m　　**13.** (ii) 4 : 1　　**14.** 49°; 131°

15. (i) $\dfrac{y}{\sqrt{3}}$　(ii) $\sqrt{3}y - 80$; $y = 40\sqrt{3}$

1. **(i)** 6 m **(ii)** 10 m **(iii)** 14 m; $15\sqrt{3}$ m^2 **2.** **(i)** 13 m **(ii)** $\dfrac{13\sqrt{3}}{3}$ m

3. **(i)** $2500 + r^2 = t^2$ **(ii)** $r = h; t = \sqrt{3}\,h$ **(iii)** **(a)** 35.4 m **(b)** 61.2 m

4. **(i)** $\sqrt{3}\,x$ **(ii)** 2 **5.** **(i)** 7 **(ii)** $2\sqrt{43}$; 67.6° **6.** **(i)** $8\sqrt{3}$ **(ii)** $\sqrt{164}$ **(iii)** 66°

13. **(i)** $90° < A < 180°$ **(ii)** $A = 90°$ **(iii)** $0° < A < 90°$ **(iv)** $A = 60°$ **(v)** $A = 120°$ **(vi)** $A = 30°$

1. **(i)** $\frac{5}{13}$ **(ii)** $\frac{12}{5}$ **(iii)** $\frac{3}{5}$ **(iv)** $\frac{3}{4}$ **(v)** $\frac{63}{65}$ **(vi)** $-\frac{16}{65}$ **(vii)** $-\frac{63}{16}$ **(viii)** $\frac{120}{169}$

2. **(a)** **(i)** $\frac{840}{841}$ **(ii)** $\frac{41}{841}$ **(iii)** $\frac{840}{41}$ **(b)** $-\frac{3}{5}$ **3.** $\dfrac{\sqrt{3}-1}{2\sqrt{2}}$ **4.** $\dfrac{\sqrt{3}+1}{2\sqrt{2}}$ **5.** $\dfrac{\sqrt{3}+1}{\sqrt{3}-1}$

6. $\dfrac{\sqrt{3}+1}{2\sqrt{2}}$ **7.** $\dfrac{\sqrt{3}-1}{2\sqrt{2}}$ **8.** $\dfrac{\sqrt{3}+1}{\sqrt{3}-1}$ **9.** $\dfrac{2\sqrt{2}}{1+\sqrt{3}}$ **10.** $\dfrac{2\sqrt{2}}{1+\sqrt{3}}$ **11.** $\dfrac{1}{\sqrt{2}}$

12. $\dfrac{\sqrt{3}}{2}$ **13.** $\sqrt{3}$ **14.** $\frac{1}{21}$ **15.** **(i)** $\frac{9}{2}$ **(ii)** $\frac{36}{85}$ **16.** $\dfrac{\pi}{4}$ or 45°

17. 225° **24.** $\pm\frac{5}{7}$ **25.** $\pm\frac{1}{5}$ **26.** **(i)** $\frac{4}{7}$ **(ii)** $\frac{3}{11}$ **33.** $\sqrt{\dfrac{\sqrt{2}+1}{2\sqrt{2}}}$ or $\sqrt{\dfrac{2+\sqrt{2}}{2}}$

1. $2\sin 3\theta \cos$ **2.** $2\cos 6\theta \cos\theta$ **3.** $-2\sin 5\theta \sin 3\theta$

4. $2\cos 4\theta \sin\theta$ **5.** $-2\sin 4\theta \sin 2\theta$ **6.** $2\cos 4\theta \cos 3\theta$

7. $2\sin 2\theta \cos\theta$ **8.** $2\cos 3\theta \cos 2\theta$ **9.** $-2\cos 5\theta \sin 3\theta$

10. $\sin 8\theta + \sin 4\theta$ **11.** $\cos 4\theta + \cos 2\theta$ **12.** $\cos 5\theta + \cos 3\theta$

13. $\sin 9\theta - \sin 3\theta$ **14.** $\cos 5\theta - \cos 3\theta$ **15.** $\sin 13\theta - \sin\theta$

16. $\frac{1}{2}(\sin 6x + \sin 4x)$ **17.** $\frac{1}{2}(\cos A - \cos 3A)$ **18.** $\frac{1}{2}(\sin 4A - \sin 2A)$

19. $\dfrac{1}{\sqrt{2}}$ **20.** $-\dfrac{\sqrt{3}}{\sqrt{2}}$ **21.** $-\dfrac{\sqrt{3}}{\sqrt{2}}$ **22.** $\dfrac{\sqrt{3}}{2}+1$ **23.** $\frac{1}{2}$ **24.** $\dfrac{1}{2\sqrt{2}}-\dfrac{1}{4}$

1. 45°, 225°　　**2.** 60°, 300°　　　**3.** 45°, 135°　　　**4.** 60°, 120°

5. 135°, 225°　　**6.** 240°, 300°　　**7.** 60°, 240°　　　**8.** 0°, 180°, 360°

9. 180°　　　**10.** 210°, 330°　　**11.** 135°, 315°　　**12.** 150°, 210°

13. 30°, 150°, 210°, 330°　　　**14.** 60°, 120°, 240°, 300°　　**15.** 45°, 135°, 225°, 315°

16. 15°, 75°, 135°, 195°, 255°, 315°　　**17.** 15°, 75°, 195°, 255°　　**18.** 300°

19. 90°, 330°　　**20.** 75°　　　**21.** 90°, 270°　　**22.** 0°, 60°, 180°, 240°, 360°

23. 15°, 95°, 135°, 215°, 255°, 335°　　**24.** 180°　　**25.** 25.5°, 154.5°

26. 51.3°, 231.3°　　**27.** 109.5°, 250.5°

1. 60°, 180°, 300°　　　**2.** 0°, 30°, 150°, 180°, 360°　　**3.** 0°, 135°, 180°, 315°, 360°

4. 60°, 90°, 270°, 300°　　**5.** 90°, 210°, 330°　　　**6.** 0°, 180°, 240°, 300°, 360°

7. 0°, 60°, 300°, 360°　　**8.** 45°, 90°, 135°, 270°　　**9.** 90°, 210°, 330°

10. 0°, 120°, 180°, 240°, 360°　　**11.** 0°, 60°, 120°, 180°, 240°, 300°, 360°

12. 0°, 90°, 180°, 360°　　**13.** 45°, 135°, 225°, 315°　　**14.** 60°, 90°, 120°, 240°, 270°, 300°

15. 60°, 180°, 300°　　**16.** 30°, 150°, 270°　　**17.** $\dfrac{\pi}{3}, \dfrac{4\pi}{3}$　　**18.** 90°, 120°

19. 0°, 45°, 135°, 180°　　**20.** $\dfrac{7\pi}{6}, \dfrac{3\pi}{2}, \dfrac{5\pi}{3}, \dfrac{11\pi}{6}$　　**21.** 60°, 90°, 120°

22. $a = 2, b = 3; 0°, 60°, 300°, 360°$　　**23.** $\dfrac{2\pi}{3}, \pi, \dfrac{4\pi}{3}$

1. $\dfrac{\pi}{6}$　　**2.** $\dfrac{\pi}{4}$　　**3.** $\dfrac{\pi}{4}$　　**4.** $-\dfrac{\pi}{4}$　　**5.** $-\dfrac{\pi}{3}$　　**6.** 0　　**7.** $-\dfrac{\pi}{4}$

8. $-\dfrac{\pi}{3}$　　**9.** $-\dfrac{\pi}{6}$　　**10.** $-\dfrac{\pi}{6}$　　**11.** $\frac{3}{4}$　　**12.** $\frac{12}{13}$　　**13.** $\sqrt{3}$　　**14.** $\frac{9}{25}$

15. $\frac{225}{64}$　　**16.** $\frac{240}{289}$　　**17.** $\frac{63}{65}$　　**18.** $\frac{56}{33}$　　**19.** $\frac{33}{65}$　　**20.** $\dfrac{1}{\sqrt{2}}$

Exercise 8.6 ▼

1. 3 **2.** 5 **3.** $\frac{1}{2}$ **4.** $\frac{1}{4}$ **5.** $\frac{3}{4}$ **6.** $\frac{3}{2}$ **7.** 8

8. 3 **9.** $\frac{1}{2}$ **10.** $\frac{1}{3}$ **11.** 1 **12.** $\frac{4}{3}$ **13.** 6 **14.** 6

15. $\frac{3}{4}$ **16.** 0 **17.** 6 **18.** $\frac{2}{3}$ **19.** 1 **20.** 1 **21.** 2

Exercise 9.1 ▼

1. period = 3; range = [0, 3] **(i)** 3 **(ii)** 0 **(iii)** 3 **(iv)** 3 **(v)** 0

2. (i) period = 10; range = [0, 3] **(ii) (a)** 3 **(b)** 0 **(c)** 3 **(d)** 0

3. (i) period = 8; range = [0, 10]

x	2	8	14	20	26	−6	−16	−34
$f(x)$	10	0	5	0	10	5	0	10

4. $k = 2, a = -2, b = 3$

x	1	4	6	7	−2	−10	−12	−16
$f(x)$	−2	3	0	−2	3	3	0	3

5. (i) 360° **(ii)** [−1, 1] **(iii)** $p = \frac{1}{2}, q = 2, r = 3, s = 2, t = -\frac{1}{2}$

(iv) (a) 0 **(b)** $\frac{1}{2}$ **(c)** $\dfrac{1}{\sqrt{2}}$ **(d)** $-\dfrac{\sqrt{3}}{2}$ **(e)** $\dfrac{1}{\sqrt{2}}$

Exercise 10.1 ▼

1. 3 **2.** 8 **3.** 5 **4.** 0 **5.** 5 **6** $\frac{1}{3}$

7. 4 **8.** 2 **9.** 12 **10** $\frac{1}{8}$ **11.** 12 **12.** $\frac{1}{27}$

13. 2 **14.** 6 **15.** 1 **16.** −4 **17.** $-\frac{1}{2}$ **18.** 2

19. 4 **20.** $\frac{1}{6}$ **21.** $\frac{1}{6}$ **22.** 4 **23.** −2 **24.** $-\frac{1}{2}$

25. 2 **26.** $\frac{4}{3}$ **27.** $\frac{2}{3}$ **28.** $\frac{4}{5}$ **29.** $\frac{3}{2}$ **30.** 0

1. $3x^2$　　**2.** $12x^3$　　**3.** $-10x$　　**4.** 3　　**5.** -2　　**6.** 0　　**7.** 0

8. $-2x^{-3}$　or　$-\dfrac{2}{x^3}$　　**9.** $-6x^{-4}$　or　$-\dfrac{6}{x^4}$　　**10.** $10x^{-6}$　or　$\dfrac{10}{x^6}$　　**11.** $2x^{-2/3}$　or　$\dfrac{2}{x^{2/3}}$

12. $-x^{-2}$　or　$-\dfrac{1}{x^2}$　　**13.** $\frac{1}{2}x^{-1/2}$　or　$\dfrac{1}{2\sqrt{x}}$　　**14.** $-2x^{-3/2}$　or　$-\dfrac{2}{x^{3/2}}$　　**15.** $-\frac{2}{3}x^{-5/3}$　or　$-\dfrac{2}{3x^{5/3}}$

16. $3x^2 - 5$　　　　**17.** $-2x$　　　　**18.** $2x + 5x^{-2}$　or　$2x + \dfrac{5}{x^2}$

19. $4x + 12x^{-5}$　or　$4x + \dfrac{12}{x^5}$　　　　**20.** $-2x^{-3} - x^{-2}$　or　$-\dfrac{2}{x^3} - \dfrac{1}{x^2}$

21. $4x^3 + 4x^{-3}$　or　$4x^3 + \dfrac{4}{x^3}$　　　　**22.** $3x^{-1/2} + x^{-3/2}$　or　$\dfrac{3}{\sqrt{x}} + \dfrac{1}{x^{3/2}}$

23. $-3x^{-2} - 4x^{-3} - 2x^{-4/3}$　or　$-\dfrac{3}{x^2} - \dfrac{4}{x^3} - \dfrac{2}{x^{4/3}}$　　　**24.** $-2x^{-2} + \frac{1}{2}x^{-3/2} - x^{-4/3}$　or　$-\dfrac{2}{x^2} + \dfrac{1}{2x^{3/2}} - \dfrac{1}{x^{4/3}}$

25. $24x + 12$　　　　**26.** $2 - 12x^2$　　　　**27.** $36x - 24$　　　　**28.** $2x^{-3}$　or　$\dfrac{2}{x^3}$

29. $2 - 16x^{-3}$　or　$2 - \dfrac{16}{x^3}$　　　　**30.** $-\frac{1}{4}x^{-3/2}$　or　$-\dfrac{1}{4x^{3/2}}$

31. $\frac{3}{4}x^{-5/2} - \frac{1}{4}x^{-3/2}$　or　$\dfrac{3}{4x^{5/2}} - \dfrac{1}{4x^{3/2}}$　　　　**32.** $-2x^{-3/2} - 6x^{-4}$　or　$-\dfrac{2}{x^{3/2}} - \dfrac{6}{x^4}$

33. $-2x^{-5/3} + 8x^{-7/3}$　or　$-\dfrac{2}{x^{5/3}} + \dfrac{8}{x^{7/3}}$　　　**34.** (i) 8　(ii) 6　　　**35.** $\frac{1}{27}$

36. 13　　　**37.** (i) -5　(ii) -4　　　**38.** -8　　　　**39.** 10π　　　**40.** 25π

41. 2　　　**42.** 3　　　**44.** (i) $0, 1$　(ii) $\frac{1}{2}$

1. $4x - 5$　　　　**2.** $3x^2 + 4x - 13$　　　　**3.** $9x^2 - 20x + 17$　　　　**4.** $3x^2 - 6x - 10$

5. $20x^3 - 84x^2 + 30x$　　**6.** $24x^3 - 21x^2 + 4x + 8$　　**7.** $\dfrac{1}{(x+1)^2}$　　**8.** $\dfrac{7}{(x+3)^2}$

9. $\dfrac{-3x^2 + 2x - 6}{(x^2 - 2)^2}$　　**10.** $\dfrac{4x}{(x^2 + 1)^2}$　　**11.** $\dfrac{-x^2 + 2x - 2}{(2x - x^2)^2}$　　**12.** $\dfrac{2(x^2 + 6)}{(x^2 + x - 6)^2}$

13. $12(3x + 2)^3$　　　　**14.** $6(x + 1)(x^2 + 2x)^2$　　　　**15.** $20x(x^2 + 1)^4$

16. $2(4x + 2)^{-1/2}$　or　$\dfrac{2}{\sqrt{4x + 2}}$　　**17.** $\dfrac{-2}{(2x - 5)^2}$　　**18.** $\dfrac{2(1 - x)}{(2x^2 - 4x)^{3/2}}$

19. $6x(x + 1)(x + 3)^3$　　　　**20.** $6(2x + 1)(x + 2)^2$　　　　**21.** $6x(2x + 3)(4x + 3)$

22. $\dfrac{x^2}{\sqrt{2x + 1}} + 2x\sqrt{2x + 1}$　　**23.** $\dfrac{x^2}{\sqrt{1 + x^2}} + \sqrt{1 + x^2}$　　**24.** $-\dfrac{1}{2x^2}\sqrt{\dfrac{x}{x + 1}}$　　**25.** $\frac{3}{16}$　　**26.** $\frac{16}{27}$

Exercise 12.3 ▼

1. $4 \cos 4x$ **2.** $-3 \sin 3x$ **3.** $2 \sec^2 2x$ **4.** $5 \sec 5x \tan 5x$

5. $6 \csc 6x \cot 6x$ **6.** $8 \csc^2 4x$ **7.** $2 \cos(2x - 3)$ **8.** $3 \sec^2(3x + 2)$

9. $2 \sec^2 x + \sec x \tan x$ **10.** $x^2 \cos x + 2x \sin x$ **11.** $3x \sec^2 x + 3 \tan x$

12. $2x \cos 2x - 2x^2 \sin 2x$ **13.** $\dfrac{x \cos x - \sin x}{x^2}$ **14.** $\dfrac{\cos x}{(1 - \sin x)^2}$

15. $\dfrac{1 + \sin x}{\cos^2 x}$ or $\dfrac{1}{1 - \sin x}$ **16.** $-3 \cos^2 x \sin x$

17. $8 \sin 4x \cos 4x$ or $4 \sin 8x$ **18.** $12 \tan^3 3x \sec^2 3x$

19. $6 \sin x \cos x(1 + \sin^2 x)^2$ or $3 \sin 2x(1 + \sin^2 x)^2$ **20.** $\dfrac{\cos x}{2\sqrt{\sin x}}$ **21.** $\dfrac{-\sin 2x}{\sqrt{\cos 2x}}$

25. 0 **26.** 0 **27.** 1

Exercise 12.4 ▼

1. $-\dfrac{x}{y}$ **2.** $\dfrac{x}{y - 1}$ or $\dfrac{-x}{1 - y}$ **3.** $\dfrac{2x}{18y^2 - 1}$ **4.** $\dfrac{x - 2}{3 - y}$ **5.** $\dfrac{-2x - y}{x + 2y}$

6. $\dfrac{-2x + 3y}{-3x + 4y}$ **7.** $\dfrac{5 - 2xy}{x^2}$ **8.** $\dfrac{-2x - y^2}{2xy}$ **9.** $\dfrac{-2xy - y^2}{2xy + x^2}$ **10.** $\frac{3}{4}$

11. 0 **12.** 1 **13.** $-\frac{12}{7}$ **14.** $-\frac{7}{5}$ **15.** $-\dfrac{1}{\pi}$

Exercise 12.5 ▼

1. t **2.** $3t^2$ **3.** $\frac{3}{2}t$ **4.** $\dfrac{1}{3t^2}$

5. $\dfrac{1 - 3t^2}{1 - 2t}$ **6.** $(2t - 1)^2$ **7.** $-t^2(2t + 4)$ **8.** $5\sqrt{t}$

9. $1 - t^2$ **10.** $\dfrac{3t}{3 - t^3}$ **11.** $-\frac{1}{3}$ **12.** $-3t^3;\ -3$

13. $t^2 - 4;\ t = \pm 2$ **16.** $\dfrac{\sin \theta}{1 - \cos \theta}$ **18.** $\frac{4}{3}$ **20.** (i) $-4 \cos \theta$ (ii) $\left(\dfrac{7k}{4}, \dfrac{7k}{8}\right)$

1. $\dfrac{2}{\sqrt{1-4x^2}}$ **2.** $\dfrac{3}{1+9x^2}$ **3.** $\dfrac{1}{\sqrt{2x-x^2}}$ **4.** $\dfrac{1}{2x^2+2x+1}$ **5.** $\dfrac{2x}{1+x^4}$

6. $\dfrac{6x^2}{\sqrt{1-4x^6}}$ **7.** $\dfrac{10\sin^{-1}5x}{\sqrt{1-25x^2}}$ **8.** $\dfrac{3}{x^2+9}$ **9.** $\dfrac{1}{2\sqrt{1-\dfrac{x^2}{4}}}$ or $\dfrac{1}{\sqrt{4-x^2}}$ **10.** -1

11. $\dfrac{x}{\sqrt{1-x^2}}+\sin^{-1}x$ **12.** $\dfrac{12x}{1+4x^2}+6\tan^{-1}2x$ **13.** 4 **15.** $-\tfrac{2}{7}$ **20.** $\dfrac{1}{1+x^2}$

1. $4e^{4x}$ **2.** $6e^{3x}$ **3.** $2xe^{x^2}$ **4.** $(2x-5)e^{x^2-5x}$ **5.** $8xe^{4x^2}$ **6.** $-e^{-x}$ or $-\dfrac{1}{e^x}$

7. $-10e^{-2x}$ or $\dfrac{-10}{e^{2x}}$ **8.** $-4xe^{-x^2}$ or $\dfrac{-4x}{e^{x^2}}$ **9.** $\cos x e^{\sin x}$ **10.** $-2\sin 2x e^{\cos 2x}$

11. $4\sec^2 x e^{4\tan x}$ **12.** $(x\cos x+\sin x)e^{x\sin x}$ **13.** $e^x(1+x)$ **14.** $xe^{5x}(5x+2)$

15. $e^{2x}(2\cos x-\sin x)$ **16.** $e^{-x^2}(\cos x-2x\sin x)$ or $\dfrac{\cos x-2x\sin x}{e^{x^2}}$

17. $2xe^{-2x}(1-x)$ or $\dfrac{2x(1-x)}{e^{2x}}$ **18.** $8xe^{x^2}(3+e^{x^2})^3$ **19.** $\dfrac{4xe^{2x^2}}{(3-e^{2x^2})^2}$

20. $\dfrac{-4e^{4x}}{\sqrt{1-2e^{4x}}}$ **22. (i)** e **(ii)** $-e^2$ **27.** $1, 2$ **32.** -1

1. $\dfrac{1}{x}$ **2.** $\dfrac{2}{2x+3}$ **3.** $\dfrac{2x}{x^2+3}$ **4.** $-\tan x$ **5.** $-\dfrac{1}{x}$ **6.** $\dfrac{e^x}{e^x+2}$

7. $2\cot 2x$ **8.** $\dfrac{3\sec^2 3x}{\tan 3x}$ **9.** 2 **10.** $2+\ln x^2$ **11.** $\dfrac{x^3}{x+1}+3x^2\ln(x+1)$

12. $x+2x\ln 4x$ **13.** $\dfrac{1}{x(x+1)}$ **14.** $\dfrac{4}{2x+3}$ **15.** -1 **16.** $\dfrac{x}{x^2+1}$

17. $\tfrac{1}{2}\cot x$ or $\dfrac{1}{2\tan x}$ **18.** $\dfrac{1}{2x(1+x)}$ **21. (i)** $3e$ **(ii)** 1 **23.** $\dfrac{1}{e}$ **24.** $\tfrac{1}{2}$

25. $-\dfrac{1}{e^3}$ **26.** e **27.** $\dfrac{t}{t+1}$ **28.** 1 **30.** -1 **33.** $a^x(1+a^x)$ **34.** $-\tfrac{5}{3}$

1. $3^x \ln 3$ **2.** $5^x \ln 5$ **3.** $3^{2x}(2 \ln 3)$ **4.** $4^{3x+1}(3 \ln 4)$

5. $2^{\sin x} \cos x \ln 2$ **6.** $\dfrac{2^{\ln x} \ln 2}{x}$ **7.** $(\sin x)^x [x \cot x + \ln(\sin x)]$

8. $2^x x^2 \left(\ln 2 + \dfrac{2}{x} \right)$ or $2^x(x^2 \ln 2 + 2x)$ **9.** $4(1 + \ln 4)$

1. $2x + y - 7 = 0$ **2.** $3x - y + 5 = 0$ **3.** $6x - y + 7 = 0$ **4.** $4x - 6y - 1 = 0$

5. $4x - 3y - 10 = 0$ **6.** $20x - 11y + 2 = 0$ **7.** $x - y + 3 = 0$ **8.** $x - y - 1 = 0$

9. $x - y + 2 = 0$ **10.** $x - y = 0$ **11.** $3x - y + 1 = 0$ **12.** $x - 2y + 1 = 0$

13. $3x - y - 5 = 0$ **14.** $x + y - 2 = 0$ **15.** $2x + y - 4 = 0; x + y + 4 = 0$

16. $3x - 4y - 35 = 0$ **17.** $(0, 0), (-2, 2), x - y = 0; x - y + 4 = 0$ **18.** $(2, 15)$

19. $a = 2; b = -5$ **20.** $p = 3; q = 4$ **21.** $p = 2; q = -8$ **22.** $(0, 2), (0, -2)$

1. **(i)** $x < 1$ **(ii)** $x > 1$ **5.** $-1 < x < 3$ **6.** $x < -3$ or $x > 1$ **9.** $x > \dfrac{1}{e}$

1. $\min(1, 4)$ **2.** $\min(-1, -8)$ **3.** $\max(-3, 19)$ **4.** $\max(1, -1), \min(3, -5), \text{poi}(2, -3)$

5. $\max(2, 16), \min(-2, -16), \text{poi}(0, 0)$ **6.** $\max(1, 17), \min(5, -15), \text{poi}(3, 1)$

7. $\max(0, 2), \min(-2, -2), \text{poi}(-1, 0)$ **8.** $\max(-1, -2), \min(1, 2)$

9. $(0, 0), (2, -16)$ **10.** $\max(0, 0), \min(1, -1), \min(-1, -1), \text{poi}\left(\dfrac{1}{\sqrt{3}}, -\dfrac{5}{9} \right), \text{poi}\left(-\dfrac{1}{\sqrt{3}}, -\dfrac{5}{9} \right)$

11. $\max(2, 1), \min(-\frac{1}{2}, -4)$ **12.** $\min(e, -e)$ **13.** $\max\left(e, \dfrac{1}{e} \right)$ **14.** $\min(0, 1)$

15. $\min\left(-1, -\dfrac{1}{e} \right)$ **16.** $\max\left(2, \dfrac{4}{e^2} \right), \min(0, 0)$ **17.** $\min(e, 0)$ **18.** **(i)** $e^{-x}(1 - x)$

(ii) $e^{-x}(x - 2); \max\left(1, \dfrac{1}{e} \right), \text{poi}\left(2, \dfrac{2}{e^2} \right)$ **19.** 75   **20.** 72   **21.** $a = -3; \max(2, 13)$

22. $p = -2$, $q = 8$, $r = 10$ **23.** $p = 2$, $q = -6$ **24.** $2e^{2x}(\cos 2x - \sin 2x)$; $-8e^{2x} \sin 2x$; $\dfrac{1}{\sqrt{2}} e^{\pi/4}$

25. $\min(0, -1)$ **26.** $\left(\ln\left(\dfrac{a}{2}\right), f\left(\ln\left(\dfrac{a}{2}\right)\right) \right)$ **28.** $\max\left(0, \dfrac{10k^3}{27}\right)$, $\min\left(\dfrac{k}{3}, \dfrac{k^3}{3}\right)$

Exercise 13.4 ▼

1. $x = -2$; $y = 1$ **2.** $x = 5$; $y = 0$ **3.** $x = 0$; $y = 0$ **4.** $x = 3$; $y = 1$

5. **(i)** $y = 1$; $x = -1$ **6.** **(iii)** $x = 3$; $y = 0$ **(v)** $x_1 + x_2 = 6$ **7.** **(i)** $x = -2$; $y = 0$ **(iv)** $(-4, -2)$

8. **(i)** $x = 2$; $y = 0$ **9.** $x = -4$; $y = 1$; $x \leqslant -6$ or $x \geqslant -2$

Exercise 13.5 ▼

1. 15   **2.** 8   **3.** 100π **4.** **(i)** $3t^2 - 18t + 15$ **(ii)** 15 m/s   **(iii)** 9 m and 23 m   **(iv)** 6 m/s^2

5. **(i)**   21 m/s   **(ii)** $\frac{20}{3}$ seconds   **(iii)** 100 m   **6.** **(i)** $\dfrac{v}{50}$ **(ii)** $\frac{8}{25}$ **7.** **(i)** $\frac{15}{2}$ m   **(ii)** $\frac{85}{9}$ m/s

8. **(i)** $k = 5$ **(ii)** $q = 3$ **9.** $v = 0$ m/s; $a = 16$ m/s^2 **10.** **(i)** 10 m/s   **(ii)** 25 m

11. $\dfrac{2}{(t + 3)^2}$ m/s; 7 seconds   **12.** **(i)** $(20 - 4t)$ rad/s   **(ii)** 5 seconds   **(iii)** 2 rads

---

Exercise 13.6 ▼

7. $20x - 15$ **8.** 6   **9.** 16   **10.** 6   **11.** 2 cm/s   **12.** $\dfrac{dx}{dt} = \dfrac{4}{x}$; $\frac{1}{4}$ cm/s

13. $\frac{1}{32}$ **14.** **(i)** $-\dfrac{5}{\pi r^2}$ cm/h   **(ii)** $-\dfrac{5}{4\pi}$ cm/h   **(iii)** -8 cm^2/h

15. $\dfrac{dA}{dt} = 12$ cm^2/s; $\dfrac{dV}{dt} = 15$ cm^3/s   **16.** $\dfrac{1}{5\pi}$ cm/s   **17.** 12 cm^3/s

---

Exercise 13.7 ▼

1. 1.75   **2.** 0.56   **3.** $\frac{23}{45}$ **4.** 3.104   **5.** $\frac{7}{4}$ **6.** $\frac{16}{7}$ **7.** $\frac{28}{9}$ **8.** $\frac{9}{8}$

9. 2; $\frac{5}{3}$ **10.** $\frac{1}{3}$; $\frac{29}{90}$ **11.** $\frac{3}{4}$; $\frac{133}{170}$ **12.** $\frac{7}{3}$; $\frac{163}{72}$ **13.** $a = 2$; $\frac{91}{72}$ **14.** $k = 8$; $\frac{50}{19}$ **15.** $a = 2$

16. **(a)** $\dfrac{2x^2 + 4x}{x + 1}$ **(b)** 1.65   **17.** **(i)** $\max(0, k)$; $\min(2, k - 4)$; poi$(1, k - 2)$ **(ii)** $0 \leqslant k \leqslant 4$ **(iii)** $\frac{25}{9}$

Exercise 14.1 ▼

1. $\frac{1}{4}x^4 + c$ **2.** $\frac{1}{3}x^3 + c$ **3.** $x^5 + c$ **4.** $-\frac{1}{2}x^2 + c$ **5.** $-\frac{2}{3}x^3 + c$

6. $5x + c$ **7.** $-2x + c$ **8.** $-\frac{1}{x} + c$ **9.** $\frac{2}{3}x^{3/2} + c$ **10.** $4\sqrt{x} + c$

11. $x^3 + 4x^2 + c$ **12.** $\frac{1}{3}x^3 + x^2 + c$ **13.** $\frac{2}{3}x^3 - \frac{5}{2}x^2 + c$

14. $\frac{1}{3}x^3 + \frac{1}{x} + c$ **15.** $x^4 + \frac{1}{x^2} + c$ **16.** $\frac{2}{3}x^{3/2} + 2\sqrt{x} + c$

17. $x^2 + \frac{1}{3}x^3 + c$ **18.** $\frac{1}{4}x^4 + \frac{5}{3}x^3 + c$ **19.** $\frac{2}{5}x^{5/2} + \frac{2}{3}x^{3/2} + c$

20. $x - \frac{1}{x^3} + c$ **21.** $-\frac{1}{x} - \frac{1}{2x^2} + c$ **22.** $\frac{6}{5}x^{5/2} - 10\sqrt{x} + c$

23. $\frac{1}{4}x^4 - \frac{2}{3}x^3 + \frac{1}{2}x^2 + c$ **24.** $\frac{1}{3}x^3 - 2x - \frac{1}{x} + c$ **25.** $\frac{1}{5}x^5 + x^2 - \frac{1}{x} + c$

26. $x^3 - x^2 + 5$ **27.** $x^3 - \frac{2}{3}x^{3/2} + 4$ **28.** $t^4 - 3t^2 + 4$

29. $4x^4 + x^2 + x + 2$ **30.** $x^3 + 4x + 2$

Exercise 14.2 ▼

1. 7 **2.** 16 **3.** $\frac{15}{4}$ **4.** $\frac{14}{3}$ **5.** $\frac{32}{3}$ **6.** -18 **7.** $\frac{16}{3}$

8. $\frac{1}{6}$ **9.** 0 **10.** $\frac{25}{4}$ **11.** -1 **12.** 7 **13.** $\frac{29}{6}$ **14.** -9

15. $\frac{7}{8}$ **16.** 5 **17.** $\frac{1}{2}(2x+3); 5$ **18.** $x^2 + 2x + 4; \frac{16}{3}$ **19.** 3 **20.** 2 **21.** 5

Exercise 14.3 ▼

1. $\frac{1}{5}(x+1)^5 + c$ **2.** $\frac{1}{4}(x^2-4)^4 + c$ **3.** $\frac{1}{4}(2x^2-3)^4 + c$ **4.** $\frac{1}{6}(x^3+1)^6 + c$

5. $\frac{1}{6}(4x+3)^{3/2} + c$ **6.** $\frac{2}{3}(4x+3)^{3/2} + c$ **7.** $\frac{1}{3}(x^2-3)^{3/2} + c$ **8.** $\frac{-1}{5(x^3+2x)^5} + c$

9. $\frac{2}{9}(x^3-2)^{3/2} + c$ **10.** $\frac{2}{3}(x-3)^{3/2} + 6(x-3)^{1/2} + c$ **11.** $\frac{1}{12}(x^2+1)^6 + c$ **12.** $\sqrt{x^2+3}$ or $(x^2+3)^{1/2}$

13. $\frac{-1}{(1+x^2)^2} + c$ **14.** $\frac{1}{7}(x+3)^7 - \frac{1}{2}(x+3)^6 + c$ **15.** $\frac{1}{6}(x-2)^6 + \frac{2}{5}(x-2)^5 + c$

16. $\frac{2}{3}(x+4)^{3/2} - 8(x+4)^{1/2} + c$ **17.** $\frac{609}{4}$ **18.** $\frac{6545}{12}$ **19.** $\frac{7}{72}$ **20.** $\frac{63}{12}$ **21.** $\frac{19}{3}$ **22.** 2

1. $\frac{1}{2}\sin 2x + c$ **2.** $-\frac{1}{4}\cos 4x + c$ **3.** $\sin 3x + c$ **4.** $-\frac{1}{2}\cos(2x+3) + c$

5. $\frac{1}{5}\sin(5x+4) + c$ **6.** $-\frac{1}{8}\cos\left(8x - \dfrac{\pi}{4}\right) + c$ **7.** $\frac{1}{4}\sin 4\theta + \frac{1}{2}\cos 2\theta + c$ **8.** $4\sin 2\theta + \cos 8\theta + c$

9. $-\frac{1}{6}\cos 6x - \frac{1}{2}\cos 2x + c$ **10.** $-\frac{1}{7}\cos 7x + \frac{1}{5}\cos 5x + c$ **11.** $\frac{1}{4}\sin 2x - \frac{1}{16}\sin 8x + c$

12. $\frac{1}{10}\sin 5x + \frac{1}{2}\sin x + c$ **13.** $\frac{1}{2}x + \frac{1}{4}\sin 2x + c$ **14.** $\theta - \frac{1}{4}\sin 4\theta + c$

15. $2x - \frac{1}{3}\sin 6x + c$ **16.** $\frac{1}{2}\theta + \frac{1}{20}\sin 10\theta + c$ **17.** $\dfrac{1}{\sqrt{2}}$ **18.** 0 **19.** $\frac{3}{2}$

20. $\frac{3}{5}$ **21.** $\frac{7}{24}$ **22.** $\dfrac{\pi}{8} + \dfrac{1}{4}$ **23.** $\dfrac{\pi}{12}$ **24.** $\dfrac{\pi}{4}$ **25.** **(i)** $\frac{1}{3}$ **(ii)** 3 **26.** $\frac{1}{3}\sin^3 x; \frac{2}{3}$

1. $\frac{1}{3}e^x + c$ **2.** $\frac{1}{2}e^{2x+3} + c$ **3.** $-\frac{1}{4}e^{-4x} + c$ **4.** $-\frac{1}{3}e^{1-3x} + c$ **5.** $-\frac{1}{2}e^{-2x} + c$

6. $4e^{x/2} + c$ **7.** $\frac{1}{2}e^{2x} + e^x + c$ **8.** $\frac{1}{3}e^{3x} + \frac{1}{3}e^{-3x} + c$ **9.** $e^{x^3} + c$ **10.** $e^{x^2+3x} + c$

11. $e^{x+\sin x} + c$ **12.** $\frac{1}{2}(e^2 - 1)$ **13.** $\dfrac{1}{3}\left(e^2 - \dfrac{1}{e^4}\right)$ **14.** $\dfrac{1}{4}\left(e^7 - \dfrac{1}{e}\right)$ **15.** $e^2 - e$

16. $e^2 + \dfrac{2}{e^2} - 3$ **17.** $\frac{1}{2}(e^3 - 1)$ **18.** $e - 1$ **19.** $\ln\left(\dfrac{1+e}{2}\right)$ **20.** $\ln(\frac{5}{4})$ **21.** $2(e - 1)$

1. $\ln(x + 2) + c$ **2.** $3\ln(x - 5) + c$ **3.** $\frac{1}{2}\ln x + c$ **4.** $\ln(4x + 5) + c$

5. $\ln(x^2 + 1) + c$ **6.** $2\ln(4x + 3) + c$ **7.** $-\ln(1 - 2x) + c$ **8.** $\frac{1}{2}\ln(1 + x^2) + c$

9. $\ln 2$ **10.** $5\ln 5$ **11.** $\ln(\frac{9}{2})$ **12.** $\ln 2$ **13.** $\frac{3}{2} + \ln 2; 4$

14. **(i)** $6 - \ln 16$ **(ii)** $1 + 2\ln 2$ **(iii)** $2 - \ln 2$ **15.** **(i)** $\frac{1}{2}$ **(ii)** $\frac{1}{2}$

1. $\sin^{-1}\left(\dfrac{x}{2}\right) + c$ **2.** $\sin^{-1}\left(\dfrac{x}{3}\right) + c$ **3.** $\sin^{-1}\left(\dfrac{x}{5}\right) + c$ **4.** $\dfrac{1}{4}\tan^{-1}\left(\dfrac{x}{4}\right) + c$

5. $\tan^{-1}\left(\dfrac{x}{3}\right) + c$ **6.** $2\tan^{-1}\left(\dfrac{x}{5}\right) + c$ **7.** $\dfrac{1}{6}\tan^{-1}\left(\dfrac{2x}{3}\right) + c$ **8.** $\dfrac{1}{12}\tan^{-1}\left(\dfrac{3x}{4}\right) + c$

9. $\dfrac{1}{5}\sin^{-1}\left(\dfrac{5x}{2}\right) + c$ **10.** $\frac{1}{4}\tan^{-1}(4x) + c$ **11.** $\tan^{-1}(2x) + c$ **12.** $\sin^{-1}\left(\dfrac{4x}{3}\right) + c$

13. $\dfrac{\pi}{8}$ **14.** $\dfrac{\pi}{12}$ **15.** $\dfrac{\pi}{6}$ **16.** $\dfrac{\pi}{3}$ **17.** $\dfrac{\pi}{12}$ **18.** $\dfrac{\pi}{6}$

19. $\dfrac{\pi}{2}$ **20.** $\dfrac{\pi}{24}$ **21.** $\dfrac{\pi}{10}$ **22.** 5 **23.** 3 **24.** $\frac{4}{3}$

1. $(x+2)^2 + 3^2$ **2.** $(x+4)^2 + 3^2$ **3.** $(x-3)^2 + 1^2$ **4.** $(x-1)^2 + 4^2$

5. $3^2 - (x+1)^2$ **6.** $4^2 - (x+3)^2$ **7.** $6^2 - (x-5)^2$ **8.** $4^2 - (x-4)^2$

9. $\dfrac{\pi}{16}$ **10.** $\dfrac{\pi}{12}$ **11.** $\dfrac{\pi}{2}$ **12.** $\dfrac{\pi}{3}$ **13.** π **14.** π

15. $p = 2, q = 3; \frac{1}{3}\tan^{-1}(\frac{1}{3})$ **16.** $4^2 - (x+3)^2; 2\pi$ **17.** 1

1. π **2.** $\dfrac{9\pi}{4}$ **3.** $\dfrac{25\pi}{4}$ **4.** $\dfrac{\pi}{8} + \dfrac{1}{4}$ **5.** $\dfrac{\pi}{8}$

6. $\dfrac{\pi}{3}$ **7.** $\dfrac{9\pi}{16}$ **8.** $\dfrac{\pi}{2} + 1$ **9.** $3\pi + \dfrac{9\sqrt{3}}{2}$ **10.** $\dfrac{8\pi}{3} + 2\sqrt{3}$

1. $\frac{21}{2}$ **2.** 9 **3.** 120 **4.** 13 **5.** $\frac{37}{12}$ **6.** $\frac{32}{3}$ **7.** $\frac{19}{3}$

8. 9 **9.** $\frac{39}{4}$ **10.** 18 **11.** $\frac{9}{2}$ **12.** $\frac{32}{3}$ **13.** (i) $2, 4; \frac{4}{3}$

14. (i) $a(1, 4), b(2, 7)$ (iii) $\frac{1}{6}$ **15.** 13 **16.** $\frac{8}{3}$ **17.** $\frac{9}{2}$

18. $\frac{32}{3}$ **19.** $\frac{14}{3}$ **20.** $6 - \ln 2$ **21.** $k = 6$ **22.** $p = 6$

23. (i) $a(2, 0), b(4, 8); \frac{32}{3}$ **25.** (i) 9π (ii) $\sqrt{r^2 - x^2}$

1. $\frac{256}{3}\pi$ **2.** $\frac{8}{3}\pi$ **3.** $\frac{112}{3}\pi$ **4.** (i) 4π (ii) 6π

5. 36π **6.** 45π **7.** $\frac{11}{3}\pi$ **8.** $a=5, b=4; \frac{20}{3}\pi$

9. $y=\dfrac{r}{h}x$ or $rx-hy=0$ **11.** 252π cm^3 **12.** (i) $(1,\sqrt{3}), (1,-\sqrt{3})$ (ii) $6\sqrt{3}\pi$

Exercise 16.1 ▼

1. 3,628,800 **2.** 28 **3.** 380 **4.** 300 **5.** $a=9; b=20$

6. $p=1; q=0$ **7.** $a=2$ **8.** $k=2$ **9.** $a=20$ **10.** 12

11. 5 **12.** 6 **13.** 10

Exercise 16.2 ▼

1. 10 **2.** 35 **3.** 28 **4.** 1 **5.** 4 **6.** 1 **7.** 792

8. 1140 **9.** 50 **10.** 4950 **12.** 6 **13.** 5 **14.** 5 **15.** 2

16. 7 **17.** 7 **18.** 7 **19.** 6 **20.** 8 **25.** 8

Exercise 16.3 ▼

1. $a^4 + 4a^3b + 6a^2b^2 + 4ab^3 + b^4$ **2.** $x^5 + 5x^4y + 10x^3y^2 + 10x^2y^3 + 5xy^4 + y^5$

3. $p^6 + 6p^5q + 15p^4q^2 + 20p^3q^3 + 15p^2q^4 + 6pq^5 + q^6$

4. $x^7 - 7x^6y + 21x^5y^2 - 35x^4y^3 + 35x^3y^4 - 21x^2y^5 + 7xy^6 - y^7$

5. $1 + 8x + 24x^2 + 32x^3 + 16x^4$ **6.** $1 - 12x + 54x^2 - 108x^3 + 81x^4$

7. $1 - 12x + 60x^2 - 160x^3 + 240x^4 - 192x^5 + 64x^6$ **8.** $1 - 20x + 150x^2 - 500x^3 + 625x^4$

9. $81 + 108y + 54y^2 + 12y^3 + y^4$

10. $64 - 192x + 240x^2 - 160x^3 + 60x^4 - 12x^5 + x^6$ **11.** $16 + 96y + 216y^2 + 216y^3 + 81y^4$

12. $32x^5 - 240x^4y + 720x^3y^2 - 1080x^2y^3 + 810xy^4 - 243y^5$

13. $1 + 3x + \frac{15}{4}x^2 + \frac{5}{2}x^3 + \frac{15}{16}x^4 + \frac{3}{16}x^5 + \frac{1}{64}x^6$ **14.** $p^5 + 5p^3 + 10p + \dfrac{10}{p} + \dfrac{5}{p^3} + \dfrac{1}{p^5}$

15. $x^8 + 16x^6 + 112x^4 + 448x^2 + 1120 + \dfrac{1792}{x^2} + \dfrac{1792}{x^4} + \dfrac{1024}{x^6} + \dfrac{256}{x^8}$

16. $16a^4 - \dfrac{32a^3}{b} + \dfrac{24a^2}{b^2} - \dfrac{8a}{b^3} + \dfrac{1}{b^4}$

17. $2 + 12x^2 + 2x^4$

18. $p = 2,\ q = 80,\ r = 160$

19. $p = 2,\ q = 12,\ r = 2$

20. $1 + 24a + 264a^2$

21. $1 - 5a + \frac{45}{4}a^2$

22. $x^{18} + 18x^{15} + 144x^{12}$

23. $\dfrac{x^4}{16} + x^2 + 6 + \dfrac{16}{x^2} + \dfrac{16}{x^4}$; the term 6 is independent of x.

Exercise 16.4 ▼

1. $17 + 12\sqrt{2}$ **2.** $76 - 44\sqrt{3}$ **3.** $576 + 256\sqrt{5}$ **4.** $196 + 80\sqrt{6}$

5. $433 + 228\sqrt{2}$ **6.** $4096 - 2220\sqrt{3}$ **7.** $1351 + 780\sqrt{3}$ **8.** $89\sqrt{3} - 109\sqrt{2}$

9. 56   **10.** 1686   **11.** 198

12. $a^5 + 5a^4b + 10a^3b^2 + 10a^2b^3 + 5ab^4 + b^5$; $20x + 160x^3 + 64x^5$; $1076\sqrt{3}$

13. $2p^4 + 12p^2q^2 + 2q^4$; $16x^4 + 16x^2 + 2$; 4354

Exercise 16.5 ▼

1. $n = 6,\ a = 15,\ b = -20$ **2.** $n = 4,\ a = 5$ **3.** $n = 7,\ a = 4$

4. $n = 6,\ k = -3$ **5.** $n = 10,\ k = 2,\ a = 960$ **6.** $n = 10,\ a = -\frac{1}{2}$

7. $n = 16,\ a = \frac{1}{2}$ **8.** $n = 16,\ a = 270,\ b = -1890$ **9.** $n = 16,\ k = \frac{1}{8}$

10. $k = 3,\ a = 18,\ b = 540$ or $k = -3,\ a = -18,\ b = -540$ **11.** $a = 2,\ b = -4,\ c = -20$

12. $n = 8$

Exercise 16.6 ▼

1. $160x^3$ **2.** $2016a^5b^4$ **3.** $264x^{10}y^2$ **4.** $28x^{12}$

5. $-x$ **6.** 70   **7.** $-\dfrac{252}{x^5}$ **8.** $15x^3$

9. $1 + 21x + 189x^2$; 99   **10.** (i) $\frac{5}{16}$ (ii) 51   **11.** $8064x^5$ **12.** $1120a^4b^4$

13. $-8064p^5q^5$ **14.** $-540a^3b^3$ **15.** $-20x^3$ **16.** $20p^3$

17. $1120x^4$ **18.** $\frac{35}{8}x^8$ **19.** 24   **20.** 70

21. 12   **22.** 15   **23.** 84   **24.** 18,564

25. 593,775   **26.** 3003   **27.** $n = 4,\ k = 216$ **28.** $n = 5;\ h = -1620$

29. $1 + 2nx + 2n(n-1)x^2 + \dfrac{4n(n-1)(n-2)}{3}x^3; \ n = 5$

30. $1 + nax + \dfrac{n(n-1)a^2}{2}x^2$ (ii) $\frac{4}{7}$

Exercise 16.7 ▼

6. 2187   **7.** 4096   **8.** 262,144

Exercise 1R.A ▼

1. $\dfrac{x^2}{x^2+4}$ **2.** $y^2 - 4y$ **3.** $x = 3, y = -1$ **4.** $x = \frac{1}{2}, y = 2$ or $x = -3, y = -5$

5. $2\sqrt{2} - 3$ **6.** $-\sqrt{3}$ **7.** 4 **8. (i)** 1 **(ii)** 3 **(iii)** 1

9. (i) $4, -\frac{10}{3}$ **(ii)** 4 **(iii)** $\sqrt{3}, \dfrac{\sqrt{3}}{4}$ **(iv)** 4 **(v)** $-\frac{1}{2}$ **(vi)** $\frac{5}{2}, \frac{1}{4}$

10. $2, 12; -4, -2, 1, 3$ **11.** $4, 5; 16, 25$ **12.** $-2, 7; -1, 2$ **13.** $a = 2, b = -9, c = -5$

14. $a = 2, b = -3, c = -11, d = 6$ **15.** $k = -8; (x+6)(x-2)$ **16.** $(2-x)(1+x)$

17. $x < -4$ **18.** $x > -2$ **19.** $x > -\frac{7}{5}$ **20.** $-1 \leqslant x \leqslant 4$ **21.** $-1 \leqslant x \leqslant 2$

22. $-\frac{3}{2} < x \leqslant 2$ **23.** $-4 \leqslant x \leqslant 2$ **24.** $0 < x < \frac{3}{2}$ **25.** $x < -\frac{3}{2}$ or $x \geqslant \frac{3}{2}$

26. $x < -\frac{7}{2}$ **27.** $-4 \leqslant x \leqslant 0$ **28.** $x < \frac{1}{2}$ or $x > 2$

29. $x = 1, y = 1$ or $x = -3, y = -3$ **30.** $x = 1, y = 2$ **31.** 3

32. $a = -11; p = -3, q = 2$ **33.** $a = 2, b = -10$ **34.** $p = 2, q = 2, r = -9$

35. $a = 3, b = -4, c = 5$ **36.** $x^4 + \dfrac{1}{x^4}$ **37. (i)** 9 **(ii)** $\frac{1}{16}$ **(iii)** $\frac{27}{8}$ **(iv)** $\frac{27}{2}$

38. -2 **39.** 5 **40. (i)** $\frac{1}{5}$ **(ii)** 3 **(iii)** 4 **(iv)** 27 **41. (i)** $a^2 - 2a$ **(ii)** $a^2 - 3a$

Exercise 1R.B ▼

1. $p + \dfrac{4}{p}$ **2.** $a = 5, b = -2, c = -3$ **3.** $x = -1, y = 3, z = 9; a = -1, b = \pm 2, c = 2$

4. $x = 3, y = 9, z = 15$ **5. (i)** 1 **(ii)** $\frac{1}{2}$ **6.** $m = 7, n = 2; (x+3)$

7. $p = 2, q = -1$ **8.** $(x+1)(x-2)(x-3); a = -6$ or 0 or 6 **9.** 9

10. (i) $-\frac{21}{4}$ **(ii)** $\frac{37}{4}$ **(iii)** $\frac{37}{49}; p = 2, q = -9, r = 2$ **11. (a)** $p^2 - 2q$ **12.** $x = 2, y = -4$

13. $x = 2, y = 1$ **14.** $\frac{5}{2}$ **15. (i)** $8y$ **(ii)** y^2 **(iii)** $2y^2; -1, 2$

16. (i) $1, 2$ **(ii)** $0, 2$ **(iii)** $0, 1$ **(iv)** $-2, 3$ **17. (i)** 1 **(ii)** 8 **(iii)** 0

22. $x < 3$ or $x > 5$ **23.** $-\frac{1}{2} < x < 2$ **23.** $0 < x < 4$

25. $x \leqslant -1$ or $x \geqslant 1$ **26.** $1 < x < 2$ **27.** $x < -9$ or $x > 5$

28. $1, 2, 3, 4, 5$ **29.** $\pm \dfrac{x}{\sqrt{1 - x^2}}; -1 < x < 1$ **30.** $-2 \leqslant k \leqslant 4$

31. (i) $-\frac{1}{2}, 1$ **(ii)** $-3, \frac{9}{2}$ **33.** $k = -1; \pm 2$ **34.** $\dfrac{q}{2p}, -\dfrac{q}{p}; px^2 + qx - q^2 = 0$

37. (i) 2 **(ii)** 1 **(iii)** 5 **(iv)** $3, 27$ **38.** $x = 7, y = 2$ or $x = -\frac{1}{2}, y = \frac{1}{2}$

Exercise 1R.C ▼

4. (i)   **(a)** $-2k$ **(b)** $k + 2$ **(c)** $4k^2 - 2k - 4$ **(iii)** $(k + 2)x^2 - 4k^2x + 4k^2 = 0$ **(iv)** -2 or 3

5. $kx^2 - 5x + 1 = 0; k \leqslant \frac{25}{4}$ **6. (i)** $(\alpha + \beta)(\alpha^2 - \alpha\beta + \beta^2); -8$

7. $p = -8, q = 19, r = -12$ **11.** $a = 9 - k^2, b = 9k; 3$ or 6 **13.** $a = 2, b = -3$ **20.** 5

24. (i) $(a + b)(a^2 - ab + b^2)$ **(ii)** $ab(a + b)$

25. (i) $(a - b)(a + b); (a - b)(a + b)(a^2 + b^2)$ **(ii)** $(a - b)^2(a + b)(a^2 + b^2)$

27. $a^2 + 2ab + b^2 - c^2; 1, \dfrac{a + b - c}{a + b + c}$

28. (i) -1 and $\dfrac{p - r - t}{p + r - t}, -1$ is rational and $\dfrac{p - r - t}{p + r - t}$ is rational as the top and bottom are integers and $(p + r - t) \neq 0$ **(ii)** -1 is an integer

29. (ii) $k = 2; -2, -1$ **31.** $x = 2, y = 1$ **32.** $p(p^2 - 3q)$

Exercise 2R.A ▼

1. no   **2.** $19x + 38y + 1 = 0$ **3.** $\frac{1}{5}$ **4.** 5 **5.** $11x - 33y - 19 = 0$

6. 5 **7 (i)** $(3, 5)$ **(ii)** $(15, 13)$ **8.** $(10, -4)$ **9.** $x - 2y + 4 = 0$

10. -5 **11.** $3x - 7y - 23 = 0$ **13.** $x + 2y - 5 = 0$ **14.** $4\frac{1}{2}$ **15.** $4x + 12y - 1 = 0$

16. $45°$ or $\dfrac{\pi}{4}$ **17.** $81x + 54y - 217 = 0$ **18.** -2 or $\frac{14}{3}$

1. $4x + 5y + 2 = 0$; $(-\frac{1}{2}, 0)$; $3 : 1$ **2.** $(4, -2)$ **3. (i)** 3 **(ii)** $(1, 2)$ **(iii)** 6

4. -2 or 1 **5.** $mx - y + (5 - 2m)$; $m = -\frac{1}{2}$ or $m = -\frac{25}{2}$

6. $5x + 8y + 21 = 0$ or $5x + 8y - 59 = 0$ **7. (i)** $13x + 17y - 6 = 0$ **(ii)** $k = -1$

8. (i) $(-2, 4)$ **(ii)** $(8, 4)$; $(-16, -8)$; $(-32, -16)$ **9. (i)** $(0, 0)$, $(3, 1)$; $(-2, 4)$ **(ii)** no **(iii)** no

10. $a(-2, 2)$, $b(-1, -1)$, $c(2, 5)$, $d(1, 8)$

1. $2x - y + 1 = 0$ or $2x - 11y + 51 = 0$ **2.** $x + 2y - 9 = 0$; $2x - y - 8 = 0$; $3x + y - 17 = 0$; $\frac{125}{2}$

3. $\frac{13}{2}$ or $-\frac{17}{2}$ **4. (i)** $k = 2$ **(ii)** $(2, 12)$ **5. (i)** $-\dfrac{t}{t-2}$ or $\dfrac{t}{2-t}$ **(ii)** -2 or $\frac{4}{3}$

6. (a) $\frac{1}{4}$ or 2; $49°$ **7. (ii)** $y = \dfrac{2x + 23}{5}$ **(iii)** $(6, 7)$ **8. (ii)** yes **9. (i)** yes

10. $(0, 0)$, $(-3, -9)$, $(7, 17)$ **(i)** $17x' - 7y' = 0$ **(ii)** $31x + 5y + 87 = 0$

11. (i) $(0, 0)$, $(3, 1)$, $(4, -1)$, $(1, -2)$ **(ii)** $x = \dfrac{2x' + y'}{7}$; $y = \dfrac{x' - 3y'}{7}$ **(v)** 7

12. $x' = 8 - 13t$; $y' = 6 - t$; $0 \leqslant t \leqslant 1$. $(\frac{5}{2}, \frac{1}{2})$; yes

13. $2x - y = 0$; $a(0, 0)$, $b(1, 2)$, $c(2, 4)$; $x = t$, $y = -t$; $0 \leqslant t \leqslant 1$; yes

1. 23.14 **3.** $30°, 330°$ **4.** $150°$ **6.** $\dfrac{t}{\sqrt{t^2 + 4}}$ **7.** $k = 2$ **8.** -1

9. (i) $\frac{5}{2}$ **(ii)** $143°$ **10.** $\frac{3}{2}$ rads **11.** 2π cm **12.** $\dfrac{1}{\sqrt{3}}$ **13.** $82.8°$

14. (i) $\frac{117}{125}$ **(ii)** $-\frac{44}{125}$ **(iii)** $-\frac{3}{4}$ **15.** $\frac{24}{25}$ **16. (i)** 3 **(ii)** $\frac{1}{5}$ **(iii)** 2 **(iv)** $\frac{7}{2}$ **(v)** 2 **(vi)** $\frac{11}{2}$

1. $0°, 60°, 300°, 360°$ **2.** $\dfrac{\pi}{2}, \pi, \dfrac{3\pi}{2}$ **3.** (i) $1 - 2\sin^2 x$ (ii) $0°, 180°, 210°, 330°, 360°$

4. (i) $2\sin 4x \cos x$ (ii) $0°, 45°, 90°, 135°, 180°$ **5.** (i) $60°, 300°$ (ii) $30°, 150°, 210°, 330°$

6. $76°, 180°$ **7.** $120°, 180°, 240°$ **8.** $a = 2, b = 1; 0°, 60°, 120°, 180°, 240°, 300°, 360°$

9. (i) $2 + \sqrt{3}$ (ii) $2 - \sqrt{3}$ **10.** $\frac{4}{3}; \frac{5}{12}$ **11.** (ii) $l = -1, k = 2$ **13.** (i) 3.96 (ii) $121°$

14. $60°, 120°; 2:1$ **15.** (i) $30°, 150°$ (ii) $4.1; 13.5$ **16.** (i) $\frac{1}{8}$ (ii) $a = 3, b = 8$

17. $33.4°$ **18.** $(15\pi - 9)\ \text{cm}^2$ **19.** (i) $3.86\ \text{cm}$ (ii) $2\ \text{cm}$ **20.** $100\left(\dfrac{\sqrt{3}}{2} - \dfrac{\pi}{6}\right)$

23. $\dfrac{\pi}{3}, \dfrac{4\pi}{3}$ **24.** (i) 1 (ii) $\frac{56}{33}$

1. $9\left(\dfrac{\pi}{3} - \dfrac{\sqrt{3}}{2}\right)$ **2.** (i) $\sin A = \frac{4}{5}, \tan A = -\frac{4}{3}$ (as $90° < A < 180°$) (ii) $\frac{11}{2}$

4. $\dfrac{1}{\sqrt{2}}(\sin A + \cos A)$ **5.** $-\frac{1}{2}(1 + \sin 2A)$ **6.** $15°, 75°$ **8.** $10\sqrt{3}\ \text{m}$

9. (i) $|pr| = \dfrac{h}{\sqrt{3}}; |qr| = \sqrt{3}h$ (ii) $\sqrt{\dfrac{8h^2}{3}}\ \text{or}\ \dfrac{2\sqrt{2}}{\sqrt{3}}h$ **13.** (i) $60°$ (ii) $60\sqrt{3}$ (iii) $110\pi + 120\sqrt{3}$

14. (i) $20\ \text{m}$ (ii) $30.6\ \text{m}$ **15.** $2\sin(A + B)\cos(A - B)$

1. $\dfrac{2}{(x + 1)^2}$ **2.** $12(4x - 1)^2$ **3.** $3x^2 + \dfrac{1}{\sqrt{x}}$ **4.** $8e^{2x + 1}$

5. $x\cos x + \sin x$ **6.** $\dfrac{x + 2}{x} + \ln x$ **7.** $e^x(2\cos 2x + \sin 2x)$

8. $x(x^2 + 1)^{-1/2}\ \text{or}\ \dfrac{x}{\sqrt{x^2 + 1}}$ **9.** $e^x\left(\dfrac{1}{x} + \ln x\right)$ **10.** $(x\cos x + \sin x)e^{x\sin x}$

11. $6\sin 3x \cos 3x$ or $3\sin 6x$ **12.** $8x\sec^2 4x^2$ **13.** $24x\tan^2 4x^2 \sec^2 4x^2$

14. $3(2x^2 - 1)^{-1/2} - 6x^2(2x^2 - 1)^{-3/2}\ \text{or}\ \dfrac{-3}{(2x^2 - 1)^{3/2}}$ **15.** $\dfrac{2}{\sqrt{1 - 4x^2}}$ **16.** $\dfrac{-1}{x^2 + 1}$

17. $2x - y - 3 = 0$ **18.** $2x - y - 2 = 0$ **19.** $\frac{8}{3}$ **20.** $52\ \text{rads/sec}$ **21.** 9

22. $\frac{5}{4}$ **23.** 3 **24.** 27 **25.** 3 **26.** 2

28. $6; [-2, 4]$ (i) -2 (ii) -1 (iii) 4 (iv) -1 (v) -1 (vi) $4; 5$

1. $\dfrac{\sec^2 x}{1 + \tan x}$ 2. $\dfrac{\cos x}{1 + \sin^2 x}$ 3. $\dfrac{x}{\sqrt{1 - x^2}} + \sin^{-1} x$ 4. $\dfrac{2x^2}{2x + 1} + 2x \ln(2x + 1)$

5. 2.57 6. $\frac{4}{3}; \frac{91}{72}$ 7. $\frac{3}{2}$ 8. $20x - 11y + 2 = 0$

10. (i) $\frac{1}{2}e^{x/2}$ (ii) 0 12. $x < -4$ and $x > 2$ 13. (i) 32 (ii) 24 14. $k = -\frac{3}{2}$

17. 2 19. $-\sin 4x$ 20. $a = 1, b = 2$ 22. $-\frac{7}{24}$

25. $\frac{3}{4}$ 26. (i) -1 27. (i) $\dfrac{1 + \sin t}{\cos^2 t} ; \dfrac{-1 - \cos t}{\sin^2 t}$ (ii) -2

28. (i) $-3 \cos^2 t \sin t; \; 3 \sin^2 t \cos t$ (ii) $a = 9, b = 4$

31. 94 32. 50 33. $(0, 0), (-3, -27); (0, 0), (-2, -16)$ 34. $\left(-1, -\dfrac{1}{2e}\right), \left(3, \dfrac{e^3}{6}\right)$

35. maximum $\left(1, \dfrac{1}{e}\right)$; inflection point $\left(2, \dfrac{2}{e^2}\right)$ 36.(i) 24 m/s (ii) 5 secs (iii) 75 m

37. (i) 12 m/s (ii) 20 secs 38. $-\dfrac{5}{96\pi}$ 39. (i) $2s + 5$ (ii) 4 (iii) $8s + 20$

40. $12(2x^2 - 2x + 1)^2$ or $48x^4 - 96x^3 + 96x^2 - 48x + 12$ 42. $5\sqrt{2}$ 43. (i) $3e$ (ii) $6e^4$

44. $\frac{1}{2}$ cm/s 45. $\frac{1}{25}$ cm/s 46. 24 cm^3/s

1. (i) $x = -1; y = 0$ 2. (i) $x = -2, y = 1$; (iii) $x < -2 - 2\sqrt{2}$ or $x > -2 + 2\sqrt{2}$

7. $\dfrac{1}{x}; k = e$ 8. (i) $4 \cos 4\theta + 4 \cos 2\theta$ (ii) $4 \sin 2\theta - 4 \sin 4\theta$ 9. $k = 6$

10. (i) 0 or $\dfrac{5k}{3}$ (ii) (b) $k = -4$ 11. $k = 4$ 12. $\left(\dfrac{1}{a}, \dfrac{1}{ae}\right); \left(\dfrac{2}{a}, \dfrac{2}{ae^2}\right)$ 14. $8\sqrt{2}$

15. $2x - y + 2 = 0$ 17. (i) $e^{3x}(3 \cos 2x - 2 \sin 2x)$ (ii) $e^{3x}(2 \cos 2x + 3 \sin 2x)$

18. $a = 2; b = -6$ 20. $p = 2, q = 1$ or $p = 2, q = -1$ 23. $a = 3, b = 1$

24. (i) $\frac{3}{5}$ (ii) parallel to the y-axis as both x coordinates are equal, both $= \dfrac{k^2 - 1}{k}$, $\therefore$ slope $= 0$

25. 1.417 27. $p = 2, q = -3$ or $p = 10, q = -2$ 28. $a = 2, b = -6, c = 0, d = 4$

Exercise 5R.A

1. $x^3 + c$

2. $2x^2 - 3x + c$

3. $\frac{1}{3}x^3 + 2x + c$

4. $2x^2 + x - \frac{1}{4x^4} + c$

5. $\frac{2}{3}x^3 - \frac{5}{2}x^2 + c$

6. $\frac{1}{3}x^3 - x + c$

7. $\frac{2}{7}x^{7/2} + \frac{2}{3}x^{3/2} + c$

8. $\frac{2}{3}x^3 + \frac{1}{2}x^2 - 3x + c$

9. $\frac{4}{3}x^3 - 2x^2 + x + c$

10. $\frac{1}{3}x^3 + 2x - \frac{1}{x} + c$

11. $x + \frac{1}{2}x^2 + \frac{4}{3}x^{3/2} + c$

12. $\frac{1}{4}x^4 + x^3 + \frac{3}{2}x^2 + x + c$ or $\frac{1}{4}(1+x)^4 + c$

13. $\frac{1}{3}x^3 + 2x - \frac{1}{x} + c$

14. $\frac{2}{3}x^{3/2} + 2x^{1/2} + c$

15. $x^2 + \ln x + c$

16. $-\frac{3}{x} + \frac{10}{3}x^{3/2} + c$

17. $\frac{1}{3}e^{3x} + c$

18. $\frac{1}{5}e^{5x-2} + c$

19. $\frac{1}{4}\sin 4x + c$

20. $-\frac{1}{5}\cos 5x + c$

21. $\sin(6x + 5) + c$

22. $\frac{1}{3}\sin 3x - \frac{1}{2}\cos 2x + c$

23. $4x + \frac{1}{2}\sin 2x + c$

24. $4x + \cos 2x + c$

25. 3

26. 30

27. $\frac{100}{3}$

28. 1

29. $e^2 - 1$

30. $\frac{1}{5}$

Exercise 5R.B

1. $\frac{15}{4}$

2. -20

3. $\frac{16}{15}$

4. $\frac{6}{5}$

5. $\frac{4}{3}$

6. 1

7. $\frac{1}{2}\ln 2$

8. $\frac{1}{2}\ln(\frac{5}{4})$

9. $\frac{1}{3}$

10. $2(e^2 - 1)$

11. $\sqrt{e} - 1$

12. $\frac{1}{2}(e^3 - 1)$

13. $\frac{\sqrt{3}}{4}$

14. $\frac{7}{12}$

15. $\frac{\pi}{2}$

16. $\frac{\pi}{4} + \frac{1}{2}$

17. $6 - 3\ln 3$

18. $\frac{10\sqrt{2}}{3}$

19. $\frac{\pi}{3}$

20. $\frac{\pi}{12}$

21. π

22. $\frac{\pi}{6}$

23. $\frac{\pi}{9}$

24. $\frac{32}{3}$

26. (a) $(x + 1)(x^2 - x + 1)$ **(b)** $\frac{5}{6}$

27. (i) $\frac{1}{3}$ **(ii)** $\frac{2}{3}$

28. $e - 1$

29. $(x + 3)^2 + 2^2; \frac{\pi}{8}$

30. $2^2 - (x - 1)^2; \frac{\pi}{6}$

31. (i) -1 **(ii)** $x^3 - 2x + 10$

32. (i) 3 **(ii)** $\ln(\frac{5}{4})$ **(iii)** $\frac{1}{4}$

33. $\frac{9}{4}$

34. $\frac{\pi}{6}$

35. $\frac{125}{6}$

36. 16

37. 36

38. $\frac{4}{3}$

39. $\frac{32}{3}$

40. $(0, 0); \ln(\frac{9}{2})$

41. 32

43. (i) $p(2, 0), q(3, \frac{1}{2})$ **(ii)** $\frac{1}{2}\ln 2$

Exercise 5R.C

1. 1

2. $\frac{7}{4}$

3. $\frac{\pi}{12}$

4. $\frac{\pi}{12}$

5. $\frac{8}{3}$

6. $\ln 2 - \frac{1}{2}$

7. $2\ln(\frac{3}{2})$

8. $\ln 2$

9. (i) 4 **(ii)** $\frac{1}{\sqrt{2}}$ **(iii)** $\frac{\pi}{12}$

10. (i) $\frac{2\pi}{3} + \frac{\sqrt{3}}{2}$ **(ii)** $\frac{\pi}{3} - \frac{\sqrt{3}}{2}$

11. $\ln\left(\frac{e+1}{2}\right)$

12. $12 - \ln 4$ **13.** $p = 3$ **14.** $(1, 1); \frac{1}{3}$ **15.** (i) $p(2, 0), q(4, -8)$ (ii) $\frac{4}{3}$ (iii) $10\frac{2}{3}$

16. $\frac{32}{3}\pi$ **17.** $a = \pm 2$ **18.** $k = -1$ or $k = -5$ **19.** $b = \pm\sqrt{a - 1}$

20. $3\sqrt{3}$ **21.** $k = 3$ **22.** $a(1, 0), b(e, 1); x = e^y$; (i) $e - 1$ (ii) 1 **23.** $k = \sqrt{3}$

Exercise 6R.A ▼

1. 40 **2.** 56 **3.** 7 **4.** $1 - 16x + 112x^2$ **5.** $10x + 20x^3 + 2x^5$

6. $362 + 209\sqrt{3}$ **7.** $1 + 10x + 40x^2 + 80x^3 + 80x^4 + 32x^5; a = 841, b = 538$

8. 970 **9.** 924 **10.** -15 **11.** $4845x^4$ **12.** 84 **13.** 495

14. $n = 6; a = -\frac{3}{2}$ **15.** -6 **16.** $p = 3, q = 1$ **17.** $r = 5$ or $r = 2$ **18.** 5

Exercise 6R.B ▼

1. $-5,376$ **2.** $a^4 + 4a^3b + 6a^2b^2 + 4ab^3 + b^4$ (i) $8x^2 + \dfrac{8}{x^2}$ **3.** $k = -3$ **4.** $k = 4$

5. $1 + 12x + 60x^2 + 160x^3 + 240x^4 + 192x^5 + 64x^6$;
$1 - 12x + 60x^2 - 160x^3 + 240x^4 - 192x^5 + 64x^6; k = 28,602$

6. 2 **7.** $k = 3$ **8.** $k = \pm 2$ **9.** $a = \pm\frac{1}{2}$

10. 8 **11.** $n = 5, a = 2$ **12.** $n = 6, a = -4$ **13.** (i) $n = 8, a = \frac{1}{4}$ (ii) $\frac{35}{128}x^3$

14. $n = 8, a = 1, b = \frac{7}{64}$ **15.** $1 + \dfrac{n}{2}x + \dfrac{n(n - 1)}{8}x^2 + \dfrac{n(n - 1)(n - 2)}{48}x^3; n = 8$

16. $\dbinom{n}{r}3^{n-r}(2x)^r$ or $\dbinom{n}{r}3^{n-r}2^r x^r$

17. $1 + 10x + 45x^2 + 120x^3 + 210x^4 + 252x^5 + 210x^6 + 120x^7 + 45x^8 + 10x^9 + x^{10}$

18. (i) $15,625$ (ii) $\frac{81}{16}$ **19.** $1 + nx + \dbinom{n}{2}x^2; \dbinom{n}{n-2}x^{n-2} + \dbinom{n}{n-1}x^{n-1} + \dbinom{n}{n}x^n$

Exercise 6R.C ▼

2. $1 + 8x + 28x^2 + 56x^3$; $2 + 13x + 32x^2 + 28x^3$ **3.** $1 + 4a + 6a^2 + 4a^3 + a^4$; $1 + 4x + 10x^2$

4. $1 - 7x + 21x^2 - 35x^3 + 35x^4 - 21x^5 + 7x^6 - x^7$; $1 - 6x + 15x^2 - 21x^3$

5. $1 - 3x + \frac{15}{4}x^2$; $a = 2, b = -7$

6. $p = a^n, q = na^{n-1}b, r = \dfrac{n(n - 1)}{2}a^{n-2}b^2$

7. $u_r = \dbinom{20}{r - 1}a^{21-r}b^{r-1}; u_{r+1} = \dbinom{20}{r}a^{20-r}b^r$